cl

PSYCHOPATHOLOGY *of* CHILDHOOD

PSYCHOPATHOLOGY
of CHILDHOOD

Edited by PAUL H. HOCH, M.D.
New York State Psychiatric Institute; College of Physicians and Surgeons, Columbia University, New York City

and JOSEPH ZUBIN, Ph.D.
New York State Psychiatric Institute; Department of Psychology, Columbia University, New York City

THE PROCEEDINGS OF THE FORTY-FOURTH AN-
NUAL MEETING OF THE AMERICAN PSYCHO-
PATHOLOGICAL ASSOCIATION, HELD IN NEW
YORK CITY, JUNE, 1954

GRUNE & STRATTON

NEW YORK · LONDON · 1955

Library of Congress Catalog Card No. 55–8799

Printed and bound in U.S.A.

CONTENTS

FOREWORD

THE ROLE OF DEVELOPMENT in relationship to causation of mental disorders is one of the fundamental problems facing research in psychopathology. Theories range from giving such a developmental process a great role in understanding etiology of certain mental disorders, while others disregard the role of development completely. We still lack understanding about the continuity between emotional alterations occurring in childhood to psychotic and neurotic disturbances observed in adults. We have some knowledge about how the former influences the latter, but we will need a great deal more knowledge before we can state that this relationship is fully clear. For this reason, the contributions of child psychiatrists and psychologists are of fundamental importance in an attempt to clarify the sources of mental illness. In order to study these problems we must not limit ourselves to the consideration of psychopathology alone, but must consider also the role of normal development. In this symposium clinical observations and systematic experimental studies of normal children are reported, together with clinical observations and experimental studies of deviant children. Animal studies too are included, since some of the attempts at manipulating early environment can hardly be done with humans.

The recent trend for paralleling the investigation of deprived and neglected children with a direct manipulation of sensory stimulation in man and animals seems to be a most fruitful approach to the problem, and the careful observation of early infant behavior is beginning to emerge from the clinical hunch stage to experimental verification. While clinicians continue to provide a plethora of rich fruitful hypotheses, they no longer feel satisfied with remaining in the "land of discovery," but are beginning to enter the "land of verification." We may expect many of the hypotheses to fall by the wayside, but those which survive will add immeasurably to our knowledge.

As in former years, the editors endeavored to sample the entire field of the topic under discussion. That some areas are not represented is not to be regarded as evidence for their unimportance. Some areas are now at a standstill, others, though alive, did not contain any investigators who were willing to participate. Nevertheless, the sampling does represent the active areas as of 1955.

THE EDITORS

DAVID M. LEVY

DAVID M. LEVY

Samuel W. Hamilton Memorial Lecturer, 1954

IT IS VERY DIFFICULT to write a short sketch which will adequately indicate even the major accomplishments of a man who has been as active and as brilliant in his contributions to psychiatry, orthopsychiatry, education, social work, and in the training of personnel, as David Levy has been in a career which stretches over 35 years. The facts about his education and training are available in any number of directories, as are his varied official positions.

Yet he has made a number of contributions that seem to me to have been insufficiently acknowledged. He developed very clever ways of ascertaining points about normal development of children and the ideas of adolescents when he was Director of Mental Hygiene Clinics for Children in the State of Illinois, associated with the Institute for Juvenile Research, in the early 1920's. The data thus obtained have not been published, so far as known, but they have been most effectively used in teaching, not only by himself, but by others to whom the material was imparted. It also seems clear that many later studies by others were sparked by his accounts of his methods and results.

When he returned in 1925 from a period of study in Zurich, he brought with him Herman Rorschach's test and text, and so introduced it for the first time in this country. A bit later he was the important counselor and training supervisor of some of the outstanding research workers in that field.

Also he brought into our work with children the once famous "amputation doll," which was the real beginning of the attempts at systematization of activity (play) therapy with children. He wrote the first paper on "Doll Play," presented at the 1925 session of the American Orthopsychiatric Association. It was never pubished, but it caused a terrific discussion.

When, in 1927, Dr. Levy became Chief-of-Staff at the New York Institute for Child Guidance, he organized sets of toy materials which could and did permit children to bring out their fantasies, fears, hopes and hostilities without feeling endangered by reprisal. And, it may be added, relieved anxieties of the people in training.

But it was his evolution of certain research methods that seems to me the most significant of his many contributions in the 1927–33 period. His book on "Over-protection" is important because of the case studies, but even more so because of the adequate report there given of a most novel method of research. His monograph on "Sibling Rivalry" is another example.

It was also during the Institute years that he developed and imparted his concepts of "Attitude Therapy." "Release Therapy" came later, but these and other points were all part of a continuing chain of research interests, and testing them out. A most remarkable series of investigations of social behavior, never reported completely enough for me, were carried out on animals to check certain concepts regarding human behavior.

In recent years, Dr. Levy has been a consultant for many agencies. But his most important assignments have been with the U. S. Public Health Service, in O.S.S., and as Director of the Screening Center Information Control Division in Germany (1945–46). For two years (1951–53) he was a member of the Institute for Advanced Study in Princeton. Currently he is associated with the Psychoanalytic Clinic at Columbia University College of Physicians and Surgeons, where he is Professor of Clinical Psychiatry (since 1945). For several years he was Research Professor of Psychiatry at Yale.

His Salmon Lectures, published in 1947 in a book entitled "New Fields of Psychiatry," perhaps give as good a picture of Levy's ideas as any particular piece of his writings.

He is a highly respected member of many organizations, but it should be mentioned that he was one of the founders of the American Orthopsychiatric Association; was its President in 1930–31; and has been a frequent and valued contributor to its meetings and its Journal. He was also an early member of the American Psychoanalytic Association, and a founding member of the Association for Psychoanalytic Medicine (past president of both organizations).

He is a member of the American Psychopathological Association and has made many contributions to its symposia, culminating in his selection for the Samuel W. Hamilton Award in 1954.

No attempt is made to list the schools and agencies where he has taught. But it seems only just to say that in my judgment very few psychiatrists in these past 35 years have done as much to advance psychiatric thinking and social psychiatry as has David Levy. And I think he has much more to contribute.—LAWSON G. LOWERY

1

NORMAL GROWTH AND DEVELOPMENT

By NANCY BAYLEY, Ph.D.*

THE PROCESSES OF NORMAL DEVELOPMENT in the human organism start off as relatively simple and undifferentiated. We do not find manifest in the human embryo those different aspects of the personality we are accustomed to describe by such terms as intelligence, motor coordinations, sensory acuities, learning ability, emotions, moods, drives, and so on. When we try to trace each of these functions back to its origins it joins with all the others, in a common, relatively undifferentiated reflexive behavior.

One problem in studying early development, therefore, is to learn how and when the many aspects of the personality become differentiated, and in what ways and to what extent they remain interdependent. Furthermore, it is obvious that from the very start the organism is developing in constant interaction with an environment that is more or less favorable to its development. What, then, are the environmental factors that are relevant at different stages in the organism's development—in the development of a human organism with its specific genetic potentialities and limitations?

The earliest action or behavior to be detected in the embryo is the preneural fetal heart beat in the third week of gestation.[13] The first response to stimulation (presumably neuromuscular) was described be Hooker[16] as a simple lateral neck bend in response to a hair prick in the area of the cheek at eight fetal weeks. By the time of birth, normally at 40 fetal weeks, we find all the reflexes necessary for life in a protected environment. The respiratory, circulatory and digestive systems are mature enough to function independently, so that the maternal placenta is no longer necessary as a source of oxygen and nourishment.

The neural and muscular development of the fetus is sufficient to

* Institute of Child Welfare, University of California, Berkeley; currently, Laboratory of Psychology, National Institute of Mental Health, Bethesda, Maryland.

allow sensory experiences for some time before birth. In the last pre-natal months, its own internal environment may afford the growing organism experiences with vague pressure sensations, as it moves. Furthermore, these movements themselves may relieve cramped positions, thus giving rise to other sensations. Also, through its move-ments, as well as its mother's movements and postural changes, the fetus may receive sensory stimulation from contact pressures. Such sensory stimuli are, of course, continued in postnatal life, together with the new stimuli which result from the new environment. Among these new environmental factors are breathing, the whole complex of digestive processes, and freedom of movement. New contact sensations are afforded by the air, clothing, handling, bathing, and so on.

With the event of birth we note activity in other sense organs which have matured enough to respond to some extent, and for which the postnatal environment affords adequate stimuli. Vision, hearing, taste, smell, feelings of warmth and of cold all become possible. The infant is now able to build up experience in these new areas, forming perceptions at the same time as sensory acuity increases. Each sense, however, probably does not function to give independent, discrete sensations. The infant's environment more likely impinges on several senses at once, thus contributing to a rather general and vague Gestalt, on the experiential side, and to more or less organized patterns of reflexes on the behavioral side.

One of the earliest organized behavior patterns is the complex process of nursing. The normal infant soon develops a smooth com-petent rhythm of sucking and swallowing that is conducted with persistence and intensity. It is evidently a potent and engrossing ex-perience. Hunger contractions of the empty stomach, and the ac-companying heightened bodily activity which eventually includes crying and general signs of distress, must give rise to strong and per-vasive internal sensations. Nursing quiets the infant: when fed he becomes relaxed and soon falls asleep. This rhythm of hunger and satiation becomes the dominant experience of the neonate's waking life. If, for some reason, the digestive process is disturbed, e.g., by food that disagrees with him, he may have additional distress from gas pressures or other sources of pain. Such distress may also be con-sidered a part, or a variation, of this important feeding rhythm.

We see, then, that the neonate's sensory-motor and perceptual development derive from, and his emotional preoccupations and drives are predominantly directed toward, his experiences of hunger, nursing, satiation and elimination, with their related activities. The prominent place held in the infant's life by these processes, which are continuously repetitive, and on which survival depends, form the basis of the freudian emphasis on the oral-anal stage as the first period in emotional development. Other sensory experiences in the very young infant are normally few and brief, in part because maternal care keeps him in a relatively constant, protected environment, and in part because he sleeps most of the time when he is not hungry or nursing.

Interpretations of the very young infant's awareness of different aspects of his environment must be made with caution. We do not know to what extent the early experiences are conscious. We may assume, however, that consciousness appears only dimly at first, and develops gradually along with the developing physical structures and functions. It seems evident that the sensory reception of stimuli and the neuromuscular reactions to them are basic to the first dim consciousness or awareness.

Part of the process of early development includes staying awake for longer periods of time. These longer waking periods afford ever more extensive experiences with the environment. This greater experience engenders more reactions to the environment, which reactions in turn yield increased and more varied experiences. This circular process combines with inherent maturational advances to foster rapid motor and mental development.

However, at first the young infant's limited ability to respond restricts his experiences. Because he lacks strength and muscular control, he lies as he is placed, and is unable to alter his position except by squirming his body, turning his head, and extending and contracting his arms and legs. At this stage, too, his actions are usually relatively unorganized and reflexive in nature; there is evidence that they start to come under cortical control along with myelinization of the relevant neural processes, at around three to four months of age.[23]

There appears to be an ordered sequence in which the various kinds of behavior become recognizably different from one another. At first there is the establishment of the reflexive life processes. With the development of the sense organs and the cortex of the brain, early reflex patterns become altered and more adaptive, and voluntary responses appear. These changes occur in both motor coordinations, on the one hand, and perceptual and intellectual functions on the other. Along with the adaptive processes, the rapidly growing and strengthening muscles form a necessary part of the developing motor abilities. The motor abilities, in turn, make possible the more adequate adaptive behaviors which are the early evidences of intellectual functioning.

The developing pattern of emotional reactions is in various ways tied in with the motor, intellectual and physical stages of maturing. That is, the individual reacts emotionally to situations only as he is able to discriminate, or at least be dimly aware of, their disturbing or satisfying qualities. Given this awareness, the infant's emotions are further determined by the ability, both physical and mental, to cope with the environment as he sees it.

We have found in the children of the Berkeley Growth Study that mental and motor behaviors become relatively independent of each other at about 18 months of age, when the r's between scores on the two scales drop from around .5 to around .2.[3] After this time most normal infants have gained enough neuromuscular maturity that the more adaptive intellectual functions are no longer closely limited by motor coordinations. The mental functions become free to differentiate and to expand pretty much on their own.

An outstanding characteristic of early behavioral growth is the speed with which all infants go through the processes of change toward more complex and more coordinated and adaptive functions. The rates at which individuals grow are similar, and individual differences are slight, relative to differences found at later ages. Where there are no gross physical indications, it is usually impossible to differentiate the potential feeble-minded from the potential genius, during the early months of life.[2, 7] They emerge in their true colors only when they reach the stage in which the more complex adaptive functions start to develop. The six-month scores of the Berkeley Growth Study children correlate .89 with their scores at 7 months, but the correlation drops to .5 at 12 months and to zero by two years and thereafter. One boy in the study whose IQ at 7 months was 81 earned an IQ of 170 at 11 years. In contrast, another boy who at 5 months had an IQ of 130 slowed down after this so that his IQ had dropped to 76 by the time he was 11 years old.

By two years of age the IQ's become fairly stable, and their correlation with later ages becomes positive. The two-year scores correlate between .4 and .5 with scores at 16 to 18 years. After school age, a fair amount of stability in IQ is the rule, but individual children can, and often do, change considerably.[4, 6] In our studies at the Institute of Child Welfare, we have concerned ourselves with trying to understand the nature and causes of these changes in IQ, or in relative intelligence. Some of the individual variations in mental growth appear to be expressions of inherent tendencies for different rates of maturing of the different functions that predominate at successive stages of development.[7] Other variations in score can be related to factors in the environment which operate to depress or to elevate the child's ability to make use of his intellectual capacities or potentialities.[5]

These factors are often matters of emotional tone. Some babies seem just to relax and vegetate. Some are highly reactive to all environmental stimulation. Some sit and look, but make little overt response. Infants of this latter type often become highly verbal children, with little urge to motor activities. Some children are unhappy, withdrawn or anxious, while others are happy and outgoing and friendly. As for environmental causes of these differences, there were usually instances of temporary or prolonged disturbances in family situations. In many instances the children's intellectual functioning was repressed by such things.[15] In others, family stresses seemed to have no effect. Differences in drive or motivation or curiosity, especially as they relate to intellectual areas, often play a role in developing mental ability. Drives seem, sometimes, to be autogenic, and at others to result from interaction with environmental factors. One girl in our study is interesting in this respect. Her strong rivalry with a brother (three years older) was expressed in several ways: she developed asthma at $4\frac{1}{2}$ years, was thin and had a strained expression; she also strove to compete with her brother on the intellectual level. Because of her asthma she was required to spend long hours in bed, or resting, where she read and played imaginative games. Her IQ rose steadily from a low of 73 at six months, to a high of 189 at 10 years.[5]

Differences in parental socioeconomic status are related to the children's scores after the first two years, but not in infancy.[5, 12] We cannot be sure whether the more able parents helped their children to better intellectual achievement by expecting and encouraging more advanced performances, and by giving better opportunities and examples. There is evidence, however, that this superior performance depends in large part upon hereditary factors, but inferences about the hereditary relationships cannot be made until the children are mature enough to permit comparison of similar kinds of intellectual functions in the parents and their children.[10]

To understand emotional factors in the personality and in the general effectiveness of an individual's functioning, it is necessary to consider early development. As already pointed out, at first the different aspects of behavior are not discrete, and even after they become differentiable they are at first closely interdependent. An infant's emotional responses are very closely tied to his general stage of maturity. And the environmental stimuli that can cause emotional reactions are limited by the infant's ability to interpret them as emotion-arousing stimuli.

Let me illustrate this from an early study on the causes of crying in the Berkeley Growth Study babies during the tests made in their first year of life.[1] Mental and physical tests were given monthly to a sample of 61 infants, at least 52 of whom were tested each month. As judged by the two examiners and the recorder, all conditions that caused crying were noted at each examination period. Crying was most frequent at one month, decreasing to four months and then increasing. But the causes of crying changed as the children grew older. Specific restricting procedures, such as measuring length and taking temperature, were provocative at all ages. Aside from these, in the first month the babies were most upset by the necessary continued handling, then by fatigue at the end of the testing period. Colic pain caused long continued crying in a fair number of infants. But crying from fatigue and from colic rapidly diminished as the babies grew older; crying from continued handling dropped, then rose again toward the end of the year. The strangeness of the place and the persons handling the infants played no role at all in the first two months, but gradually became a potent stimulus as the babies developed enough to discriminate between the strange and the familiar. By 10 months of age this was the predominant source of disturbance in our testing schedule. In the second half-year some babies "used" crying as a means to gain attention or special consideration, and, starting at 10 months, a few cried because of specific learning or memories of disliked procedures. After about 18 months the children rarely cried in the testing situation. They had become able to cope with the experiences they met there. They felt that they knew the experimenters; the games were fun; the measuring instruments could be understood, or could be fought off by other forms of refusal and noncooperation. By 3 or 4 years of age "negativism" had also disappeared, and the children enjoyed their experiences at the Institute.

The emotional potential of our testing schedules did not remain stable, however. When the children were around 12 to 14 years old, many of them rebelled strongly against pressures put on them to keep their appointments with us. In some instances we had to forego the physical examinations. We missed a few examinations on some, and actually lost two cases at this time. Fortunately for our study, however, this rebellion did not last. As one girl said to me at 16 years: "I don't mind the physicals at all now. I was silly to be bothered by them when I was 13." Now, when I ask them to come for a three-hour session at 25 years, they are interested and often willing to go to considerable inconvenience to make and keep an appointment.

The period of early adolescence has been mentioned as one in which the children disliked the testing situation, and in particular the physical examination. This is notoriously a period of storm and stress. In our studies at the Institute of Child Welfare we have endeavored to find some explanations for this, and have found some interesting relationships.

On the physical side, there are rapid changes that make a difference in the children's drives and in their attitudes toward themselves. Pubescence seems to be initiated by the rapid increase of androgens and estrogens. These sex hormones stimulate the maturing of the reproductive organs and their accompanying drives, and also the growth and maturing of the whole body. Before nine years there is very little difference in children's physiques. But at about this age the girls start to grow rapidly; they forge ahead in their maturing two years or more beyond the boys. By 13 years the average girl is taller than the average boy; she has developed almost mature feminine contours and she has had, or is about to have, her first menstruation. Her interests have changed, along with her build, toward more "grown-up" things, and social activities that include the opposite sex. The average 13-year-old boy, on the other hand, is still physically immature; he is growing rapidly, and by the time he is 15 he will have reached the physical maturity equivalent to that of the 13-year-old girl. In the meantime, his interests have been primarily with boys' games—outdoor sports and the like. There is a strong need in the adolescent boy to be manly, to be big and strong and skillful.[17, 18, 20, 25]

We are all aware of these contrasting patterns. But we often forget that these descriptions are of averages. There is, within each sex group, great individual variation in the rates of physical maturing. For example, we often find, in the same junior high school class of boys and girls the same age, a normal range of six years in their degrees of physical maturity, as indicated by such criteria as secondary sex characteristics and skeletal age.[6] We have found that the children who are most out of line, the early-maturing girls and the late-maturing boys, are most likely to be the unhappy, emotionally-disturbed children.[19, 20] Neither fits into the ideal the boys and girls have for themselves of what they wish to be or think they ought to be. The mature girl worries about being too big and fat; the immature boy worries over whether he will ever grow to be normally tall and strong. Neither realizes that theirs is often just a temporary deviation. Also, in keeping with their physical maturities, their interests are out of line. The physically precocious girl would like to mix socially with a crowd two or three years older than she, while the immature boy is still interested in the little-boy games his classmates have outgrown.

Those who deviate in the other directions tend to get along well. The early-maturing boy is admired for his size and strength. He is often considered good-looking, mature and socially at ease. He is physically on a par with the average girl his age. The late-maturing girl (unless very retarded) is, similarly, in step with the average boy her age, in her interests and general physical maturity. Furthermore, she is still small and slender—characteristics that are considered appropriate for girls.

On the intellectual side another factor contributes to the turbulence of adolescence. The teen-ager has almost adult intelligence, and with physical maturity he begins to consider himself an adult, and consequently deserving of adult privileges. But he is lacking in the wisdom of experience, and is also developing new and strong sexual drives which he has not learned to cope with. Consequently, he very often acts unwisely when he is given responsibility. This behavior accentuates the parents' natural reluctance to see their babies grow up and become independent. As a result there is often strife within the family. The 13- or 14-year-old is likely to rebel against parental authority, and to reject all adults, at least to some extent, in favor of friends his own age.[17, 25]

We find in this period an almost slavish adherence to the mores of small groups or cliques with which the child identifies. Styles in clothes, in vocabulary, in social activities, are closely adhered to, for fear of ostracism by the in-group.[25] This is a period of trial and error, of practice in adult manners and ways of life. With it go wide swings of emotional behavior. Things are either "divine," or hopelessly intolerable. In our studies at the Institute, Rorschach and TAT protocols taken at these ages in our normal children indicate emotional disturbances which in adults would be considered strong signs of pathology.[22] But, as a rule, each child works out an acceptable role or pattern of behavior, and comes through with an integrated personality. He can then accept others outside his own group; he likes and gets along with adults and children—and himself. He once more becomes a willing member of his own family.

Of course, there are great individual differences in the adequacy with which the children cope with the hazards of their environment. There seem to be innate differences in susceptibility to environmental influences, as well as differences in the environments with which they must try to cope.

We have, in our studies, made some efforts to relate personality to constitutional factors. This is a difficult task, and our comparisons have been limited to such things as variations in somatotype and in masculinity-femininity of physique. These studies have brought out some relationships that are suggestive. Hanley[14] compared ratings of personality factors of physically mature boys with their somatotypes. His findings tended to corroborate those of Sheldon, but the correlations were low, indicating only general tendencies for the mesomorph (with well-developed musculature) to be the active boy who takes chances and is good at games, and the slender, skinny ectomorph to be bashful, unhappy and submissive. He found no significant correlates witl endomorphy (the tendency to be fat), for which Sheldon found traits of sociability, love of comfort and of food, and related characteristics. So far, we have no comparable data for the girls. We find, however, that girls do not fit so well into the somatotypes which were, after all, set up to describe the physiques of young men.

Leona Bayer and I have worked out a set of standards for assessing somatic androgyny.[11] We used the nude photographs of both boys and girls aged 17 to 18 years, and sorted them according to eight variables that showed sex differences in body form. In addition to the typical masculine and feminine builds, our standards include the hypermasculine and hyperfeminine, the hypo (or underdeveloped) masculine and feminine, and bisexual builds in which the boy or girl has characteristics of the opposite as well as of the same sex. One comparison has been made with masculinity-femininity of interests as derived from the Kuder Interest Records, which the subjects took when about 16½ years old.[9] The boys with atypical builds (that is, those who were classed as bisexual or hypomasculine) tended to have the most masculine interests. It seems that at this age many such boys felt the need to protest against their inappropriate physiques by strongly compensating—at least in the verbal claim to masculinity. From other studies[24] we may expect these boys to change their interests as they mature.

The relations in the girls are less clear, but those who could afford to be more feminine in their interests appeared to be the ones who more often than not had typically feminine builds. Those with atypical physiques, including the hyperfeminine, were a little more likely to express more masculine interests.

The changing emotional patterns, with growth, of normal children are reflected in a recently-completed monograph by Macfarlane, Allen and Honzik.[21] These authors have summarized the incidence of problems reported by the mothers of over 100 normal children in an open-question interview of 35 items taken at the times the children were brought in for mental tests. Many problems were reported so frequently at some ages as to be considered very normal occurrences in the developmental process. The incidence of some problems decreased with age, others increased, others had one or more ages of high incidence. For the most part the periods of high incidence could be related to conditions characteristic for the ages at which they occurred.

Of those that declined with age, the earliest reported were associated with the control of elimination: at 21 months of age 74 per cent of the mothers reported nocturnal enuresis, while about half reported diurnal enuresis and a quarter reported soiling. Problems associated with speech (30 per cent of the boys and 17 per cent of the girls) and thumbsucking (21 per cent of the boys and 33 per cent of the girls) were also most frequent at 31 months and 3 years. Specific fears were most frequent at 3 and 3½ years (67 per cent of the girls, 56 per cent of boys at 3½). Then, around 5 years, overactivity (46 per cent of the boys and 35 per cent of the girls) and destructiveness (28 per cent of the boys and 10 per cent of the girls) were problems that later diminished. Tempers were predominant at 3 years (69 per cent of the boys and 63 per cent of the girls). Although tempers grew less frequent with age, they were more persistent among the boys, a third of whom were still having tempers at 13 years.

There was a systematic increase with age in nailbiting. In girls it reached the high of 40 per cent at 11 years, after which it subsided, probably in response to social pressures for good grooming. At 14 years, the age at the last interview, 33 per cent of the boys were still nailbiters.

The period of insufficient appetite, 4 to 6 years, with an incidence of 31 per cent in boys at 4 years and 37 per cent in girls at 6, coincided with a period of a high level of communicable diseases.

Lying was a problem in about half of the children getween 4 and 6 years, it appeared a little earlier in the girls, and evidently dropped out when it proved to be an unacceptable coping device.

A group of problems had two periods of high frequency, usually during the preschool ages and again in late pubescence. These are restless sleep, disturbing dreams, physical timidity, irritability and attention-demanding. Another group had peaks on entering school and in early adolescence. These are overdependence, somberness, jealousy and, in boys, food finickiness.

Oversensitiveness, once it was established at about 5 years, continued in about half of the cases. It evidently was a succesful coping device in dealing with parents. In the boys, however, oversensitiveness dropped out rapidly after 11 years, being incompatible with "pressures to be a man."

In relating problems to birth order among siblings, these authors found that first-born boys showed more withdrawing and internalizing patterns, non-first were more overt, aggressive and competitive.

The second-born girls had a greater incidence of thumbsucking and oversensitiveness. For the first-born girls: ". . . life appeared to be more difficult than for others. They had more problems, and more incompatible combinations of both aggressive and withdrawing behavior."

As for the continuity of problem behavior in the same children, correlation coefficients were usually low between the younger and older ages. The greatest persistence was found in overdependence, moodiness, somberness and irritability. A child's characteristic behaviors were relatively unstable at around 11 and 12 years, at the beginning of adolescence. After this age the children tended to return to their earlier characteristics.

Some problems were more likely to go together in the same children. Those problems with the greatest number of correlates are, in order: irritability, overdependence, moodiness, negativism, somberness and reserve. The girls' problems were more intercorrelated at 5 years, while problems among the boys were more intercorrelated at 12 years. There appear to be differential cultural pressures that build up periods of stress—earlier in the girls than in the boys.

Overt conformity was established earlier in girls. The authors suggest this may be due in part to biologic differences, the girls being more docile and responsive to cultural pressures to conform. We may guess that boys become troubled when they are faced, in adolescence, with the prospect of having to become economically independent, and to make careers for themselves,

The personality characteristics of the mothers for the most part showed little relation to the children's problems. On the basis of low correlations (of the order of .3 or less), Macfarlane says, "The mother who is painfully self-conscious and feels inferior is likely to have children who are overdependent, excessively reserved, destructive, have mood swings, are irritable, and somber." If the mother is talkative and cheerful, the children are less likely to be somber and reserved. The unhappy and silent mothers tend to have inhibited and somber children. There is no relation between children's problems and the mother's restlessness, worrisomeness, interest in her child, cooperation in the study, concern over her child's personality traits, or disturbance over her child's sexual behavior.

I have summarized this study in some detail because it seems to me relevant to an understanding of the relations between pathologic and normal behavior. Children do not grow up without at times exhibiting behavior over which their parents become concerned. Certain periods in the growing-up process are more conducive to problems; certain conditions in the environment and interpersonal relations present difficulties for a child to adjust to. But a very large proportion of children manage to work out more or less adequate methods of coping with these hazards. In the process, their behavior is often socially unacceptable; and periods of trial and error, or "problems," are inevitable until the adjustments are made. Some children do not work out of their problems. It is well to be aware of the critical conditions, and the times and places when difficulties are likely to occur. Such knowledge will help in giving wise guidance. But we need not be unduly oppressed by many of the problem-behaviors exhibited by children—most of them will be outgrown.

We should remember, furthermore, that normal development is a dynamic process of interaction between the organism and its environment. Those aspects of the environment that are potent in affecting the organism are dependent to a considerable extent on the degree of maturity that the organism has attained, as well as the organism's inherent vulnerability or capacity to cope with environmental hazards. If pathologic development is in any degree environmentally determined, or if it is to yield to environmental controls, then we need to know the relevant facts about the patient's developmental stage, and those environmental factors that are pertinent to it.

REFERENCES

1. BAYLEY, N.: A study of the crying of infants during mental and physical tests. J. Genet. Psychol. *40:* 306–329, 1932.
2. ———: Mental growth during the first three years. Genet. Psychol. Monogr. *14:* 92, 1933.
3. ———: The development of motor abilities during the first three years. Monogr. Soc. Res. Child Devel. *1:* 26, 1935.
4. ———: Mental growth in young children. Yearbook Nat. Soc. Study of Educ. *39:* 11–47, 1940.
5. ———: Factors influencing the growth of intelligence in young children. Yearbook Nat. Soc. Study of Educ. *39:* 49–79, 1940.
6. ———: Skeletal maturing in adolescence as a basis for determining percentage of completed growth. Child Devel. *14:* 1–46, 1943.
7. ———: Consistency and variability in the growth of intelligence from birth to eighteen years. J. Genet. Psychol. *75:* 165–196, 1949.

8. ——: Development and Maturation. *In* Theoretical Foundations of Psychology (H. Helson, ed.). New York, Van Nostrand, 1951, pp. 145–199.

9. ——: Some psychological correlates of somatic androgyny. Child Devel. *22:* 47–60, 1951.

10. ——: Some increasing parent-child similarities during the growth of children. J. Educ. Psychol. *45:* 1–21, 1954.

11. —— AND BAYER, L. M.: The assessment of somatic androgyny. Am. J. Phys. Anthropol. *5:* 433–461, 1946.

12. —— AND JONES, H. E.: Environmental correlates of mental and motor development: A cumulative study from infancy to six years. Child Devel. *8:* 329–341, 1937.

13. CARMICHAEL, L.: The Onset and Early Development of Behavior. *In* Manual of Child Psychology (L. Carmichael, ed.). New York, John Wiley & Sons, 1946, pp. 43–166.

14. HANLEY, C.: Physique and reputation of junior high school boys. Child Devel. *22:* 247–260, 1951.

15. HONZIK, M. P., MACFARLANE, J. W. AND ALLEN, L.: The stability of mental test performance between two and eighteen years. J. Exper. Educ. 309–324, 1948.

16. HOOKER, D.: Reflex Activities in the Human Fetus. *In* Child Behavior and Development (Roger Barker, J. S. Kounin and H. F. Wright, eds.). New York, McGraw-Hill, 1943, pp. 17–28.

17. JONES, H. E.: Development in Adolescence. New York, Appleton-Century, 1943, p. 166.

18. ——: Motor performance and growth: A developmental study of static dynamometric strength. University of California Publications in Child Development *1:* 1–182, 1949.

19. ——: The Adolescent in Our Society. *In* The Family in a Democratic Society. New York, Columbia University Press, 1949, 70–84.

20. JONES, M. C. AND BAYLEY, N.: Physical maturing among boys as related to behavior. J. Educ. Psychol. *41:* 129–148, 1950.

21. MACFARLANE, J. W., ALLEN, L. AND HONZIK, M. P.: A developmental study of the behavior problems of normal children between 21 months and 14 years. University of California Publications in Child Development, Berkeley, University of California Press, 1954, vol. 2, pp. 1–222.

22. McFATE, M. Z. AND ORR, F. G.: Through adolescence with the Rorschach. Rorschach Res. Exchange & J. Proj. Tech. *13:* 302–319, 1949.

23. McGRAW, M. B.: The Neuro-Muscular Maturation of the Human Infant. New York, Columbia University Press, 1942, p. 140.

24. SELTZER, C. C.: The relationship between the masculine component and personality. Am. J. Phys. Anthropol. *3:* 33–47, 1945.

25. TRYON, C. M.: The adolescent peer culture. Yearbook Nat. Soc. Study of Educ., 1944, part I, pp. 217–239.

2

SCIENTIFIC MODELS FOR THE INVESTIGATION OF CHILD DEVELOPMENT

By WAYNE DENNIS, Ph.D.*

PSYCHOLOGIC STUDIES OF CHILDREN have been conducted for a number of decades. These researches might reasonably be expected to provide information of great value to those concerned with child care. Yet the cautious child psychologist will be the first to indicate that, as yet, his field possesses only a modest amount of scientific data.

The recent appearance of the second edition of the *Manual of Child Psychology*, edited by Carmichael, provides a convenient sourcebook for assessing recent advances. An interesting base line for comparison is supplied by Murchison's *Handbook of Child Psychology*, the second edition of which was published in 1933. One notes that of the 19 authors or senior authors of chapters in the new Carmichael book, eleven were contributors to Murchison's book which appeared 21 years ago. Judging from Carmichael's choice of contributors, one must conclude that few new persons of importance have appeared in child psychology in the past two decades. The subject matter, too, shows little change. Of the 19 chapter headings in the recent book, 16 were present in Murchison. Since 1933 the advancement of knowledge about children has apparently increased at a slow pace. By contrast, within this same interval of time, we have expanded dramatically our knowledge of rats, monkeys and chimpanzees. During the past two decades whole areas of psychology, such as military psychology, clinical psychology and human engineering have come into prominence. The total personnel in psychology has increased greatly. But in these decades the number of persons engaged in research upon child

* Professor of Psychology and Chairman, Department of Psychology, Brooklyn College, Brooklyn, New York.

behavior has grown but little. Thus, by several standards of comparison, progress in child psychology has been relatively slow.

How can this backwardness be understood? No doubt a full understanding of it would involve many factors. The present paper will limit itself to an examination of the research procedures in the field of child development, with a view to finding their shortcomings and discussing their possible improvement.

For our present purposes let us note that the major activities of scientists fall into three categories: the first is the discovery and exploration of phenomena in some segment of the universe; the second is the analysis of relationships existing among these phenomena; and the third activity consists in discovering which of these relationships are causal. The significance of these distinctions will become clearer as we proceed.

These three activities go on concurrently, and are closely interrelated. This should be kept in mind, even though, in the interest of simplicity of exposition they will be discussed separately.

Let us take up first the discovery and exploration of the subject matter of child behavior. By those with naive notions of psychology and related disciplines, it is often assumed that there are no new phenomena to discover, since human behavior is observable to all. This view, however, is no more reasonable than the notion that since plants and animals and stars are visible to all, biologists and astronomers cannot discover new species or new stars.

One can point to many discoveries of psychologic phenomena. Two familiar, if elementary, instances are the discovery of the blind spot and of color blindness. These characteristics have been present in man for doubtless thousands of years, yet they were discovered only in 1668 and 1798 respectively. Discoveries concerning child development are even more recent. For example, very recently Minkowski and Hooker observed for the first time the early responses of the human fetus. In the neonatal period, too, much that is new has been discovered. The scientist studying the newborn infant has observed things which had been neglected by parents, midwives, obstetricians and pediatricians. For example, prior to systematic researches no one seems to have known about the young infant's ability to support himself by the grasp of his hand. Robinson, to play up the probable evolutionary significance of this response, photographed a newborn infant supporting himself on the limb of a tree. Only recently discovered, too, is the newborn infant's ability to swim, if one means by swimming propelling himself in water, face downward, while holding his breath. As noted earlier, because children have been universally available for observation for some time, it might be assumed that there is nothing new to be uncovered about them. But the illustrations mentioned above indicate that as we find new technics for observation, and new conditions under which to observe the child, we may indeed find new phenomena, just as the biologist discovers species and the astronomer, new stars. Nor have discoveries been limited to the period of early infancy. One of our speakers, Piaget, has made major discoveries in regard to child thought. He has done this by questioning children in ways in which they had seldom been questioned before, and by exposing them to ingenious experimental problems. It should be mentioned that Rorschach's fame rests largely upon the invention of a new way of tapping psychologic data. The application of his method to children has as yet not been as extensive as one could wish. Notwithstanding the fact that examples such as those just mentioned can be cited, on the whole perhaps psychologists have not been very inventive or imaginative. Child psychologists, especially, have found only a few new avenues of information. This may be because we have not been sufficiently aware of the possibilities of discovery. We seem prone to become statisticians rather than explorers. Psychologists have shown more interest in research design than they do in invention and creativity. Once we make the acquaintance of a phenomenon, such as Ebbinghaus' nonsense syllables or Pavlov's conditioned reflex, we can train students to subject these phenomena to innumerable experimental variations. But we cannot tell anyone how to produce an original idea, such as occurred to Ebbinghaus and Pavlov. Let us hope that eventually we may learn how to facilitate the process of discovery. Meanwhile we will probably do best by being continually on the alert for new procedures—in some cases lucky accidents—which will give us information not previously available. We can also be more alert in applying to children new technics which arise in other fields of psychology. For, while we cannot as yet instruct anyone with regard to how to achieve scientific originality, it seems likely that the advances will be made by those who are actively looking for new ideas rather than by those who are indifferent to such ideas. We should entertain continually the possibility that new methods of obtaining information about children may someday revolutionize child psychology to the degree that the telescope and the microscope have revolutionized certain other areas of science.

Let us turn now to a second activity of the scientist. Having discovered or become acquainted with a certain phenomenon, he looks for relationships between it and other things. For example, how are temper tantrums related to health, to the daily cycle and to parental behavior? How is thumb-sucking related to infant feeding? Galton's invention of correlation provided a useful tool for the search for relationships. However, relationships can be expressed not only by coefficients of correlation but by other methods as well. We need not discuss these methods, since presentations of them are readily available in textbooks on statistic methods.

The majority of studies in child psychology are in the nature of establishing statistic associations among variables. Given a large number of variables, the number of possible relationships is enormous. It would seem that the list of potential studies is beyond the possibility of execution. Factor analysis has been proposed as a method of simplifying the situation, but its eventual contribution is still uncertain.

Compared to other fields of psychology, the relationships to be examined by developmental psychology are complicated and enriched by the fact that developmental psychology seeks to analyze the relations existing not merely at a given moment of time but among different parts of the human life-span. Relationships are viewed as progressively changing, not as being static. Child psychology has been almost alone in undertaking longitudinal studies. Perhaps child psychology moves slowly because longitudinal studies are inherently slow. Furthermore, as suggested above, they result in an embarrassing increase in the number of correlations which can be computed.

While statisticians have made great progress in determining how to test for the presence of relationships, they have no special way of determining which of the millions of possible relationships should be examined. This, it seems to me, is the function of theory. A particular relationship should be examined not to establish an isolated fact but to find a fact which plays a key role in a set of interrelated propositions.

In regard to theory, as well as in regard to discoveries, child psychology does not have a brilliant record. In most child psychology textbooks, one will find few theories worthy of the name. Psychoanalytic theories are the most comprehensive, but as Sears, as well as others, has indicated, they prove difficult to test.

The emergence of new theories would doubtless be a vitalizing factor in child psychology. In its day, even the old theory of recapitulation was a powerful stimulant. But its impetus is gone. We need new stimulants today. Unfortunately no one, it seems, can tell us how to concoct an exciting theory, just as no one can tell us how to make a discovery.

Let us turn now to another activity of scientists, the establishment of causal relations. It has been suggested above that most researches dealing with child behavior have been so conducted that they reveal mere statistic associations and not causal relationships. What we want to learn, as scientists, are not mere correlations but an understanding of causes. In our courses, we teach that correlation does not prove causation, but this precept seems to have little effect upon researches dealing with children.

Many of our investigations follow a schema which results in finding, for example, that neurotic parents and neurotic children are associated. It should be obvious that this fact does not tell us whether neurotic behavior on the part of the parent causes neurotic behavior in the child, or whether the neurotic child induces neuroticism in the parent, or whether a situation which surrounds both child and parent is producing like behavior in both, or whether parent-child resemblance in neuroticism is due to common genes, or whether the explanation lies in some other direction.

A concrete example of the difficulty of interpreting results arising from the pursuit of correlations is to be found in the recent book by Whiting and Child, *Child Training and Personality*. Using data on a number of societies, they have produced evidence for certain associations between child care and adult personality. The authors argue for a particular causal interpretation, but they are aware that the proof of an association between a certain kind of child care and certain forms of adult behavior does not indicate which one is producing the other, or indeed, that there is any causal relation between the two. Both may be produced by some third factor.

It is this weakness in research procedures which seems to me to be a major reason for the backwardness of child psychology. It is my opinion that so long as we use correlational research models, little advance will occur.

The correct direction in which to proceed is clear. It is generally understood that the way to determine a causal factor or a causal complex of factors is first to establish groups of subjects who may reasonably be assumed to be equivalent. The simplest and perhaps the best approach to obtaining equivalent groups is to assign subjects to groups in a random manner. The independent variable is then applied to one or more of these groups and not to others, and the differences which appear are noted. Since other influences may be assumed to be equal for the various groups, the manipulated variable is the *cause* of any differences which appear. This is, of course, the experimental method which has been applied with such fruitfulness in many areas of science, including other fields of psychology.

In research with children, experimentation in the sense in which this term is here used has not been totally lacking. It has been used extensively with newborn subjects. Outstanding are the studies of Irvin and others on the causes of infant movement, of Wickens and others on conditioning, and of Sears and his collaborators on the sucking response. Probably experimental studies have been performed with newborn infants because hospital nurseries, under cooperative medical supervision, lend themselves particularly well to such research. Newborn infants are accessible, they can easily be tagged, and it is easy to assign them to experimental and control groups in a random manner, and to determine the effects of experimental variables. It should be possible to to this at all ages throughout childhood. Let us consider, for example, the possibility of experimentation in the schools. Between age 6 and 16 the majority of American children attend educational institutions. They must be assigned to rooms, assigned to teachers and, therefore, assigned to certain personalities and certain human relations. If one wished to find the effect of some variable which is already present in the school system, it should be possible to divide a given pool of children into experimental and control groups in a satisfactory manner. But the number of studies of school children which have met the requirements of randomization of subjects among groups are few.

We have an anomalous situation in America. We support science to an extent to which it has never been supported before. At the same time, there is much public concern with problems of child rearing, personality development and education. But a genuine experimental attack upon the problems in these fields is almost lacking. The introduction of active research departments attached to public schools could contribute greatly to our knowledge of child development.

Other promising opportunities for fundamental research in child development are to be found in residential institutions, such as foundling homes, orphanages and children's homes. Here every aspect of the child's life can be supervised. Here great variation presently exists in child rearing practices. Many of these practices are probably psychologically bad. There is pressure for change in institutional care. If institutions interested in improving their programs could be induced first to apply a change to some of their children and to determine the effect of the change before applying it to all, our knowledge of causal influences in child development would soon be increased a hundred-fold. Research thinking of this type has penetrated the field of public health, but not the field of child welfare. A polio vaccine is not applied indiscriminately until it has been tested, but the truth of a new concept in child welfare is often considered to be self-evident. Apparently we need an Arrowsmith in child development.

Institutions for feeble-minded children and for delinquent youth are among those which could assist in building a science of child development. Since these institutions are maintained at public expense, they can reasonably be expected to contribute to civic welfare by maintaining research programs. Because an organization of this sort serves many children and because it has a central management, it would be a simple matter to set up the institution into two or more parallel and equivalent units. If this were done, any authorized investigator could be supplied with experimental and control groups almost upon request. Yet, despite the advantages of the organization of an institution into parallel and equivalent groups (from a research point of view), I do not know of any institution which has such an organization.

A search for causal explanations for child behavior need not be limited to residential institutions. Undoubtedly the major influences affecting most children spring from the family. There are many organizations serving the family and enlisting the cooperation of parents—agencies such as child guidance centers, psychiatric clinics, child welfare agencies, remedial education clinics, etc. These, too, have opportunities for playing an important role in the science of child development. The fundamental requirements are, first, that a service agency occasionally have two or more ways of approaching a problem, rather than one, and, second, that families or children be assigned to these programs at random. For example, a clinic engaged in child therapy should not try just therapy A but also therapy B. If this represents too radical a break with tradition, then it might at least try form A_1 and form A_2. One variation might consist in delaying therapy—therapy must often be delayed anyway—but those to be delayed should be assigned at random. Only in this way will reliable knowledge be obtained. If I appear to be obsessive about this elementary point, it is because, in general, those responsible for child service programs have shown little awareness of it.

At this point it should be made clear that I am cognizant that research institutes concerned with child development already exist. There are half a dozen or more such institutes, several of them dating from 1930 or earlier. Nearly all are associated with colleges and universities. Considering the small staffs and small budgets which are characteristic of them, their output has been excellent. But the research in which they are now engaged is small in quantity. Undoubtedly they could do much more if they were more liberally financed.

While there should always be child research centers in universities, it is my belief that the major portion of child research should be done in service centers, as indicated above. In order to obtain child subjects, the university center usually feels it must develop a kindergarten or elementary school or clinic. Such facilities, since they must compete with other items in the university budget, remain small. The cases available to the center are few and often are highly selected. No child research center has, nor can attain, the human laboratory which is afforded by other social institutions for children if these centers were organized to facilitate research. For example, no university child research center is ever likely to have a budget which is one-tenth of the budget of any large state institution for the feeble-minded.

There is the further fact that the results of research are more likely to be assimilated into practice if they are an outgrowth of institutional cooperation. Time does not permit an expansion on this point, but it is an important one.

It may be urged that there are difficulties associated with research on child behavior which rule out the approach which I have advocated. The possible difficulties are of two sorts: difficulties in regard to public attitudes about child research and difficulties in financing and organizing child research. I do not believe that either of these difficulties is insurmountable.

Let us consider first the fact that some people object to the idea of subjecting children to experimental regimes. Those who understand the purpose of research on children do not object to it. Its purpose is humanitarian. In almost all instances the scientist promotes the purposes of the society in which he lives. He seldom wishes to violate its standards. Thus, medical research on child health meets little objection because the medical researcher wants to discover ways to make children well, not ways to make them ill. Likewise, the psychologist is interested in reducing the incidence of school failures, of delinquency and of parent-child conflict—not in increasing them. A wider understanding of the purposes of research, and of the ethical standards under which the investigator conducts his studies, should insure public approval.

So far as finances are concerned, it should be noted that large-scale experimental studies of child behavior do not require the establishment of new social institutions. Institutions for the welfare of children are already in existence. Variations in their approach to child care already exist. All that is needed is a method whereby the present and future variation can be caused to yield scientific answers—answers which cannot be obtained so long as environmental variables do not conform to the most elementary research design.

If I am correct, the general direction which child research should take is clear. The basic research model is simple and well-known. It is the experimental group-control group concept. What is needed is a more widespread appreciation of the necessity of following this model among those who have responsibilities for child development. The kind of research thinking which in the past century has led to great reductions in disease and death in childhood needs to be applied to the psychologic aspects of child life.

3

CURRENT TRENDS OF RESEARCH IN CHILD DEVELOPMENT

By ALFRED L. BALDWIN, Ph.D.*

IT GIVES ME GREAT PLEASURE to have this opportunity to speak to this group on some of the current trends of research in child development. Research in any field has its ups and downs; child development is no different. Some of us who are in the field have been of the opinion that child development theory and research has been at ebb tide for the last several years, despite a few outstanding exceptions. A few years ago I would have appeared before you with a certain apologetic air, but today I can hopefully discern some important current trends of child development which lead me to anticipate a resurgence of interest in the field and a recognition of the importance of the developmental area for any theory of human behavior.

I doubt if the present trends in the field can be understood without some historical background. I must say that I feel out of place talking about the history of child development during the last quarter century in the presence of these people who have helped make that history and who know it much better than I. It seems to me, however, that child development since 1920 can be roughly divided into two main periods, if you do not worry too much about a few notable exceptions and about a sharp dividing line between periods. The period of 1920 to the mid-thirties was marked by a predominance of research concerned with the developmental process—its predictability, stability and the influence of genetic factors on development. This is the period of studies of constancy of IQ, of the relative importance of maturation and learning and of heredity and environment. It is also the period of the theoretic controversies on the nature of the growth process—its mathematic description, and whether it is a process of differentiation or of integration. Many of the empiric studies of this

* Department of Child Development and Family Relationships, Cornell University, Ithaca, New York.

period charted the development of physical and mental characteristics either through cross-sectional or through longitudinal studies. It is the period when most of the large longitudinal studies were begun.

During the late thirties, it seems to me, the emphasis of research changed. In this recent period our science has been largely living off the hypotheses coming from psychoanalysis. Some of them have been indigestible; others have been digested so thoroughly that they are hardly identifiable; and many form an integral, obvious part of our current beliefs. As I see it, the interest in psychoanalytic hypotheses accompanied the tremendous upsurge of interest in psychiatry and clinical psychology, and has brought with it a general interest in the effects of childhood experiences and environment upon the adult who emerges from these experiences.

At first, our attempts to investigate psychoanalytic hypotheses were pretty naive. We took some of Freud's casual statements too literally, and tried to test them completely out of context. But we have gradually improved, I think. A rereading now of Sears' "Survey of Objective Studies of Psychoanalytic Concepts," published in 1943,[11] is comforting because it is clear that child development research has become more sophisticated in the last fifteen years. At first, we tried to investigate the influence of single factors in childhood—breast feeding or a childhood traumatic experience. Now we are more concerned with the atmosphere of child rearing—with the habitual practices rather than the isolated experiences.

The practical problems of psychopathology perhaps forced the shift in research emphasis in child development. It was a healthy influence, although it left many important problems of previous decades unsolved. It also changed the quality of publications in child development research. Barker,[1] in describing child psychology in 1950, pointed out how much research on the behavior and development of children was in the hands of practitioners; how many of the publications comprised didactic, programmatic writing; and how only one-fourth of the articles in the field reported any original observations or experiments. We were at a familiar impasse in behavioral science; the problems suitable for rigorous investigation were thought to be superficial, while the problems most people considered significant did not lend themselves to rigorous research. The methods which were employed to investigate these significant problems were adapted to discover fruitful hypotheses but were not designed to test them. Thus it was possible for Orlansky,[9] in 1949, to review the research on the influence of childhood experience on personality and to leave his readers with the impression that nobody had shown that any childhood experience had any effect upon personality development.

Last summer I had the opportunity, provided me by the Ford Foundation, to visit a number of investigators in the field of child development and to meet in conference with a number of others. I could not possibly tell you about all the research projects I saw or heard about. Instead of attempting an unbiased survey, I want to tell you about a few of the foci of research interest which, I believe, point to important future developments.

Certainly the most popular problem under current investigation is that of childhood antecedents of adult personality. In other words, we are still working along the same theme which characterizes the second period in my historical analysis. It seems to me that the experiences of infancy and early childhood are receiving the most attention within this broad area.

We have, for example, some empiric fact-finding research. Escalona[5] has for a number of years been describing individual differences among young infants, especially non-normative differences. Her basic scientific assumption is, I take it, that differences in perceptual sensitivity, in the amount of oral behavior, and other such differences in young infants, interact with the differences in the way mothers handle their babies, and provide the basis for an explanation of personality development during the early years. She gives us facts which are both refreshing and disillusioning to a person who has been too captivated by the descriptions of normative behavior. For example, her research does not confirm the common belief that all infants wake up and go to sleep gradually and imperceptibly. Some do so, but others snap out of a nap as quickly as any adult. Katherine Wolf is directing an intensive fact-finding longitudinal study of a small number of infants which is designed, as I see it, to describe the course of the infant's interactions with his parents and siblings during the early years.

A second important focus of research on childhood antecedents of personality is the work on socialization by Sears and his colleagues.

This group has been operating under the assumption that a reinforcement theory of learning can account for personality development. This learning theory, which they have called "General Behavior Theory," is an extremely complicated and sophisticated theoretic structure. Many portions are explicit reformulations of psychoanalytic hypotheses in a new theoretic language. One concrete result of this research interest has been a pilot study followed by a full-scale investigation of the relationships between child behavior and child training practices of parents.[12] The hypotheses originally tested were fairly simple. Frustration should lead to aggression; and that behavior which was rewarded should appear overtly, while punished behavior should disappear. Thus, children from a frustrating home would tend to be aggressive, but in many of these same frustrating homes aggressive behavior would be punished. This combination of factors suggested many interesting problems. Aggressive behavior, therefore, has been studied in nursery school and doll play situations. The findings have not been easy to explain: there are differences between sexes; there are age trends. Aggression apparently depends on many factors. Thus, the theoretic structure has become more and more complex. It has been necessary to introduce dependence and identification as theoretic constructs in the system. Some aspects of the data are rather nicely explained by a hypothesis of identification with the aggressor, as proposed by Anna Freud.[6]

The "General Behavior Theory" has become, it seems to me, sufficiently broad and complex to be a true candidate for a theory of child development. It is my personal opinion that some concept of maturation must be integrated into the learning theory, and that reinforcement alone will not account for all childhood learning; but it will certainly be interesting to see if these research workers can account for personality development with such a parsimonious set of assumptions.

Another focus of the research efforts stemming from the "General Behavior Theory" has been cross-cultural investigations. Cultural differences provide an inviting opportunity to investigate the childhood antecedents of personality characteristics. If we make the assumption that the personality differences from one culture to another are at least partially a consequence of the patterns of child rearing in that culture, then we have a method of investigation which offers certain advantages over the study of children and adults in our own culture. In the first place, there are much greater differences in child rearing practices between cultures than within a single culture. Secondly, practices which are normal in one culture may be extremely deviant in another. Therefore, if we search for extreme child raising practices in our own culture, we cannot be sure whether the consequences depend solely upon the practice or partly upon the fact that the practice is atypical. On the other hand, cross-cultural research is bedeviled with its own set of difficult methodologic problems, because the child training practices appear in a different cultural context in different cultures. Nobody knows, for example, whether parental authoritarianism has the same effect in a culture with well-defined age and sex roles that it has in a culture in which age and sex roles are relatively vague, as in our own society.

Some of the fruits of cross-cultural studies of socialization have been published by Whiting and Child.[14] Just to illustrate the ingenuity of their research, let me give you an example of their findings. They noted certain aspects of child training practices in some 75 cultures from a careful study of ethnographies; at the same time, they categorized the beliefs about illness prevalent in each culture. In some cultures, for example, illness is thought to be the responsibility of the patient. It is the result of some sin or stupidity on his part. In other cultures, the illness is attributed to something else: bad luck, the spirits, witchcraft, etc. Whiting and Child make the assumption that the belief in patient responsibility is indicative of guilt feelings. Thus, they predict that cultures which raise children in such a way as to produce guilt, tend to be those which have such a belief. Lo and behold, it panned out. Cultures which are rated high in the amount of anxiety produced by socialization practices tend to be those which believe in patient responsibility for illness.

It would be much better, of course, not to depend upon published ethnographies for obtaining information about child training practices, and to have more direct measures of adult personality than those obtained by this sort of ingenious but tortuous reasoning. Whiting, Child and Lambert are supervising a research project during the next three years to collect and analyze comparable child raising and personality data from five different cultures.

Still a third important focus of interest in childhood antecedents of adult personality has been on the effect of institutionalization of infants and separation from the mother. We will hear tomorrow from Dr. Goldfarb about one such study. Bowlby,[2] of the Tavistock Clinic, has also made important contributions to this area of research.

I would like to speak about a recent theoretic contribution of Bowlby,[3] which stems from his research, rather than about the research project itself, because it seems to me to be one of the indications of a new theoretic orientation toward child development which holds great promise. Dr. Bowlby has evidently been influenced by the work of Tinbergen[13] on instincts. In the article in *New Biology* to which I refer, he discusses critical periods in the development of social behavior in terms of the maturation of instinctive reactions, and their modification through learning.

The notion of critical periods of development has been in the air for a long time. It appeared in several of the early studies of maturation by McGraw,[8] for example. Erikson[4] formulated it in psychoanalytic terminology a few years ago. It seems to me that tying this idea into the theories of Tinbergen is a very promising trend.

In the first place, I have been impressed, as no doubt many of you have, with the structural similarity between psychoanalytic theory and Tinbergen's theory of instincts. Tinbergen has investigated fairly simple responses of the lower animals. He has described the instinct as an innate behavior-releasing mechanism. The organism makes a predictable response to the appropriate releasing stimuli. In some sorts of instinctive behavior there is one set of stimuli which evokes the behavior, and other sets which guide it. When Tinbergen tries to describe the properties of this mechanism he finds it necessary to conceive of an instinct as a dynamic tension system in which tension can accumulate. The consequence of this accumulation is that the organism becomes more and more sensitive to those stimuli which release the instinctual behavior. The tension can accumulate sufficiently to produce spontaneous instinctive behavior in the absence of appropriate stimuli. Tinbergen describes, for example, flycatching behavior in certain species of birds even in the absence of any "fly-like" stimulus, provided the instinctual mechanism is very sensitive. The tension can find discharge in irrelevant instinctual behavior—which Tinbergen calls "displacement"—when the appropriate behavior is blocked or when two incompatible instincts are simultaneously elicited. The basic resemblance to psychoanalytic theory is obvious.

The advantage of the Tinbergen formulation over the usual psychoanalytic one is that he describes a releasing mechanism. It has always seemed to me that psychoanalytic theory lacked an adequate set of constructs for predicting what external situations elicit what instinctive behavior. Furthermore, the Tinbergen theory permits a broader range of instinctive activities than does psychoanalytic theory, although they do not differ so much if one considers all the behavior Freud called partial instincts. The Tinbergen formulation, on the other hand, seems far too simple and too automatic in its present form to account for many aspects of human behavior. Tinbergen does not face many of the problems of control of instincts. Certainly, his belief that the releasers for instinctive behavior are simple unitary stimuli makes it extremely difficult to describe socalled intelligent behavior in his terms. Tinbergen says practically nothing about the development of instincts; he speaks of learning but does not integrate learning concepts into his theory of instincts.

The general sort of mechanism described by Tinbergen is not an uncommon one. Piaget[10] for example, has described the "schema." The schema, as it appears in early infancy, strongly resembles the instinct as described by Tinbergen. Piaget has devoted himself to the study of the development of the schema. As he conceives of it, the schema can become detached from its historical origin and become usable as a means to various ends. Grasping develops out of the grasp reflex, but we can grasp many different objects for many different purposes. At an older age level the schema may be a complex system of abstract relations. There is , for example, a number of assumptions which are tacit in our use of the concept of number: that the sum of the parts equals the total, and that the total number is not changed by rearranging the order or distribution of parts. While Piaget has not, in my opinion, formulated a true theory either of learning or maturation, he has described some of the changes that occur during development and has shown how these changes make it possible for the mature organism to adjust to remote consequences, to conventional signs and to abstract relationships.

McClelland[7] is another psychologist who has tried to describe the differences between adult motivation and instinctive behavior as formulated by Tinbergen. He conceives of the releasing stimuli as operating in the adult, but instead of releasing overt behavior, they release feelings, emotions or motives. Then the overt behavior which satisfies these evoked motives may be quite varied and indirect.

Now we find Bowlby adopting a Tinbergen formulation of social behavior, with modifications providing for a maturation process as well as a learning process. Furthermore, he sees the maturational process as having critical periods, during which the entire course of future development is easily modified.

We should not describe all these new developments without recognizing the long history of instincts which lies behind it. This is no brand new concept, nor a completely revolutionary way of looking at it. It does perhaps represent a new and improved 1954 model of an old idea which is not plagued with some of the more troublesome characteristics of the earlier instinct hypotheses.

This situation seems to me to be ripe for important developments. It suggests the possibility of an integrating theory which might encompass and reconcile many of the theoretic differences which have hampered the progress of an adequate developmental theory.

Even if no integrating theory does emerge, these formulations suggest various interesting lines of research. What we need and what this line of thinking may provide is a theory of action as opposed to a theory of development, or a theory of learning. Tinbergen, right or wrong, points to the importance of the stimulus situation in eliciting human behavior. It seems to me that one weakness of child development research in the last fifteen years has been its attention to the developmental consequences of experiences, without any comparable study of the immediate behavioral response to situations. We have available in our everyday knowledge of human behavior myriad hypotheses which could well be tested. The hypotheses that people tend to resist impositions, that people tend to hide their defects from the public, that people are motivated to repay kindness and revenge wrongs—any one of these hypotheses could be tested and refined. They are all too simple: they all have exceptions, but they seem to have enough general validity that we guide our everyday actions by them. We try to word requests and communicate orders in such a way that they do not arouse resistance. We do not expose a person's defects to public gaze if we want him to be a friend of ours.

The importance of a theory of action is, as I see it, that it forms the basic framework which defines the personality dispositions, in whose development we are all so concerned.

This, then, is the trend in current child development research which to me offers the most promise of future theoretic developments and important practical applications. Many of you could survey the current scene and describe other exciting vistas of the future. Each of us has his own predilections and his own enthusiasms. There are, no doubt, many different directions in which research could profitably proceed. The more people who explore them, the better the outlook for the future of research in child development.

REFERENCES

1. BARKER, ROGER G.: Child psychology. Ann. Rev. Psychol., vol. II, 1951.
2. BOWLBY, JOHN: Maternal care and mental health. World Health Organization Monogr., no. 2, 1951.
3. ——: Critical phases in the development of social responses in man. New Biology, no. 14, 1953.
4. ERIKSON, ERIK H.: Childhood and Society. New York, Norton, 1950, chap. 7.
5. ESCALONA, S. K.: A non-normative study of infant behavior. Child Development Monogr., 1953.
6. FREUD, ANNA: The Ego and Mechanisms of Defense. London, Hogarth, 1937.
7. McCLELLAND, DAVID C.: The Achievement Motive. New York, Appleton-Century, 1954.
8. McGRAW, MYRTLE B.: Maturation of Behavior. In Manual of Child Psychology (Carmichael, ed.). New York, Wiley, 1946.
9. ORLANSKY, HAROLD: Infant care and personality. Psychol. Bull. 46: 1–48, 1949.
10. PIAGET, JEAN: Origins of Intelligence in Children. New York, International Universities Press, 1952.
11. SEARS, R. R.: Survey of objective studies of psychoanalytic concepts. Social Science Research Council Bull., no. 51, 1943.
12. ——, WHITING, J. W. M., NOWLIS, V. AND SEARS, P. S.: Some child rearing antecedents of aggression and dependency in young children. Genet. Psychol. Monogr., no. 47, part 2, 1953.
13. TINBERGEN, N.: The Study of Instinct. London, Oxford, 1951.
14. WHITING, J. W. M. AND CHILD, I. L.: Child Training and Personality. New Haven, Yale Press, 1953.

4

THE DEVELOPMENT OF TIME CONCEPTS IN THE CHILD*

By JEAN PIAGET, D. ès Sc.†

THE TOPIC OF THIS DISCUSSION is not the *perception of time*. Rather, we shall concern ourselves with *time concepts*, their formation and elaboration. Time, let us note, can be perceived: a brief time interval appears to us as long or short. Temporal simultaneity and successiveness can be perceived: two lamps are seen as lighting up simultaneously or successively, one after the other. Finally, there is perceived speed, which is intrinsically related to the perception of time.

But, in the first place, such perceptions are subject to more or less systematic errors. For example, at a distance of two or three meters from two lamps it is very difficult to judge whether or not they light up simultaneously. The lamp which is fixated by the observer generally appears to light up earlier.

In the second place, accurate perception is not a sufficient condition for the formation of an adequate time concept. A child, for instance, can perceive accurately two moving objects stopping at the same time. He realizes, and says, that when one stopped the other one no longer moves, and vice versa. But such perceived simultaneity does not suffice for the logical concept of simultaneity. If one of the two objects moves faster than the other, the child will refuse to accept the statement that "both stopped at the same time," because in the case of different speeds the concept of simultaneity of arrest is meaningless to him. In this case, the percept does not yet correspond to a concept.

* Professor Piaget's paper was delivered in French and was translated by Dr. Marianne L. Simmel, Illinois State Psychopathic Institute and College of Medicine, University of Illinois. The Editors are grateful to Dr. Barbeli Inhelder and Dr. Leonore Boehm for their assistance during the symposium in translating Dr. Piaget's responses to the questions from the audience, and to Miss Florence Pene and Mr. David Peretz for a preliminary translation of Professor Piaget's paper.

† Professor of Psychology, University of Geneva; Director, International Bureau of Education and the Institute Jean-Jacques Rousseau, Geneva, Switzerland.

34

The child lacks the intellectual operations by means of which the perceptual data can be analysed, integrated and interpreted.

For the above two reasons we do not believe that the perception of time provides a sufficient condition for the development of time concepts. This leads us beyond the study of the perception of time to the investigation of the intellectual operations involving time relationships. Let us discuss these now.

Classical mechanics defines speed by the ratio $v = \dfrac{d}{t}$, i.e., velocity = distance divided by time. This implies that the distance covered and the time are given as simple intuitions, as "absolutes," while speed is conceived of as a ratio. By contrast, relativity mechanics considers time as a function of speed, and speed itself as the elementary datum. We now ask: Which of these two conceptions is parallelled most closely by the psychologic development of time concepts in the child?

Time as a logical concept has two aspects: the order of the succession of events (before, after, at the same time), and the duration of intervals separating successive events. Comparison of durations can be expressed by the simple relations of inequality of more or less than ($>$ or $<$) or of the relation of equality, the same ($=$); or it can lead to a system of time measurements, such as hours, minutes, etc.

Three important stages can be distinguished in the development of the concept of time: the prelanguage stage of sensorimotor intelligence; an intermediate, "preoperative" stage between two to seven or eight years, in the course of which the child gradually attempts to execute the equivalent of sensorimotor acts on the plane of thought; and, finally, the stage of concrete operations which is attained at about seven or eight years of age.* A discussion of temporal schemata on the level of sensorimotor intelligence has previously appeared in English.† We shall therefore limit ourselves in the following to the two later stages.

* Some of the following experiments have been made in collaboration with Dr. Edith Meyer Taylor, now at Children's Hospital, Boston. Compare our joint publication *Le developpement de la notion de temps chez l'enfant* (J. Piaget in collaboration with Esther Bussmann, Edith Meyer, Vroni Richli and Myriam Van Remoortel, published in French by Presses Universitaires de France, Paris, and in German by Rascher, Zurich, but not yet published in English).

† Piaget, J.: The Construction of Reality in the Child. New York, Basic Books, 1954, chap. IV.

I. The Order of Successive Events

(1) Our studies of simultaneity reveal a close relationship between the child's notions of time and speed. Our experimental technics consist, for instance, of running with the child at either the same or different speeds between a number of fixed points. Or, small dolls or cars can be made to move across a table surface at identical or different speeds. The latter procedure does not involve the child as actively as the former, but it yields more reliable observations.

When the two moving bodies A and B start together at the same place and arrive together at another identical spot, having followed the same path and moved with the same speed, even the youngest children we tested acknowledged without difficulty the simultaneity of both arrival and departure. Certain perceptual errors occur at times, due to more prolonged visual fixation of one or the other of the two objects, but that is not a problem of intelligence.

(2) By contrast, let us consider the situation in which two moving bodies start simultaneously from the same point: B, moving more rapidly than A, has covered more distance at the moment of simultaneous arrest. Here, children of approximately four to six years of age admit without difficulty the simultaneity of departure, but not that of arrest. Yet, this is not due to any perceptual errors. The subject acknowledges easily that when B stops, A no longer moves, and vice versa. He refuses to say, however, that the objects came to rest at the same time, "together." (It is important to observe the vocabulary carefully, and to use the same expressions which the child himself uses to describe the simultaneity of events.) The child thinks that B stopped "before" A, because the former is "ahead" of the latter in the spatial sense; or he thinks that A stopped before B, stopped "first," in the sense that it is spatially closer.

In either case, he does not yet understand that both objects stopped moving "at the same time," because the notion of the "same time" as applied to two objects moving at different speeds is quite meaningless to him. He does not yet have the concept of "same time" or "common time" insofar as this implies a homogeneous, constant flow of time independent of the speeds of bodies which happen to move through it.

(3) Moreover, there is the case of two objects A and B which start at the same point and move at identical speeds, with one of

them, however, coming to rest before the second, i.e., the former having moved through less distance than the latter. Here, children between four and six years of age show considerable difficulty in trying to dissociate temporal and spatial priority. Similar phenomena can be observed in adults, given certain stimulus configurations and greater speeds of movement. This can be demonstrated, for instance, with the technics which Michotte used to study the perception of causality. But we are dealing here, in the adult, with perceptual errors, not with concepts.

In summary it can be said that, at the "preoperative" level of development, the child's judgments of simultaneity or successiveness in time depend on the equality or inequality of the speed of objects moving along the same path.

II. DURATION

(4) When a single object A leaves from position 1, moves along a straight line to position 2, then continues to position 3, the child understands without difficulty that the trajectory 1–3 takes "more time" than the trajectory 1–2. As a matter of fact, duration in this case is measured directly in terms of spatial distance, and duration is understood as a simple extension of the action symbolized by the distance covered. Thus, the child's answers are correct, without, however, indicating to us whether time concepts are adequately differentiated from perceived space.

(5) But as soon as comparisons between two separate movements are to be made, the same difficulties arise again, and are once more related to speed. For instance, in experiment (2) above, where A and B started and stopped at the same time, with B having gone faster and thus traversed greater distance, we find that children dispute the equality of the two synchronous durations, and that this equality is even more difficult to comprehend than simultaneity of the specific moments of arrest. We have found subjects between six and one-half and seven and one-half years of age who think that A and B "started at the same time" and that they "stopped moving at the same time," but that since B went farther than A, B "took more time" than A. In this case time, i.e., duration, has not been differentiated from the space traversed, from the "work accomplished" in terms of spatial displacement, and consequently also not from speed.

(6) In this connection it is interesting to note that the statement "faster" implies "more time" for the child. This can be observed in a large proportion of children between the ages of four and six, and even up to seven or eight years, the exact proportions depending on the specific experimental condition. For example, we ask the child how long it takes to walk from his home to school. He answers: "Not long at all" or "Ten minutes."

"And if you run, is it faster or slower?"

"Faster, of course."

"Does it take more time or less time?"

"More time." This answer, which is frequent before age seven, is not simply a verbal automatism. (In French, the word *"plus"* is part of both expressions *"plus vite,"* faster, and *"plus de temps,"* a longer time, and one might think the child is simply perseverating in this response.)

Comparison of two objects rolling at different speeds down two planes inclined at different angles leads the child often to the statement that the faster object takes more time, even if the question of speed has not been introduced previously. Such cases are not the general rule, but they are frequent nevertheless. They demonstrate that the expression "more time" is translated to mean "more work" or "more effort," etc.

(7) For the study of concepts of equality of synchronous durations of events the following experiment yields more precise observations than (5) above. We use a glass tube with two arms, an inverted Y, with one stopcock controlling the flow in the two arms. The latter is to facilitate the understanding of simultaneity of start and cessation of flow. Equal amounts of a colored liquid flow through each of the two arms and then fall into two receptacles, e.g., glasses, which are placed side by side underneath the outflows. If the receptacles have the same shape and size, such that the water collected in one is, at any given time, at the same level as that in the other, the child agrees readily that the water has run "the same (length of) time" to fill the two containers. But if one of the two glasses is narrower and longer, such that the water in it rises to a higher level than that in the other glass, the child between four and six believes that the water in the former flowed "longer" than that in the latter, even though he clearly perceived the simultaneity of beginning and end of flow, having ob-

served the whole transparent apparatus during the entire procedure. In this experiment the relation "longer" can be linked either to the speed with which the water rises in the narrower receptacle, or to the distance traversed, i.e., the greater height of the latter; both cases demonstrate again that duration is evaluated in terms of work accomplished.

III. The Coordination of Successive Events and Their Duration

(8) Approximately one-half of the children succeed in mastering the operations of temporal succession (grouping of "before," "after" and "simultaneously") before they grasp the operations of duration in time (inclusion of time intervals and synchronization). The remainder learn to manipulate duration before succession of events. This is in marked contrast to the "preoperative" stage (before age seven to eight), where we rarely find simultaneous organization of two such systems. Their lack of mutual integration is precisely one of the signs of the inadequacy of primitive time concepts. (See [7] above: simultaneity does not imply equality of synchronous durations.)

(9) Successive events are organized seriatim; "before" and "after" are the definitive relationships in a chain of events. A before B, B before C; therefore, A before C, etc. Duration of events, by contrast, presupposes a system of inclusions (parallel to that of the inclusion of logical classes): for example, interval AB < interval AC < interval AD, etc.

Once either of these two systems of "operation" has been mastered, there remains the problem of integrating it with the other system. This qualitative synthesis is a most interesting subject for further study. It results in the logical coordination which, strictly speaking, is a systematic concept of time prior to the attainment of measuring operations (system of time measurements).

The following procedure demonstrates this clearly. Two connected containers are placed one above the other. They may have the same cylindric shape or, better still, the upper one may be balloon or pear shaped, and the lower one cylindric. The outflow of the upper vessel into the lower is regulated step-wise by a stopcock. Prior to the experiment a series of multicolored line drawings of the two containers are prepared. On these separate sheets the child fills in the levels of liquid observed successively in the upper and lower vessels. This completed, the diagrams are shuffled and the child is asked to rearrange them in the correct series, i.e., to reconstruct the successive order of liquid levels in the two vessels. Thereupon the sheets are cut in the middle, separating the upper and the lower containers, and then shuffled once more. Now the child is to indicate the level of water in the upper vessel corresponding to a given level in the lower container, and vice versa, by selecting the proper drawing. This implies the ordering of two series which are inversely related: a high level of the liquid in one container corresponds to a low level in the other. At the same time, these drawings can be used as a basis for questions concerning duration. For instance, we ask the child whether intervals A–C between the first three levels depicted in the upper container have consumed more or less time than the corresponding intervals A–B–C in the lower containers. The same problem is also demonstrated on the vessels themselves. Finally, by means of this arrangement the child can be led to the discovery of a system of measurement of time. If the intervals A–B, B–C, C–D, etc., between successive water levels in one container are equal, then the consideration of n such intervals constitutes a system of measurement of time.

Thus, the above-described experimental device lends itself to quite an extensive study of the coordination of a sequence of events and the inclusion of time intervals. Once more it demonstrates that logical operations presuppose reversibility of intellectual operations. Even though time itself is physically irreversible, i.e., the flow of time during which events occur cannot be turned back upon itself, it is logically and mathematically possible to reorder the events in reverse sequence. This is what small children may object to. A boy of six years told us that it was impossible to compare the intervals A–B and D–E, which were correctly depicted on his diagrams, "because when the water is here (pointing to D–E), it is no longer here (at A–B), and therefore I can't tell." At approximately seven to eight years the sequential operations pertaining to series of events and inclusions of time intervals are sufficiently coordinated to allow for the resolution of these problems.

(10) We can study the coordination of temporal successions and durations also at the purely verbal level in the following manner:

(a) First we ask the child if he has a friend who is older than he.

If the subject is six years old, he may tell us about a friend who is seven. Usually he will spontaneously add that his friend is older "because he is bigger," as if age were measured in terms of height. This is another example of the estimation of time as a function of spatial distance covered or work accomplished, because height is a spatial characteristic and height attained an indication of accomplishment.

(b) We then proceed to ask the six year old whether his seven year old friend was born before him or after him. Since there is yet no coordination of temporal succession and duration, the child answers, "I don't know, I have never asked him," or "I have to ask his mother," etc. Age and birthdate are not coordinated before the ages of seven or eight by about 75 per cent of the Geneva children we have studied.

(11) Once the coordination of operations of temporal succession and time duration is accomplished, we can go on to the organization of systems of time measurements. Prior to that time nothing is gained by the utilization of a watch or an hourglass while we question the child concerning the above problems, because the small child of four to six years does not understand that the speed of movement of hands on a watch, or the speed of flow of sand in an hourglass are constant. For example, if the child observes a watch in order to estimate the time taken by an object to execute a rapid movement, the hand of the watch appears to him to move more slowly than if he tries to estimate the time taken by an object in slower motion. This is due to perceptual contrast. The opposite may also happen. The watch hand appears to move faster for the faster moving object, due to perceptual assimilation. Even as adults we experience such perceptual illusions, but they do not enter into our reasoning processes, while the child sees no reason why he should assume that the rate of displacement of the watch hand or the rate of flow of sand in the hourglass is constant. He has not yet the intellectual tools to understand the problem of conservation of speed.

We see, therefore, that the construction of a system of time measurements presupposes also the concept of speed, as did all the preceding temporal operations. The development of systematic time concepts is thus at no point independent of the understanding of concepts of speed.

IV. The Concept of Speed

(12) Speed can be perceived, but the *perception* of speed is not a sufficient condition for the development of the *systematic concept* of speed—and for two reasons. In the first place, the perception of speed is subject to multiple errors. We are now engaged in a study of these errors and their relation to Michotte's experiments on the perception of causality. Secondly, even the correct perception of speed does not necessarily imply the transition to its conceptual representation in the form of the relationship $v = \dfrac{d}{t}$. In fact, we have already established (see above [5]–[11]) that duration itself is such a relationship: $t = \dfrac{d}{v}$. The problem for the child is now to construct the two relations simultaneously $\left(t = \dfrac{d}{v} \text{ and } v = \dfrac{d}{t} \right)$, for which the perception of speed is not a sufficient condition at all.

However, an intuitive representation of speed does exist, which is accessible at all ages, and which is that of "passing" or "overtaking." If one moving object overtakes another on a straight path, the child at all ages understands that the former goes faster than the latter. It is easy to show that this is due specifically to the act of overtaking, and not to the comprehension of $v = \dfrac{d}{t}$. For instance, we let the child compare two objects, moving along parallel paths, one from A to B, and the other from A to C, such that AC > AB. If the objects move through opaque tunnels, the child between four and six years holds that they move with the same speed, "because they arrive at the same time at the other end of the tunnel," even though he just previously told us that tunnel AC is longer than tunnel AB, a clarification which always precedes the experiment proper. If we now remove the tunnels, the child sees that the object moving along AC goes faster than the other one, because the former overtakes the latter. Thereupon the child extends the intuition of "passing" from "catching up" to literal "overtaking," by simply extending in his thought the path of the seen movement. These forms of judgment of speed are essentially independent of the concept of time, since catching up and overtaking are directly perceived as a function of the order of successive positions.

(13) The conservation of relationships of speed is achieved only around the age of seven to eight years. One may ask a child to draw the successive paths of a toy automobile which is made to move in a succession of steps, the movement for each step being of the same duration and the same speed. Before ages seven to eight the child reproduces trajectories of unequal lengths, but around age seven or eight this problem can be solved without difficulty.

(14) The equation $v = \dfrac{d}{t}$ (velocity is a ratio of the distance traversed to the time it takes to cover it) can be understood only once the coordination of temporal duration and temporal succession has been attained, i.e., when the concepts of time and speed (as defined by $\dfrac{d}{t}$) are solidly established. In other words, the child has arrived at a systematic notion of duration when he understands that duration is not simply a function of the distance traversed or the work accomplished $(t = d)$, but when duration has become inversely proportional to speed $\left(t = \dfrac{d}{v} \right)$. Once this is clearly established, he is ready to comprehend that speed itself is a similar ratio $\left(v = \dfrac{d}{t} \right)$.

V. Conclusions

I. The elaboration of the concept of time is not simply a function of perceptual data, but implies a progressive structurization of these data, which is accomplished by a sequence of logical operations.

II. The structure of these logical operations is at first simple, i.e., they are qualitative. They consist of the following:

(a) The seriation of before and after, i.e., the sequential ordering of asymmetric, transitive successive events, such as

   (1) $A \rightarrow B \rightarrow C \rightarrow etc.$

(a′) The special case is that of simultaneity, i.e., not succession, as in

   (2) $A \rightarrow B \rightarrow C$
       $\updownarrow \quad \updownarrow \quad \updownarrow$
       $A' \rightarrow B' \rightarrow C'$

where A and A′, B and B′, etc., are simultaneous events.

(b) The inclusive relationship of intervals which constitute duration:

(3) AB < AC < AD < *etc.*

from which follows

(4) AB + BC = AC *etc.*

AC − BC = AB *etc.*

(c) The coordination of durations *qua* intervals between events within the sequence of succession of such events:

(5) A → B → C → *etc.*

$$\underbrace{\underbrace{\text{A} \to \text{B}}_{\text{AB}} \underbrace{\to \text{C}}_{\text{BC}}}_{\text{AC}} \to etc.$$

III. Once these qualitative operations have been accomplished, operations of measurement can be attained with the introduction of temporal units:

(6) if   AB = BC = CD = *etc.*
then AC = 2AB, AD = 3AB *etc.*

IV. To each of the above operations of succession and duration there is a corresponding parallel operational structure of speed: $t = \dfrac{d}{v}$ and $v = \dfrac{d}{t}$. Thus, psychologically speaking, time is defined by the coordination of speeds, just as space is defined by the coordination of displacements, i.e., movements irrespective of the attribute of speed.

Discussion of Chapters 1–4

By DOROTHEA McCARTHY, Ph.D.*

IT SEEMS APPROPRIATE after this paper on the concept of time that we discuss the *last* paper *first*. It is indeed a great pleasure for me to be here today and to have this opportunity to meet and hear Dr. Piaget, whose work I have found most stimulating over the past thirty years. It is, however, frustrating and somewhat ironic that we, who are so interested in children's language, should find ourselves separated by a barrier of communication. As I read the brief English abstract of Dr. Piaget's paper, I found myself trying to relate his observations on children's perceptions of time and speed to certain aspects of language. For example, does he find the child progressing to more advanced stages in these concepts at about the same ages that he begins to use past and future tense in his spontaneous speech? It would also be interesting to try to relate such observations as Dr. Piaget has reported to the child's ability to refer to remote as well as to immediate time. Ames[1] found that at about four years of age children were able to use past and future about 10 per cent of the time, but that they rarely referred to past and future times earlier or later than the day of speaking.

Another aspect of this problem which intrigues me is perhaps a semantic one. Dr. Piaget's method, as I understand it, is essentially that of verbal report with children whose language is in the process of developing sharpness and clarity of meaning. The use of verbal terms such as "before," "after," "faster," "sooner," etc., are inherent in the method. The child may not yet have clear concepts for those words and may not be using them in the same sense as adults. Some of the illustrations given in the paper seem to indicate that the child may be using such words as "faster," "first," and the like, as generalized *quantity* words which are in the process of becoming more specific. When the method involves the child's use of language, how much can we conclude about his concepts, or is all concept formation inextricably bound up with the ability to express concepts verbally?

* Professor of Psychiatry, Fordham University Graduate School, New York City.

It seems to me we should establish first that the child is using certain key words for such an experiment in the same sense that the examiner is, and then proceed to study his use of these terms in a series of increasingly complex problems. Perhaps Dr. Piaget has done this very thing, but it was not clear to me from the abstract.

I would also like to be able to relate some of Dr. Piaget's findings to a recent manuscript by de Hirsch[8] which reports that children with specific language disturbances show marked difficulty in experiencing Gestalten in terms of spatial and temporal relationships. De Hirsch relates this phenomenon to the difficulties experienced by the brain-injured in distinguishing figure from background. She considers speech as a temporal succession of sounds against a background of silence, and she claims that children with language disturbances have difficulty in making the necessary figure-ground distinctions. In clinical tests, for instance, she reports that children who suffer from various language disorders have great difficulty in reproducing a series of taps.

I enjoyed thoroughly Dr. Bayley's charming, delightful and dynamic sketch of the developmental process. She presented the highlights of what is known on fetal behavior as well as an accurate picture on into adolescence, with due regard for the magnitude of individual differences. My only serious doubt about the studies she reports concerns the interpretation of the reasons for crying behavior observed during physical examinations. I suppose most people would agree that when a baby cries while someone is taking his temperature, that particular process may reasonably be considered a cause of crying. I am rather disturbed, however, by the subjective interpretations of the examiners regarding such vague things as "fatigue," "strangeness of the situation," and the "use" of crying to gain attention. Perhaps we need to remind ourselves once more of the pioneer study of Sherman,[17] using the motion picture technic in observing emotional behavior, in which it was found that the interpretation was related to the background of the observer and to his knowledge of the stimulus, rather than to the behavior of the child. We could grant concomitance in the study Dr. Bayley reported, but I wonder if we could agree with her on the matter of causation?

I was especially interested in the description of emotional tone of the babies as unhappy, withdrawn or anxious. It seems so similar to the picture of clinical cases at higher ages who do not learn to read. If we could really find out why some children are so adversely affected by disturbances in family situations, and others are not, I think we would have solved a very basic problem having tremendous implications for mental health.

With regard to the measurement of intelligence in infancy, I have a strong suspicion that the reason most infant tests have not proved satisfactory before about 18 months to two years of age is that children have not developed language before that age. At higher age levels, the verbal factor has had the best predictive value, but the infant tests have largely neglected the verbal factor at the earliest levels. Contrary to Dr. Bayley's report that differences in parental socioeconomic status are not related to children's intelligence test scores in infancy, we have the very interesting study by Brodbeck and Irwin[4] who found marked socioeconomic differences in the prelinguistic babblings of infants even in the first six months of life. By using a phonetic analysis, developmental curves of such measures as consonant frequency and consonant-vowel frequency ratio show excellent differentiation between upper and lower socioeconomic levels, and between children living in institution settings and those living in family environments. An article by Catalano and myself[6] indicates that various phonetic measures of infant speech correlate $+.45$ with Stanford Binet IQ at 42 months of age. This was for only 23 cases in the lower ranges of ability. This method of studying infant speech seems promising, however, and worth studying on a larger scale. I would also like to see what the new British infant scale by Ruth Griffiths[7] will yield, as it has a separate speech and hearing scale. My hunch is that if we can measure the verbal factor in its incipient stages in infancy, we may have something which will behave in a manner similar to the standard intelligence tests at higher age levels.

I was especially interested in Dr. Bayley's presentation of the study by Macfarlane, Allen and Honzik on the behavior problems reported by the mothers over such a wide age range. It seems to show so well the importance of the attitude of the parents in determining what is and what is not problem behavior. I would like to check the findings of the study with the many statements regarding the characteristic problems of various age levels which are repeatedly presented as established facts in certain syndicated columns of the daily press. It seems to me, however, that such a study should be done on 500 or 1000 cases to give us dependable norms for each age level over such a wide age range.

I would also like to know how the personality characteristics of the mothers were measured in the study of Macfarlane et al., and just what traits were studied. I find it difficult to harmonize the statement that, "The personality characteristics of the mothers for the most part showed little relation to the children's problems," with the material reported earlier on children who were disturbed by periods of family stress. This is a phenomenon with which every clinician is familiar. Bayley states that there was little relation, and that the correlations were "of the order of .3 or less," yet she quotes Macfarlane to the effect that, "The mother who is painfully self-conscious and feels inferior is likely to have children who are overdependent, excessively reserved, destructive, have mood swings, are irritable and somber." Is this Macfarlane the research worker or Macfarlane the clinician speaking? Is this the correct interpretation of the data, is she going beyond the data, or were the instruments for measuring mothers' attitudes sufficiently reliable to yield a satisfactory indication of this crucial matter?

The two papers by Dr. Baldwin and Dr. Dennis can be discussed together since both are concerned with a broad overview of the field of child psychology, taking stock of how far we have come and whither we are going. It would be hard to find two such different descriptions of the same period of development of the same science. Dr. Baldwin admits there has been an "ebb-tide" in the field, but he is full of hope and optimism and is vigorously looking forward to new strides. Dr. Dennis takes a much more pessimistic view. Some of his points may be justified, but I would like to try to account for them, and to suggest reasons why certain conditions seem to exist in the field today. I definitely disagree with certain other points made by Dr. Dennis.

I liked very much Dr. Baldwin's cogent description of the two main periods in the field of child development. They indicate quite accurately the stages I too have sensed as I have worked in the field during both periods. I like to think of the two emphases as the *what* phase and the *why* phase. In the twenties and thirties we were very busy with normative studies, surveying the field and merely describing what happens and showing how children grow. The picture is by no means complete and there will always be room for filling in details, confirmation and correction of norms to suit the time and the place. Descriptions of normal behavior are, of course, important, and give necessary frames of reference, but they seldom go far to help with a particular problem of a disturbed child and his parent who come to the clinic for help.

Thy *why* period, which has come as the result of the rapid increase in demands for clinical services in community agencies, is the one which Dr. Baldwin describes as "living off the hypotheses coming from psychoanalysis." I was particularly interested in his apt reference to those who have been "too captivated by the descriptions of normative behavior." I also feel that too many able persons in the field have developed a fixation, and have continued to worship too long at the shrine of maturation. They seem to have been too content with the *what* and the *how* of the developmental process, and have not progressed to the *why*. Perhaps they have not yet arrived at the age of asking "the *whys* of causal relationships," described elsewhere by Piaget.[16]

Dr. Baldwin seems to sense a change in the quality of the research being reported recently. He seems to feel we are working on more significant problems, but with cruder tools, and arriving at less conclusive results than in the earlier more precise studies.

Dr. Dennis is describing much the same phenomena in the history of child psychology when he speaks of the three kinds of activities: exploration, analysis of relationships and the search for causality. I think we are moving away from the first two kinds of activity and are increasing our research in the third. I agree with Dr. Dennis in his pleas for originality and creativeness, but I do not agree that the field has been backward, unproductive or at a standstill, as he seems to imply. If we examine his own yardstick and compare Murchison's[15] *Handbook of Child Psychology* (1933) with Carmichael's[5] *Manual of Child Psychology* (1954), we find that over 3000 more references appear in the latter volume. This represents an increase of about 110 per cent. In other words, the amount of material reviewed has more than doubled in the twenty-one year period. That is not backwardness, to my way of thinking. Apparently, the "backwardness" is only relative to certain fields of psychology which have mushroomed since World War II, for some very good reasons which I shall point out in a moment. While speaking of the Carmichael *Manual*, it should be pointed out that the authors finally represented are not always the editor's first choices, but rather are those who could, and would co-operate in such a laborious but unrewarding undertaking. Eight of the 1933 authors died in the intervening years, or there might have been considerably more overlapping of the two volumes in authorship. Continued activity of certain individuals in the field does not imply absence of newcomers in this instance. One of the main reasons for continuing with the same authors, where possible, was because the tremendous spade work of bibliographic background had already been done by those individuals. It further seems that *we*, as developmental psychologists, should be the last to imply that, because the same persons have contributed to two volumes, there will not be change. People *can* and *do* change. They grow and mature in their professional point of view, in their outlook and in their ability to interpret and synthesize material. This is definitely reflected in the new volume. Jersild,[12] in the preface to the fourth edition of his *Child Psychology* (1954), which has spanned the same twenty-one year period, states:

> I can say it has become virtually a new book. I have again treated the objective and behavioral aspects of human development as thoroughly as feasible, but I have given much more attention than before to the personal and subjective aspects of the child's life . . . now I have taken a full leap in emphasizing the concept of the self as an essential consideration in the study of all features and phases of developmental psychology.

If Dr. Escalona, who I am replacing on the program this morning, had been able to be here, I am sure she would have made a plea for recognition of Lewin's[13] topological psychology as an attempt at formulation of a theory which has had a considerable impact on the thinking of many people. I feel that Irwin's[9-11] phonetic analysis of infant speech represents an advance somewhat analogous to that of piercing the sound barrier in aviation. The attention given to this work in George Thompson's[18] text would seem to indicate that he, too, considers it an important advance in method, opening up new vistas.

Since the publication of Bradley's[3] *Childhood Schizophrenia* in 1941 we have seen notable contributions in the field of child psychiatry by several contributors to today's program, especially by Dr. Bender and Dr. Despert. In fact, there has occurred in recent years the birth of the whole new field of child psychiatry, which is intricately involved with the older field of child psychology. The founding of two new journals, *The Journal of Child Psychiatry* and the *Quarterly Journal of Child Behavior* in the past six years must also indicate flourishing growth in this field.

Then, too, the outstanding contributions of Dr. Benda[2] in the area of psychopathology, especially that regarding the role of the endocrines in the causation of mongolism and cretinism, is also a milestone of first importance. We shall indeed be privileged to hear from these investigators this afternoon.

I also feel that there has been a marked convergence of the developmental approach and the clinical point of view. This is a healthy thing in some ways because it tends to make researchers attack more vital problems. It is difficult to do this, however, without lowering our scientific standards, because of the eternal conflict between service and research orientations. I think this is what Dr. Baldwin means when he complains of the poorer quality of publications nowadays and that research is in the hands of the practitioners. I am not too concerned on this score, however, because I think it is only an indication of transition, as we emerge from the ebb-tide into the flow of a new era in child psychology. Mowrer[14] says in the preface of his *Learning and Personality Dynamics:*

> Our knowledge in this area (contemporary psychologic science) has been derived from two distinct scientific approaches, two roads to the same destination; that of the laboratory and that of the clinic. A few decades ago these two approaches seemed to have little in common and to be aiming in different directions. But today, with a growing number of younger psychologists who have respectable training in the concepts and techniques of both experimental and clinical psychology, the trend toward integration and unification is widespread and vigorous. Today it is by no means uncommon to find psychologists who are equally versed and interested in laboratory research and in psychotherapy or other clinical work and who move freely, both in their thinking and in their activities, from one to the other.

Now, as to the reasons for the relative lag in child psychology compared to the rapid developments in clinical and military psychology and human engineering (mentioned by Dr. Dennis), many of you will recall that the big impetus to research in child development was sparked by the large grants of money from the Laura Spellman Rockefeller Foundation which started several child welfare institutes in various universities which have been most productive of research. A big spurt in the clinical field came at about the same time, when the Commonwealth Fund started child guidance clinics as demonstration centers in several of our large cities. Funds in support of research with children have subsequently been withdrawn in many instances, and have been given instead to work with the aging, allegedly because of the increasing average age of the population. Now, however, with the increasing birthrate, we should be able to attract more financial support for child development research on normal children. Much of the available money seems to go for work with handicapped groups. Irwin, for example, is now working entirely with the small group of cerebral palsied children.

Another aspect of the problem is that most of the major descriptive normative studies have been done, and there is less glory in improving and refining norms than there is in blazing a new trail. The next major investigations which need to be done require foundation support over a long time. They are beyond the scope of what is feasible in the usual Ph.D. dissertations, which so far have contributed the bulk of our knowledge in the field.

In many universities there is little money available for research, and clinical facilities and demonstration schools and clinics are expensive ways to teach. Many colleges offer child psychology as a next course after an introductory psychology course, but do not offer advanced work in the area for graduate students, which would lead them into research in the field. Too often this is due to lack of appreciation of the developmental point of view by psychologists in other fields who administer training programs. Young students are often introduced to the abnormal early in their training, before they have the proper frames of reference regarding the normal. Students with a general interest in psychology who are about to specialize, are naturally attracted to areas where money is available, and in recent years the government-supported-project research has given many of them their first jobs. This has tended to foster research oriented toward practical problems of interest to the Armed Forces, the Veterans Administration or the United States Public Health Service. This is not the type of research which is likely to lead to important contributions to theory, and it is discouraging to others whose interest remains in the field of child psychology. Economic conditions are such that few persons find it possible to do research for the love of it, as in the old days, and many who could are less motivated, unable to do it without remuneration, when on every hand their associates and their students are being well paid for working on what seem to them like less significant problems.

Another difficulty is that child psychology has attracted large numbers of women. Few young men of research-producing age are sufficiently mature in their attitudes, and sufficiently secure in their masculine roles to dedicate their lives to research in child psychology. Many also go directly into military service and become sidetracked. Among the women trained in the field, many marry and apply their knowledge in bringing up their own children, but they are lost to research for a number of years. Those who return to the field after their children are grown find themselves barred from university positions because of insurance and pension plans which necessitate refusing permanent appointments to persons in their early forties. Many other women attracted to work with children go into nursery school and parent education work, and still others into routine clinical work. Those who are seeing patients from nine to five have little remaining energy or opportunity to do research of a high order, just as the practicing physician ordinarily does not make outstanding contributions to medical research.

I am in hearty agreement with Dr. Dennis on the need for more experimental work using control groups. The research worker's Utopia which he describes, however, I am afraid is not likely to be realized in the near future. Taxpayers are not yet supporting schools and institutions adequately in regard to minimum essentials of classroom space, and teachers' salaries and teaching materials. School administrators are not likely to give office space and equipment or pay salaries to research workers until they have solved these other problems which to them are more urgent. I believe it would be possible to get many administrators to group children for experimental purposes, but I believe the support for the research would have to come from outside the school or institutional budget. Sometimes there are ethical issues involved also in assigning human beings to experimental and control groups. On many issues there is preliminary evidence in favor of one practice or another which makes it difficult for school administrators to justify the denial of what seems to be the better practice to half the population of his school.

Another difficulty in getting control subjects is the problem of securing cooperation from the families of well-adjusted children. We need to do a job of selling ourselves so that families having no problems serious enough to require clinical service will cooperate by divulging personal matters comparable to the information contained in social histories secured on clinical cases.

It seems to me, therefore, that child psychologists need to do a good job of public relations in selling themselves to the public in order to gain support for, and cooperation in, research. I get a little tired of the perennial jokes in magazine cartoons and on television in which the child psychologist or the psychiatrist is the scapegoat. It makes me wonder where we have failed. Every such incident lessens the chance for therapy and cooperation in research of many potential subjects. We have not been proud either of the large numbers of children needing clinical help who were brought up "by the books" based on the rigid habit-training principles of the era of watsonian behaviorism. But we have moved a long way in a more constructive direction. We need to see many more evaluative follow-up studies in settings where research results have been applied, in order to judge their effectiveness. Such studies need to be reported, not only in scientific journals, but in more popular outlets as well, so as to gain the support of those who are in a position to contribute to the cause of research in child psychology.

REFERENCES

1. AMES, L. B.: The development of the sense of time in the young child. J. Genet. Psychol. *68:* 97–125, 1946.
2. BENDA, C. E.: Mongolism and Cretinism. New York, Grune & Stratton. 1949.
3. BRADLEY, C.: Schizophrenia in Childhood. New York, Macmillan, 1941.
4. BRODBECK, A. J. AND IRWIN, O. C.: The speech behavior of infants without families. Child Devel. *17:* 145–156, 1946.
5. CARMICHAEL, L.: Manual of Child Psychology. New York, Wiley, 1954.
6. CATALANO, F. L. AND McCARTHY, D.: Infant speech as a possible predictor of later intelligence. J. Psychol. *38:* 203–209, 1954.
7. GRIFFITHS, RUTH: The Abilities of Babies. New York, McGraw-Hill. 1954.
8. DE HIRSCH, K.: J. Nerv. & Ment. Dis., 1954 (In press).
9. IRWIN, O. C.: Research on speech sounds for the first six months of life. Psychol. Bull. *38:* 277–285, 1941.
10. ——: Infant Speech. *In* Encyclopedia of Psychology (Harriman, ed.). New York, Philosophical Library, 1946, pp. 274–276.
11. ——: Infant speech. Scient. Am. *18:* 22–24, 1949.

12. JERSILD, A. T.: Child Psychology (ed. 4). New York, Prentice Hall, 1954.
13. LEWIN, K.: The Principles of Topological Psychology. New York, McGraw-Hill, 1936.
14. MOWRER, O. H.: Learning and Personality Dynamics. New York, Ronald Press, 1950.
15. MURCHISON, C.: Handbook of Child Psychology. Worcester, Mass., Clark University Press, 1933.
16. PIAGET, J.: The Child's Conception of Physical Casuality (Gabain, transl.). New York, Harcourt Brace, 1930.
17. SHERMAN, M.: The differentiation of emotional responses in infants. J. Comp. Psychol. *7:* 265–284, 335–351, 1927.
18. THOMPSON, GEORGE G.: Child Psychology. Boston, Houghton Mifflin, 1952.

5

PSYCHOPATHOLOGY OF MENTAL DEFICIENCY IN CHILDREN

By CLEMENS E. BENDA, M.D.* *and* MALCOLM J. FARRELL, M.D.†

IT IS A GREAT PRIVILEGE to participate in a symposium on the psychopathology of childhood, a symposium which deals with the concepts of growth and development in the normal child and the pathologic deviations from such standards.

The subject of this paper is mental deficiency in children, but since it happens that one of us (MJF) is a member of the Joint Expert Committee on the mentally subnormal child convened by WHO with the participation of the United Nations, ILO and UNESCO (the newest report on the mentally subnormal child having just been issued), it may be worth while to make a few comments on the nomenclature presently in use and the suggestions made by the World Health Organization (table 1). In the United States the term "mental deficiency" has now replaced terms like "feeblemindedness" and "idiocy," terms which have been used almost interchangeably in previous decades or centuries. Britains maintain the term "feeblemindedness" for one group of the mentally defective which has been called the "moron" in the United States. The term "mental deficiency" usually covers all degrees of severity previously called "idiots," "imbeciles" and "morons." However, mental deficiency is not only used in some areas for the description of an incomplete development of intelligence, but applies also to incomplete emotional development with normal levels of intelligence, and in England includes even the term "moral defectives." The committee of the World Health Organization proposes at present the term "mental sub-

* Director of Research and Clinical Psychiatry, W. E. Fernald State School, Waverley, Massachusetts; Instructor, Harvard Medical School; Lecturer in Pediatrics, Tufts College Medical School, Boston.

† Superintendent, W. E. Fernald State School, Waverley, Massachusetts; Instructor in Psychiatry, Boston University Medical School and Tufts College Medical School; Lecturer, Harvard Graduate School of Public Health, Boston.

TABLE 1.—*Current and Proposed Nomenclature of Mental Subnormality**

Recommended Terms	Current Usage				Intelligence Test	
Degree of Mental Subnormality	British	American	French	German	IQ (children)	Mental Age in Years† (adults)
Mild subnormality	feeble-minded	moron	débile	debil	50–69	8–12
Moderate subnormality	imbecile	imbecile	imbécile	imbezill / schwach-sinnig	20–49	3–7
Severe subnormality	idiot	idiot	idiot	idiotisch / blödsinnig	0–19	0–2
All grades of mental subnormality	mentally defective	feeble-minded	arriéré	geistes-schwach	0–69	0–12
	amentia	mentally deficient / mentally retarded	oligo-phrène	oligo-phren		

* *From* World Health Organization Technical Report Series No. 75: The Mentally Subnormal Child, p. 8, table 1 (Geneva, April 1954).

† *According to* World Health Organization (1948) Manual of the International Statistical Classification of Diseases, Injuries and Causes of Death, Geneva, vol. 1, p. 114.

normality," to describe the mentally subnormal child. It also proposes replacement of the previous terms referring to degrees of severity by statements like "most severe," "moderately subnormal," "most mild." The term "mental retardation" is used in the report on the mentally subnormal child to refer to those whose educational and social performance is markedly lower than would be expected from what is known of their intellectual abilities. Attention may be called to the fact that although intelligence tests have a useful though limited function in the diagnosis of mental subnormality, "they describe only one aspect and it must be recognized that overlapping of the IQ's of children who on clinical grounds are in different grades is unavoidable, and that an individual's ascertained IQ may differ from time to time."

As to the frequency, there is still much argument, and different estimates vary greatly. The proportion of children regarded as educationally subnormal in Holland, based on eight large cities, is given as 2.6 per cent. French estimates range from 1.5 to 8.6 per cent, depending on age. English educational practices make provisions for 1 per cent of school children in special schools, while a further 8 to 9 per cent are considered to require special educational provisions within the ordinary school system. The estimates in the United States vary greatly in different States. Our own experiences would indicate an estimate similar to that found in England, that is, 10 per cent of children of school age require special attention. Some of these requirements are merely of the nature of counseling or psychiatric help, while 4 per cent represent actual educational difficulties. In general, uniform statistics cannot be given, since the proportions of children regarded as educationally subnormal in different countries vary greatly, both with society and with social and economic conditions.

To analyze the group of mental defectives, we would start with the idea that each child is entitled to a normal mental development, and if we find evidence that this has not been achieved, we must ask ourselves as physicians: Why is the child not functioning properly? What factors have interfered with the normal process of mentation?

By analyzing the whole group of children with inadequate performance, one may segregate those children who reveal severe emotional difficulties which interfere with their mental performance in spite of the fact that intellectual endowment appears adequate. In this way we may exclude the psychoneuroses of childhood from the discussion of mental deficiency; the inadequate mental performance is then a result of emotional factors, and the mental deficiency in this case is what has been called "pseudofeeblemindedness" (which is a rather poor term). We personally prefer to cover the whole field with the term "disorders of mentation," the term "mentation" lending itself well to the designation of mental development in general.

A more difficult discrimination is the differentiation between mental deficiency and the early forms of childhood schizophrenia in which a child is so thoroughly disturbed and lacking contact formation with the outside world that we have only indirect evidence of his mental facilities. His intellectual faculties will be revealed only in sudden flashes or must be surmised from some performances which could not be achieved if judgment and understanding of the outside world were not adequate. We may remember that the term "idiot" originally meant a "private" person not able to take public office, a term derived from the Greek and implying that the idiot is a person living in his own world, unable to *communicate*. With the discovery of childhood autism and childhood schizophrenia, it was not surprising to find among the "idiots" of old State institutions many children with autism and schizophrenia mixed in with those who may be properly designated as mentally defective. Since the problem of childhood autism and schizophrenia is left to the expert presentation of other speakers, we may restrict ourselves completely to that group of patients whose intellectual performance shows definite deficiencies in certain areas. In these cases we are justified in talking of mental defects.

It has been the main purpose of research in mental deficiency to delineate the different groups of mental deficiencies, in order to arrive at a better understanding of each group. No progress can be expected in the handling of mental deficiencies as long as they are treated as a more or less uniform group of subnormal intelligence, divided by the psychologist into different levels of defects, but left by the medical profession as an undifferentiated field. As is true in the whole field of medicine, progress can be made only if the pathology of the different conditions is established. Many scholars still talk in terms of "functional" and "organic," and distinguish between psychopathology and organic pathology as though the research deals with two different subjects, instead of realizing that we are dealing with different aspects of the same matter.

Mental performance is possible only with an adequate instrument of mentation, and there can be no doubt that our central nervous system is the instrument on which the mind plays, just as a violin is the virtuoso's means of playing his solo. With an inadequate instrument even the most accomplished artist is unable to perform to the satisfaction of his listeners. The researcher who deals with mental deficiencies has to establish, in the first place, the kind of nervous system which is at the disposal of the mentally defective patient and, as a second step, try to establish the factors which have interfered with the completion of this nervous system, the defects of which have been discovered at autopsy. Needless to say, this type of developmental neuropathology is not so much concerned with causes of death or recent histopathologic alterations, but is concerned with the developmental aspects of the nervous system and tries to establish the original failure of development underlying the abnormal performance which the psychiatrist and psychologist were able to observe.

As a first step, therefore, one of us (CEB) has collected data on about 300 autopsies done on various types of mental deficiency over a period of eighteen years, and analyzed the material according to seven different categories. Of course, these seven categories are somewhat arbitrary; they could be many times increased and they could be somewhat reduced, but it was felt that these categories were most adequate for a basic understanding of the matter under discussion.

THE MATERIAL

The actual analysis is based on 267 cases in which microscopic study was completed.

One of the most important distinctions in developmental pathology is the classification of material into the three important periods: the antenatal, the natal and the postnatal. This classification cannot take into account the differentiation between genetic, germinal and extrinsic disorders. Genetic factors which play an important role in all metabolic disorders and in some of the malformations such as cleft formations may become manifest at any time in life. In cases of amaurotic idiocy, for example, we know a difference in appearance is distinguished in the infantile, late infantile and juvenile forms. Juvenile amaurotic idiocy does not manifest itself before about ten years. A similar variation in appearance can be seen in gargoylism. A genetic disorder like Huntington's chorea may manifest itself as late as in the 20's or 30's, and the same is true for some of the genetic forms of schizophrenia. It is therefore impossible to differentiate between genetic and extrinsic disorders by an analysis of the structural pathology, since both types of disorders may have identical structural alterations. We have mentioned the germinal disorders which are due to noxious factors influencing the germ cell itself without evidence of genetic anomalies.

The prenatal disorders were divided into two groups: congenital malformations and mongolism. Disorders of the prenatal period are usually associated with congenital malformations, and comparative

TABLE 2.—*Material of the Study*

	No. of Cases	Percentage
Total Material............................	267	
Questionable, Material Excluded..........	9	
Total Material Analyzed..................	258	100
Prenatal Disorders.........................	91	35
Congenital Malformations (36, 14%) Mongolism (55, 21%)		
Paranatal Cerebral Palsies.................	61	24
Postinfectious Cerebral Palsies.............	37	14
Metabolic Disorders.......................	17	7
Neoplastic Disorders......................	12	5
Oligoencephaly...........................	40	15

pathology and experimental teratology enable us to establish a nearly exact timetable in which specific human malformations may occur in the first half of the gestation period. Although mongolism is clearly a prenatal developmental disorder, the large percentage of mongoloid autopsies and the particular pathology of mongolism justified the treatment of mongolism as a specific entity. As table 2 shows, the number of congenital malformations including mongolism was 91, or 35 per cent. Congenital malformations like agyria, microgyria, microcephalia vera and Arnold-Chiari malformation accounted for 36 cases, or 14 per cent, while there were 55 cases of mongolism, or 21 per cent.

The largest single group in our material is listed under the term "cerebral palsy," of which there were 61 cases, or 24 per cent. The use of the term "cerebral palsy" needs some explanation. The term was used in this study for all conditions of a disorder of motor expression due to cerebral defects not caused by prenatal congenital malformations or infectious diseases. The term is therefore, used here synonymously with paranatal disorders, the originally normal development of the nervous system having been interrupted by trauma or by some noninfectious agent of a vascular nature, or by asphyxiation, with cerebral motor disorders resulting. We did not use the term "birth injuries" because some paranatal disorders occur probably several weeks before the actual birth takes place, through thrombosis or infarction of the placenta, premature separation of the pla-

centa (placenta previa) or toxemias and abnormal movements of the
fetus causing strangulation by the cord around the neck. On the
other hand, some birth injuries occur after completion of the actual
birth. The term indicates the presence of lesions caused by circulatory
defects resulting in actual hemorrhages, traumatization of the brain
or anoxia.

The next group encompasses the infectious diseases of childhood
which play an important part in the causation of mental deficiency.
There were 37 cases in this material in which there was definite evidence from the history and histopathology that the condition of the
child was due to an early infection of the central nervous system.

The next important group is the group of metabolic disorders,
and this term also needs some comment. The term is used as a common denominator for a great variety of conditions ranging from cretinism, gargoylism and phenylpyruvic oligophrenia to amaurotic
idiocy, leukencephalitis and other forms of disorders of lipoid, sugar
or protein metabolism. This interesting and relatively undeveloped
field of pediatric neuropsychiatry and histopathology is bound to be
enlarged as time goes on.

Twelve cases of neoplastic malformations are included, among them
tuberosclerosis, neurofibromatosis, Sturge-Weber disease and other
phakomatoses. We also found three new cases of megalocephaly, or
macrocephaly, which is apparently a somewhat more important condition than had previously been realized. The histologic study of
these new cases indicates clearly that they should be included in the
group of neoplastic malformations related to tuberosclerosis, as
van Bogaert and others have suspected before.

The last and most problematic category is composed of 40 cases
which we have grouped under the term of "oligoencephaly" as one
type of oligophrenia distinguished by an insufficient structural development of the nervous system which is different from true microcephaly. Patients were classified as oligoencephalic after the possibility of the presence of morbid entities such as post-traumatic,
postinfectious, metabolic or neoplastic disorders had been excluded.

CONGENITAL MALFORMATIONS

Congenital malformations have to be understood as developmental
arrests or decelerations of growth in the prenatal period secondary

to interference with normal development by noxious factors. There is no doubt that a number of developmental arrests are due to genetic factors, especially cleft formations, microcephalia vera, some of the anomalies of the cerebellum, spina bifida and related conditions. However, data collected on the role of infectious diseases such as German measles or, particularly, virus diseases in the mother as well as our wealth of data on cases of mongolism have provided conclusive evidence that there is too much emphasis on the importance of genetic factors in the causation of severe forms of mental deficiency, and that the assumption of many embryologists and experimental teratologists that human malformations are mainly due to extrinsic factors is fully justified. Developmental arrests of the nervous system include anencephaly, agyria or lissencephaly, microgyria interna, microcephaly as a whole and mongolism.

With regard to mongolism, our material provides evidence that mongolism is a congenital acromicria in which the growth of the embryo has been decelerated between the 6th and 12th week of gestation. The unfortunate term "mongolism" and the implication that it is some strange "racial regression" should be abandoned. Circumstantial evidence points to the fact that the child who turns out to be mongoloid shows a fairly normal development in the very first period of organogenetic development, but that in the so-called neofetal period, growth and development are considerably slowed down, so that at the beginning of the fetal period the mongoloid fetus shows subnormal growth and incomplete development which results in essential immaturity and underdevelopment of the child at the time of birth. The mongoloid newborn shows many characteristics of "fetalism" such as the epicanthal skin-folds of the eyes, the slanting orbits, the open sutures and enlarged fontanels, incompletion of development of the sex organs and many other features. Most important in this respect is the immaturity of the nervous system, with crowding of nerve cells, incomplete differentiation of the neuronic systems and delay in myelination. The structural anomalies are clinically evident in the extreme deceleration of mental development and rate of progress.

Experimental teratology has provided a wealth of evidence that malformations are stage-specific according to the time of development in which a noxious agent operates, and a great variety of noxious agents—poisons, changes in CO_2 concentration, asphyxiation, mechanical traumata, vitamin and nutritional deficiencies and, last but not least, radiation—can be used to produce a malformation. The type of malformation depends upon the stage through which the developing embryo is passing at the specific moment when the noxious agent is operating, because those tissues will be affected which show the highest rate of developmental metabolism and which are, therefore, most susceptible to any noxious interference. Tissues which have reached a certain degree of maturity or are still in a dormant condition are slightly or not at all affected. These observations have recently been fully confirmed by the use of x-ray radiation. I refer specifically to only one of the many investigations presently under way—the studies of Samuel P. Hicks and Liane B. Russell, whose experiments show that by radiating different animals on each day of the gestation period and examining the surviving embryos at full term, a perfect timetable of developmental variations can be established. The data of their independent experiments reveal that x-ray radiation of rats on the 12th and 13th day of the gestation period produces general stunted growth and an underdevelopment of the visceral skull and the skull basis. It appears that the specific stage through which the rat passes at about the 12th day can be compared with the stage through which the human embryo passes at the 7th to 9th week. The noxious agent has a specific decelerating effect upon general growth, producing acromicria if applied during that period, but has none of these effects if radiation is applied before or after the critical stage. It is remarkable that the radiated animal of 11 days shows normal development of facial and visceral structures and the long skull, although the cranium is open, while the animal of 12th day radiation shows the acromicria and roundness of features so typical of mongoloid deficiency. The acromicric rat embryo continues to develop at a much slower rate than in other malformations.

Paranatal Brain Damage with Cerebral Palsy

As has been mentioned, the term "cerebral palsy" in this study has been identified with cerebral pathology developing in the paranatal period, and the large number of cases (61, or 24 per cent of the whole material), emphasizes the importance of circulatory nutritional factors in the causation of mental defects. There has been considerable argument whether asphyxiation or a vascular defect is more important, and investigators like Courville have recently stressed the role of asphyxiation, feeling that others overemphasize the importance of vascular involvement. From a neuropathologic viewpoint it would seem that a definite separation of these two factors cannot be made. Anoxia of the fetus, owing to strangulation by the cord, to placental thrombosis and embolism or to a long-lasting birth, as well as anoxia due to extensive anesthesia of the mother, will result in lowering of the oxygen supply to the brain tissues, but at the same time will result in circulatory anomalies, stasis, stagnation of blood flow, hyperemia, weakening of the vascular walls, petechial bleedings, subarachnoid seepage and perivascular necrosis.

The histopathologic appearance of the brain of children who were exposed to any type of anoxia, such as mentioned above, is rather uniform. An analysis of the material shows that the pathology can be divided into three main categories. There is some degree of correlation between the clinical picture and pathology.

The first group is that of more or less extensive degeneration and liquefaction of the white matter in which cystic holes appear which are confluent in later stages and may lead to a complete degeneration of the white matter. This condition has been called central porencephaly (Schwartz), encephaloclastic porencephaly (Yakovlev), false porencephaly and central encephalomalacia. The term cystic degeneration, however, seems to describe the condition most adequately.

The cortex and the white cores of the convolutions are not primarily involved in this condition. The cysts are formed outside of the basal ganglia and are in communication with the ventricular system only after large parts of the central white matter have been destroyed. The cysts vary greatly in size, the smaller ones being filled with a fiber meshwork, the larger ones with a clear fluid and only a few fiber strands. The cavity wall contains numerous glia cells but the glia wall is not very strong and is likely to break down gradually. In this way progressively larger cavities are formed and a whole lobe may be destroyed, leaving a cyst covered by greatly thickened leptomeningeal membranes. In this stage the cortical architecture is destroyed, but remnants of the gray matter may still be recognizable.

This type of lesion is not related to any particular vascular patterns, but seems to depend upon ischemic necrosis. Microscopic examination of the brain in general seems to indicate that the glia is destroyed in the same manner as the nerve tissue, which may account for the lack of reparatory response. This condition is associated with decerebrate rigidity, or the true type of Little's spastic rigidity, or "Starre."

The second type of pathologic condition is that of mantle sclerosis, which is also known as granular or parchment atrophy of the brain, subcortical encephalomalacia and subcortical porencephaly.

The brain lesions consist of degeneration of the cortical layers with necrosis of the subcortical white matter. The white matter may present a status spongiosus in which small subcortical cysts are sometimes found. The gray matter is devoid of nerve cells which are replaced by gliosis. The leptomeningeal covering of the affected areas is greatly thickened. The subarachnoid spaces are fibrotic and contain enlarged vessels suspended in the fibrous meshwork. The pia is greatly thickened and tightly fused with the gliotic cortex. There are areas of calcification and residues of hemorrhages. The condition may affect parts of one lobe or a whole lobe or even one hemisphere. The condition is asymmetric, but may be bilateral. The distribution of the lesions indicates that their development depends upon lesions of the vascular tree. In some cases, occlusion of branches of the main arteries is the cause. In some cases, venous thromboses and sinus thrombosis are suggested as causes. In at least three of five cases under study, the sagittal sinus was found fibrotic and obliterated with little or no canalization.

The third type, clinically associated with the so-called extrapyramidal-pyramidal movements and principally with the choreoathetoid movements of the arms with spastic paraplegia of the legs, is characterized by a status marmoratus of the basal ganglia (Anton) in a high percentage of cases. Although Oscar and Cecile Vogt in their original paper considered status marmoratus a congenital malformation, they have apparently come to the conclusion that it should be considered the product of factors which are operating at the time of birth. As a matter of fact, status marmoratus can often be found in adults suffering from longlasting vascular encephalopathy.

The theory that status marmoratus is caused by a circulatory defect and oxygenation has been supported by a variety of independent investigators: Spatz, Hallervorden and Scholz in Germany,

Benda and Courville in America, Greenfield in England, and others. The assumption is based on circumstantial evidence provided by the normal development of the rest of the brain, although there may be a vascular breakdown and even status marmoratus of other areas, including the cortex. A study of status marmoratus indicates that the hypermyelination of certain fiber tracts is due to a reparative activity of the oligodendroglia. H. Spatz pointed out that the same type of diffuse and undirected outgrowth of myelinated fibers can be found after the separation of a peripheral nerve in the form of amputation neuromas. Status marmoratus cannot be considered a "scar" in itself, but the surrounding tissues show vascular necrosis, stagnation of circulation and focal gliosis in certain areas. There is also destruction of nerve cells in the affected region. The sources of the veins in the white matter are enlarged, and perivascular necrosis is found also in the putamen. The brain in general shows a confusing mixture of pale and red infarction. The symmetry of status marmoratus in the basal ganglia and its restriction to the basal ganglia in some cases (but by no means in all) indicate the importance of the great vein of Galen in the production of this condition. The great vein of Galen is the only place from which both hemispheres can be equally and symmetrically affected.

POSTINFECTIOUS DEFECTS

The influence of infectious diseases upon mentation has been recognized for a long time. In 14 per cent of the autopsy material, mental deficiency was considered due to infectious agents—a number as large as the number of congenital malformations, excluding mongolism. Congenital syphilis is gradually disappearing as a factor in mental deficiency because of the attention given to the health of the mother in the prenatal period. Toxoplasmosis, on the other hand, seems to gain increasing importance, as publications from all parts of the world indicate. This condition may affect a child prenatally, and in this instance the brain often appears hydrocephalic and cystic—the "Swiss cheese brain," as it is sometimes called. The histopathologic examination reveals granulomatous encephalitis with extensive scar formation, calcifications, cystic areas filled with gitter cells and a general encephalomyelitis. It is often possible to establish the diagnosis by the finding of toxoplasmic "cysts."

TABLE 3.—*Encephalitis and Meningitis as Causes of Mental Deficiency (Out-Patient Clinic, January 1949–March 1954)*

	No. of Cases
Cases Seen	2155
FORMS OF ENCEPHALITIS	
Measles	12
Pneumonia	4
Whooping Cough	5
Tuberculosis	1
Scarlet Fever	2
Meningoencephalitis	1
Unknown Type	23
Total Encephalitis	48 (2.2%)
FORMS OF MENINGITIS	
Influenza	3
Tuberculosis	1
Pneumococcus	1
Meningococcus	2
Otitis Media	2
Unknown Type	5
Total Meningitis	14 (0.6%)
Total, All Cases	62 (2.8%)

In order to evaluate more exactly the importance of infectious diseases in the causation of mental deficiency, we have examined all out-patient records from January 1949 to March 1954 to establish in how many instances there was evidence that mental deficiency was caused by infectious agents. Among the total number of 2155 cases seen in the out-patient clinic during that period, infectious diseases were found to account for 62 cases, or 2.8 per cent (table 3).

The cases are grouped in table 4 into 14 categories within the two large divisions of encephalitis and meningitis. An analysis of the material seems to indicate that meningitis is of less importance than encephalitis. The three cases of poliomyelitis are presented in a separate category. Further details will be found in the table with regard to the types of infections, the age at which the patient was afflicted and the chronologic and mental ages of patients when tested.

Among the different types of encephalitis, measles accounted for 12 cases; pneumonia, 4; whooping cough, 5; tuberculosis, 1; scarlet fever, 2; meningoencephalitis, 1 and encephalitis of unknown type, 23 cases. Among the cases of meningitis, influenza meningitis accounted for 3, tuberculosis for 1, pneumococcus for 1, meningococcus for 2, otitis media for 2, and meningitis of unknown type for 5 cases.

As far as statistics from other institutions are concerned, the Department of Mental Hygiene of the State of New York reported a percentage of .009 cases due to meningitis among 21,734 institutionalized patients, and the various institutions of Massachusetts reported an incidence of about .005 of meningitis on record. These very low figures for meningitis alone are probably indicative of the fact that it is often difficult to separate meningitis and encephalitis.

As to the number of mental deficiencies due to encephalitis, about $2\frac{1}{2}$ per cent of all children seen in the out-patient clinic in a period of over five years showed evidence that their mental status was due to a previous encephalitis. We have to remember that such a clinic sees all types of school problems, including perfectly normal children with emotional difficulties, reading disabilities, slow learners, behavior disorders, border-line cases and patients with IQ levels between 50 and 70 which form by far the largest group among mentally inadequate persons. Mental inadequacy on the moron level is due in about 80 per cent of the cases to "familial" or genetic factors, while infectious agents account primarily for the more severe forms.

The nature of the acute stages of meningitis and encephalitis has been thoroughly studied from post mortem material of patients who died while the active disease was in progress. These studies provide knowledge of the original alterations which take place. For the problem of mental deficiency it is significant that the ability of the nervous system to repair damage is not only very limited but the reparative processes, manifested in scar formations and fibrotic organization, often overshoot the goal. Dr. Dickinson W. Richards has recently written an illuminating paper on homeostasis and hyperexis in which he emphasizes, we think for the first time, that there is not only a tendency in nature to return to an equilibrium, as indicated by the term homeostasis, but that it is also unfortunately a characteristic

TABLE 4.—*Postinfectious Cases (Out-Patient Clinic, January 1949–March 1954)*

Type of Infection	Sex	Age Afflicted		Age Tested		Stanford-Binet IQ	Mental Age	
		yr.	mo.	yr.	mo.		yr.	mo.
ENCEPHALITIS								
Measle	M	–	18	7	11	51	4	–
Encephalitis	M	3	–	8	–	75	6	–
(12 cases)	F	–	3	3	11	11 est.	–	5
	F	3	–	7	–	33	2	4
	M	2	–	12	1	48 est.	5	10
	F	–	16	11	2	79	8	10
	M	infancy		1	5	unmanageable	?	
	F	2	–	12	3	42	5	2
	M	–	9	4	9	26	1	3
	F	1	–	7	–	38	2	8
	F	5	6	7	–	86	6	–
	F	11	–	15	4	80	11	8
Pneumonia	M	–	15	9	10	25 est.	2	4
Encephalitis	F	–	18	6	7	46	3	–
(4 cases)	M	–	3	9	3	65	6	–
	M	–	8	6	10	56	3	10
Whooping Cough	M	2	6	8	11	45	4	–
Encephalitis	F	–	3	9	5	66	6	2
(5 cases)	M	–	8	13	8	50 est.	6	10
	M	–	9	8	11	41 est.	3	8
	F	–	8	36	6	49	7	10
Tuberculosis Encephalitis (1 case)	F	1	9	4	7	14 est.		
Scarlet fever	M	3	–	24	9	47 est.	7	6
Encephalitis (2 cases)	M	1	6	4	2	unmanageable	?	
Meningo-Encephalitis (1 case)	M	–	9	18	–	35	5	6
Encephalitis of unknown type	F	?		6	–	untestable	?	
(23 cases)	M	–	7	57	11	49	7	10
	M	–	11	16	11	64	11	2
	F	prenatal		4	3	06 est.	–	3
	F	–	8	4	5	13 est.	–	7
	F	early childhood		6	–	10	–	7
	F	–	13	3	10	30 est.	–	14
	F	2	–	4	7	not tested		

70

Type of Infection	Sex	Age Afflicted		Age Tested		Stanford-Binet IQ	Mental Age	
		yr.	*mo.*	*yr.*	*mo.*		*yr.*	*mo.*
	F	2	–	13	11	04 est.	–	6
	F	infancy		5	2	10 est.	–	6
	M	–	18	7	4	10 est.	–	9
	F	–	17	4	6	20 est.	–	11
	F	–	15	4	7	31 est.	1	5
	F	infancy		3	4	45 est.	1	6
	M	–	6	10	4	51		
	M	–	15	5	7	17 est.	–	11
	F	infancy		37	11	39		
	F	early childhood		25	10	63	10	1
	M	3	–	3	11	77 est.	3	–
	M	2	–	4	9	60	2	10
	M	unknown		19	4	54	8	7
	F	1	–	16	5	49	7	10
	F	–	8	4	5	13 est.	–	7
MENINGITIS Influenza Meningitis (3 cases)	F	9	–	13	5	51	6	7
	M	5	1	7	4	68 est.	5	–
	F	2	–	4	4	56	2	8
Tuberculosis Meningitis (1 case)	M	4	–	6	5	Not tested		
Pneumococcus Meningitis (1 case)	M	–	4	1	–	untestable	?	
Meningococcus Meningitis (2 cases)	M	–	8	4	10	38 est.	1	1
	F	–	3 wk.	10	6	57 est.	6	–
Otitis Media Meningitis (2 cases)	M	1	6	8	7	35 est.	3	–
	M	3	–	18	11	62	9	11
Meningitis of un- known type (5 cases)	M	–	9	5	5	22 est.	–	14
	M	4	–	7	1	68	4	10
	M	5	–	9	10	67	6	6
	F	9	–	26	8	66	10	6
	M	–	3	7	7	05		5
POLIOMYELITIS (3 cases)	M	5	–	10	5	83	8	8
	F	9	–	14	6	75	10	10
	M	–	4	13	11	38	5	2

71

of pathologic processes to overshoot the goal, and hyperexis accounts for much of the chronic damage found after many severe illnesses. Indeed, hyperexis plays a significant role in postinfectious mental deficiency, as the meninges show evidence of profound fibrosis which interferes with circulation of spinal fluid and vascular circulation, causing stasis, retrograde congestion and brain sclerosis as secondary phenomena due to anoxia of the brain tissue. Postinfectious mental deficiency is further complicated by atrophy of the brain and hydrocephalic enlargement of the ventricles.

As to the clinical symptoms, a study of 16 cases confirmed by autopsy indicated that 7 of the 16 cases had convulsions at the beginning of the disease, and 6 of the 7 continued to have epileptic seizures. Thirteen of the 16 cases showed speech defects of a more or less severe nature; 12 of the 16 showed some form of cerebral palsy. The severity of the symptoms depends somewhat upon the age of the patient at the time of acute illness. If a child is very young and his nervous system still immature, the damage is usually wide-spread, and the ensuing mental deficiency most severe. If encephalitis occurs after the second year of life, and patterns of speech and gait have already been established, many children lose temporarily or permanently their ability to walk and talk. Encephalitis in later years often causes those well-known behavior patterns of hyperactivity, unlimited aggressiveness and destructiveness, while the IQ seems only slightly impaired.

Among the postnatal infectious bacterial and virus diseases, whooping cough, measles, pneumonias, influenza, meningitis and others may cause an encephalomyelitis with considerable damage to brain tissue. This aspect has recently been thoroughly presented by Ludo van Bogaert, who made a significant contribution on the relationship between exanthematous processes and encephalitis. Van Bogaert concludes that the "form of the neurological disease is determined not only by the nature of the causative agent but by the reactive state of the tissues." Therefore, identical clinical pictures may result from different etiologic agents.

The significance of rheumatic encephalitis has been emphasized by Walter Bruetsch. Our own material seems fully to corroborate the data of Bruetsch which indicate that there is a chronic form of rheumatic encephalitis with specific histologic lesions and a definite influence upon mentation.

The features of kernicterus owing to erythroblastosis fetalis have been brought out by a number of investigators, and histopathology confirms kernicterus as a cause of cerebral palsy.

METABOLIC DISORDERS

The area of metabolic disorders is a large one, but we shall restrict our discussion to a few remarks.

Considering the countless amino acids involved in brain and body metabolism, one may safely assume that a large number of metabolic disorders will be discovered as soon as adequate histochemical methods have been established to differentiate clinically abnormal amino acid metabolism.

Phenylpyruvic oligophrenia or Foelling's disease, is the first definitely established disorder of protein metabolism, and deserves some attention. Its histopathologic manifestations have been recently described by Alvord, Stevenson, Vogel and Engle from autopsy material of 5 cases. Our material (2 cases) confirmed the fact that demyelination seems to be a persistent feature in this disorder, and indicated an accumulation of macromolecular substances in the spinal cord, bodies which seemed to be composed of myelin and amyloid. It may be assumed that the amyloidosis in phenylpyruvic oligophrenia is more than a coincidence.

Knowledge of lipoid metabolism is much better established, and what may be called the group of amaurotic idiocies has received much attention. Gargoylism, which has only been recognized since 1917 (Hunter) and 1919 (Hurler) is now seen to be responsible for a large share of cases, and we may assume that in many instances gargoylism has been, and is still, mistakenly diagnosed as cretinism, mongolism or other conditions. Autopsy observations indicate that gargoylism is a metabolic disorder of a lipoid protein structure which is not identical with any of the known lipoidoses but resembles some of the better known diseases in its pathologic appearance. Gargoylism is associated with profound degeneration of the nerve cells, lipoid storage, a perivascular fibrosis with a mesh-work filled with lipoid bodies and glycogen, and an extensive hyperplasia of the leptomeninges.

Time does not permit dealing with the different leukencephalopathies as established by Krabbe, Scholz, Ferraro, van Bogaert,

Nyssen, Pelizaeus, Merzbacher; and the metachromatic leuken-cephalopathy, the knowledge of which has been so greatly enhanced by a series of publications by Einarson and Neel, and Greenfield.

Oligoencephaly or Oligophrenia Vera

The last group which we would like to discuss, the group which may be called oligophrenia vera or oligoencephaly, is that category of mental inadequacy which offers the most complicated problems to neuropathology. In this group are included those cases which show no definite specific lesions which would permit classification of a case in any one of the other categories.

Oligoencephaly, as we like to call the neuropathologic representation of oligophrenia vera, comprises a group of patients who range in mentality from dull normal to low levels of morons and, in rare instances, imbecility. Some writers, having found no lesions in these cases, have talked of "functional" mental deficiency, which is a most unfortunate expression. Recent discoveries indicate that a number of cases which had been classified as idiots are actually instances of childhood schizophrenia, and the discussion of the neuropathology of these conditions therefore touches upon the whole problem of the neuropathology of mental illness. In our material there was one extremely interesting autopsy on an eight-year-old child who had been diagnosed as a case of dementia infantilis, or Heller's disease. The autopsy, which one of us (CEB) described in his book *Developmental Disorders of Mentation and Cerebral Palsies*, showed a degenerative process of the brain with degeneration of nerve cells, formation of multinucleated giant cells, extreme meningeal fibrosis and fibrosis of the perivascular spaces. The giant cells remind one of Gaucher cells, as described by Hallervorden in two brains. Yet the remainder of the autopsy did not provide any evidence for a diagnosis of Gaucher's disease. Although the classification of this case is undetermined, there is no doubt that there was actually evidence of cerebral lesions. In another somewhat similar case biopsy specimens of the frontal lobes showed severe degeneration of the nerve cells in the frontal areas. Electroencephalographic studies of the frontal lobes indicated a severe frontal arrhythmia.

As far as oligoencephaly as such is concerned, the problem touches upon a more universal question: "Do mental brilliance and mental inadequacy manifest themselves in structural differences of the brain, or are these classic assumptions ill-defined?" The idea that the brain of more highly intelligent persons is characterized by a higher brain weight has been definitely abandoned, and we now know that brain weight and intelligence have no correlation as far as the normal range of weights is concerned. However, it cannot be denied that a brain weight below the normal range is of some significance if the brain is that of a person at the peak of his development, and an abnormally low brain weight is not a manifestation of brain atrophy or senile processes. Our material, covering 15 carefully studied cases of oligophrenia vera, showed two cases with brain weights of as low as 950 grams in patients 39 and 48 years of age respectively; 3 cases had brain weights of 1190, 1170 and 1140 grams respectively, and determination of the brain volume indicated actually a low volume. However, the rest of the cases fell within the average range.

The idea that special faculties of a person have their structural representation in a specific development of certain brain areas has intrigued scientists for at least 150 years, and several careful investigations have dealt with the neuroanatomy of outstanding scientists. We may only mention the studies of Edward Anthony Spitzka (1906), dealing with brains of six eminent scientists and scholars belonging to the American Anthropometric Society, together with a description of the skull of Professor E. D. Cope; or the study of David Hansemann (1907) of the three great Germans, Theodor Mommsen, H. W. Bunsen and the great painter Adolf von Menzel and the latest study along these lines by Walther Riese and Kurt Goldstein on the brain of Ludwig Edinger. These last writers came to the conclusion that the brain of Edinger was characterized by a remarkable asymmetry as regards both convolutions and fissures, and that "in view of former morphological investigations of the brains of prominent people one is justified to correlate the cerebral asymmetry with Edinger's general mental gifts and can argue that a wide deviation from the average (probably in either direction) creates favorable conditions for the development of asymmetries."

In more general terms, cortical evolution as a representation of intellectual evolution is emphasized by Gerhardt von Bonin, who outlined the evolution of the human brain contrasted with the brain of other animal species. He feels that "what impresses one most is the astounding homogeneity of the cerebral cortex of men.... We gain perhaps more by thinking of the ability of these vast stretches of the cortex to function as a unit than to dwell on the concept of elementary organs as the classical school did."

If intellectual superiority is manifested in greater differentiation of brain structure, it is only logical to assume that deficiencies in intellectual development would represent themselves in structural anomalies of the opposite nature. "Feeblemindedness" or "oligophrenia" refers to a limitation in the use of the human mind, and inadequacy of those functions which we expect from an average person and which we admire in those persons who excel by superior contributions to human culture. To expect to find a structural representation of the inadequacy of the human mind would mean to be able to demonstrate a close relationship between the functioning of the mind and brain structure. Although this has been a dream of certain scientists for the last few hundred years, the results of related investigations are not convincing, which may be due, not to an inadequacy of employed methods of a lack of brilliance on the part of the scientists, but to a basic misconception of the human mind. This was clearly brought out in a recent symposium of the American Neurological Association, given in June 1951 on "The Brain and the Mind." Stanley Cobb, in his contribution, "On the Nature and Locus of Mind," restates the formulation of Russell Brain, which is well worth quoting:

> Not only are there twelve thousand million nerve cells out of which the patterns can be made, but nervous patterns exist in time, like a melody, as well as in space. If you look at a tapestry through a magnifying glass you will see the individual threads but not the pattern: if you stand away from it you will see the pattern but not the threads. My guess is that in the nervous system we are looking at the threads, while in the mind we perceive the patterns, and that one day we shall discover how the patterns are made of the threads.

And Cobb goes on to say:

> A changing dynamic mechanism seems to offer the only tenable hypothesis. It is the integration itself, the relationship of one functioning part to another, which is mind and which causes the phenomenon of consciousness. There can be no center. There is not one seat of consciousness. It is the streaming of impulses in a complex series of circuits that makes mind feasible. Many of these circuits pass from cortex to thalamus and brain stem and back. Probably these are the circuits most important for mental functions; but because it is the working

together and the sequence in time that count, no part is higher or lower than the others. Some are concerned largely with alertness and awareness; others, with discrimination and choice.

I would express it this way: The brain is the organ of mind; its great complexity in man makes his thinking possible, but no study of the anatomy and physiology of one brain will ever explain mind. Thinking is a sequence of events, depending on the interplay of messages from one part of the brain to another in response to external stimuli, including messages from other brains. In other words, *mind is the relationship*. If one takes the analogy of thought to a melody, it is obvious that no amount of histological study, no matter how advanced, could show in a brain more than the pattern left by one note. The sequence of the notes in time makes the melody. Ideas are such sequences.

Prepared by these thoughts for a study of the structural anatomy of those mental inadequacies which are not due to visible anomalies described above, we realize that it is impossible to establish a clear relationship between levels of intelligence and brain structure. It is obvious that even the most minute study of millions of nerve cells and fiber tracts would not enable one to discover defects in thinking and judgment or in any of those processes which we associate with the concept of human intelligence.

The human mind and brain activity rely as much on factors which are related to what we vaguely call "mental energy," "vitality" or "élan vital." Whatever the expression, it is this central "vis a tergo" which is behind the indefinable phenomenon which we admire in those men who manifest a great power of mind, and which we miss in those men whom we consider as mentally inadequate. The histopathology of oligophrenia can never discover differences of this type, and we deal, therefore, only with one aspect of the human mind—the lack of scope—which we are able to recognize in one group of the oligophrenias, the so-called "oligoencephaly."

Defects in differentiation of the brain in oligoencephaly have been suspected since the classic studies of Carl Hammarberg (1895) in which he mentioned that "the psychological defects could be related to a lack of functionally adequate nerve cells." He claimed that "in every case it could be demonstrated that the development of the cortex has been inhibited in its normal development." Similar conclusions were presented by Joseph Shaw Bolton and A. F. Tredgold (1903) who emphasized paucity of cells, badly arranged and ill-developed, and diminution in the number of fibers.

Our own studies of oligoencephalic brains have revealed several aberrations which may be summarized as asymmetry of the hemispheres, irregularity of the convolutional patterns with folding of the main fissures or abnormal "cauliflower-like" arrangements; crowded cell layers alternating with empty spaces; broadening of the gray matter owing to lack of tangential fibrillation; small white cores and lack of myelination; presence of underdeveloped "fetal" nerve cells in various cortical layers; arrested nerve cells in the white matter; asymmetry and anomalies of main centers as inferior olives, dentate nuclei and basal ganglia, and irregularities in the distribution of Purkinje cells.

The interpretation of these findings is only partially possible, since the brains of outstanding men seem also characterized by great asymmetry. However, the actual evidence of fetal nerve cells, of disorders of migration, or neuroblasts, and anomalies in the formation of symmetric nerve centers seem to provide a certain basis for the idea that oligophrenia, at least in its severer degrees, is represented by disorders of differentiation. This concept has been greatly confirmed through a study of the spinal cord of oligophrenic patients.

Assuming that differentiation is a process involving the whole nervous system and, therefore, the spinal cord too, one of us (CEB) concentrated primarily on a study of the spinal cord in order to proceed from the more uniform and less complicated conditions in the spinal cord to a study of brain differentiation. Studies on the spinal cord of oligoencephalic patients provided amazing material which confirms the classic concept of constitutional inadequacy and spinal dysraphism (Henneberg, Bremer) or myelodysplasia (Fuchs). Ever since Ira van Gieson's classic study on artifacts of the nervous system in 1892, neuropathologists have been hesitant in the evaluation of myelodysplasias because of the possibility that heterotopias and myelodysplasias may be caused through artifacts at autopsy. H. Zingerle's elaborate study in 1902 seems indeed somewhat unaware of the possibility of artifacts and, though we feel that Zingerle probably dealt with actual anomalies, his findings were confused through additional artifacts. The study of spinal cords, made with the greatest precaution, reveals that myelodysplasia of the spinal cord is a sensitive indicator for developmental anomalies, in contrast to those disorders like birth injuries in which the spinal cord is found perfectly normal. Instances of true oligophrenias revealed more or less severe degrees of spinal dysraphism, or we may rather say that we included in the diagnosis of oligoencephaly only those cases where the spinal cord examination, if it was available, indicated disorders of differentiation.

Studying the brains of patients with spinal dysraphism, one comes to the conclusion that differentiation of the hemispheres is indeed at fault in many instances. There are many striking asymmetric anomalies between the hemispheres, and the occipital lobes are often cone-shaped and far apart. The nerve cells are either too crowded in younger children or rare and degenerated in older ones. The presence of arrested nerve cells in the white matter and especially arrested Purkinje cells in the granular matter provides further evidence of a disorder of brain differentiation.

SUMMARY

A study of mental deficiency or subnormality indicates that the severe and moderate forms are due to various factors which operate either in the prenatal, paranatal or postnatal period. This distinction does not differentiate between genetic and extrinsic factors. Genetic factors account primarily for certain developmental anomalies like cleft formations and the metabolic disorders which may become manifest at any period in the life-span. It may be said that the importance of genetic disorders in the causation of severe forms of mental deficiency is often overestimated, and it becomes increasingly apparent that extrinsic factors play a paramount role.

Among the prenatal disorders, congenital malformations which are of great importance manifest themselves usually in physical and mental defects at the same time. Congenital acromicria or mongolism takes first place in frequency. Mongolism occurs in many degrees of severity and can be best understood as a deceleration of fetal growth in the neofetal period, caused by factors which slow down the physical development and interfere severely with the differentiation of the nervous system.

The paranatal disorders are due to various factors interfering with oxygenation of the brain, and resulting in more or less localized cerebral anomalies which manifest themselves neurologically in cerebral palsy, and psychologically in more or less severe anomalies of mentation.

A study of the infectious causes of mental deficiency indicates that various infectious factors play an important role in the causation of mental deficiency.

Metabolic disorders are of great interest. Only a few, like the amaurotic idiocies, gargoylism and phenylpyruvic oligophrenia are better known, but it may be assumed that, with increased knowledge, many more mental deficiencies will be recognized as stemming from specific metabolic anomalies.

The majority of mental defects are intellectual deficiencies of a milder form which may be covered by the general term "oligophrenia vera." The inadequate intellectuality associated with this disorder is primarily due to genetic factors. Anatomically, it represents itself in deficiencies in differentiation of the nervous system, which seem to account for a general constitutional inadequacy.

BIBLIOGRAPHY

ANTON, G.: Über die Beteiligung der grossen basalen Gehirnganglien bei Bewegungsstörungen, insbesondere bei der Chorea. Jahrb. Psychiat. Neurol. *14:* 141, 1896.

BENDA, C. E.: Mongolism and Cretinism (ed. 2). New York, Grune & Stratton, 1949.

——: Developmental Disorders of Mentation and Cerebral Palsies. New York, Grune & Stratton, 1952.

——: Acromicria Congenita, Or the Mongoloid Deficiency. *In* The Biology of Mental Health and Disease. New York, Hoeber, 1952, p. 402.

——: Psychopathology of Childhood. *In* Manual of Child Psychology (Carmichael, ed.). New York, Wiley & Sons, 1954, p. 1115.

BENDER, L., FREEDMAN, A. M., CRUGETT, A. E., JR., AND HELME, W.: Schizophrenia in Childhood—A Confirmation of the Diagnosis. *In* Transactions of American Neurological Association. Virginia, Wm. Byrd Press, 1952.

BRAIN, R.: Physical Basis of Mind: A Symposium (P. Laslet , ed.). Oxford, Basil Blackwell & Mott, Ltd., 1950.

BREMER, F. W.: Klinische Untersuchungen zur Ätiologie der Syringomyelie, der "Status Dysraphicus." Deutsche Ztschr. Nervenhk. *95:* 1, 1926.

COBB, S.: On the nature and locus of mind. Arch. Neurol. & Psychiat. *67:* 172, 1952.

COURVILLE, C. B.: Contributions to the study of cerebral anoxia. Bull. Los Angeles Neurol. Soc. *15:* 99, 1950.

FARRELL, M. J.: The Mentally Subnormal Child. Technical Report Series No. 75, World Health Organization, Geneva, April, 1954.

FOELLING, A.: Ueber Ausscheidung von Phenylbrenztraubensäure im Harn als Stoffwechselanomalie in Verbindung mit Imbecillität. Ztschr. f. physiolog. Chem. *227:* 169, 1934.

HALLERVORDEN, J.: Kreislaufstörungen in der Aetiologie des angeborenen Schwachsinns. Ztschr. f. d. ges. Neurol. u. Psychiat. *167:* 527, 1939.

HAMMARBERG, C.: Studien über Klinik und Pathologie der Idiotie. Nebst Untersuchungen über die normale Anatomie der Hirnrinde. Upsala, E. Berling, 1895.

HICKS, S. P.: Some effects of ionizing radiation and metabolic inhibition on the developing mammalian nervous system. J. Pediat. *40:* 489, 1952.

HURLER, G.: Über einen Typ multipler Abartungen, vorwiegend am Skelettsystem. Ztschr. f. Kinderh. *24:* 220, 1919.

RICHARDS, D. W.: Homeostasis Versus Hyperexis: or St. George and the Dragon. Scient. Monthly *12:* 289, 1953.

RIESE, W., AND GOLDSTEIN, K.: The brain of Ludwig Edinger. J. Comp. Neurol. *92:* 133, 1950.

RUSSELL, L. B.: X-ray induced developmental abnormalities in the mouse and their use in the analysis of embryological patterns. 1. External and gross visceral changes. J. Exper. Zool. *114:* 545, 1950.

SJÖGREN, T.: Die juvenile amaurotische Idiotie. Klinische und erblichkeitsmedizinische Untersuchungen. Hereditas *14:* 197, 1931.

SPATZ, H.: Pathologische Anatomie der Kreislaufstörungen des Gehirns. Ztschr. Neurol. *167:* 301, 1939.

SPITZKA, E. A.: A study of the brains of six eminent scientists and scholars belonging to the American Anthropometric Society, together with a description of the skull of Professor E. D. Cope. American Philosophical Soc. *21:* 175, 1907.

VAN BOGAERT, L.: Post-infectious encephalomyelitis and multiple sclerosis. J. Neuropath. & Exper. Neurol. *9:* 219, 1950.

VON BONIN, G.: Notes on cortical evolution. Arch. Neurol. & Psychiat. *67:* 135, 1952.

6

ORGANIC FACTORS IN THE PSYCHOPATHOLOGY OF CHILDHOOD

By CHARLES BRADLEY, M.D.*

O RGANIC FACTORS in the psychopathologic reactions of children are attracting a great deal of attention at the present time, and to some workers seem to be of more frequent occurrence than had been previously supposed. Psychiatrists working with children have for many years tended to focus primarily on the emotional reactions to past life experience as major determinants of current attitudes and adjustment. Extension of the clinician's serious attention to organic and constitutional factors, as well as those of psychodynamic significance, indicates a broadening of clinical interest which should eventually enrich our understanding of many disturbed children.

DEFINITION OF TERMS

A few definitions are in order at the start of the present discussion. The term "factor" in the title assigned for this presentation is a happy one. No item of human behavior is the result of a single preceding or predisposing cause, but appears rather as a result of multiple, correlated antecedents. Believing that a child's symptoms are determined *either* by the physical effects of a preceding illness *or* by his emotional reaction to having been ill is not as important as recognizing that both factors have some bearing on his present activity. The idea that an organic factor is but one of several elements involved in a clinical problem is a more realistic hypothesis than assuming the situation is *either* organically *or* psychodynamically determined.

In line with present clinical custom, this discussion will consider "organic" factors as those stemming from damage to, structural changes in, or disordered physiologic action of the brain as a physical

* Associate Professor of Pediatrics and Psychiatry, University of Oregon Medical School, Portland, Oregon.

structure. Cobb[1] and others rightly suggest that at some future time we will very likely be able to understand much of human behavior in terms of the physical and chemical changes taking place in the nervous system, and if we use "organic" to imply "cerebral lesion," why not use the latter term specifically? Actually, the crude but currently popular expression "brain injury" may be considered synonomous with "organic factors." Attempts so far to introduce some specific, technically accurate designation covering clinical conditions which are largely influenced by organic factors have not met with wide acceptance.

At the moment, we are concerned with the psychopathology of childhood. Theoretically, trauma and illness may injure the brain at any chronologic point in a child's life. Practical clinical experience indicates that damage originating during the prenatal or infancy periods is generally the source of organic factors which bring a child to clinical attention. Whether this is due to the fact that the young organism is more likely to encounter traumatic illness or injury during this early period, whether the tissues of the central nervous system are more vulnerable to trauma at this time, or whether the fact that damage occurring in the relatively undeveloped individual will be reflected in widespread and clinically important developmental deviations later, are still open questions. Whatever the reasons may be, the present discussion will concern itself largely with children whose organic factors originated in early life.

Since we are to be concerned with the psychopathologic manifestations of organic factors, it seems wise to consider specific sequelae of brain damage, such as mental retardation, cerebral palsy, impaired vision and other sensory and motor handicaps, as complications of the more general effects with which we are mainly dealing. Damage to the brain does result in some rather definite psychopathologic problems, whether or not these specific complications are present. It is to these problems that we will now turn.

HISTORICAL PERSPECTIVE

While there is at present widespread interest in organic factors in childhood psychopathology, the literature on the subject is by no means voluminous. This is understandable in view of the period in the history of psychiatry when our knowledge of children's development and behavior difficulties really began to expand. Prior to the second and third decades of the present century, children's psychiatric problems were felt to differ in no way except in degree from those of adults. Child psychiatry and child guidance clinic activity, from which much of our understanding of children's problems has been derived, had their origins about the time of Healy's work with delinquents in Chicago, just prior to 1910. At this period, enlightened psychiatrists in America were just beginning to break away from preoccupation with Kraepelinian descriptions of mental illness and were becoming intrigued with the newer dynamic concepts derived from the psychoanalytic contributions of Freud, the psychobiologic outlook of Adolf Meyer, and the earlier observations of the developmental and clinical psychologists. Subsequent child guidance clinic activities, for many years, have been significantly influenced by psychoanalytic concepts, with diagnosis and treatment revolving about the child's life experiences and his reactions to them. Many advances in this particular field have been shared by psychiatrists with workers from other disciplines, particularly those of psychiatric social work and clinical psychology. Workers from the latter two categories have naturally, as a result of both background and experience, been more familiar with psychodynamic than with physical and medical concepts. While due respect has been paid to illness and the physical development of the child in this teamwork approach, appraisal of his physical and neurologic status, in terms of thorough and expert examination by a member of the clinic team itself, has not necessarily been an integral part of study. Attention has rarely been primarily focused on organic factors. The limitations of our present knowledge reflect this to a considerable degree.

Our awareness of significant organic factors in childhood psychopathology has been stimulated by a handful of writers who have been interested in the subject. Several have emphasized how frequently these factors are encountered by those who are alert to them. Kurt Goldstein,[2] by his extensive studies of brain-injured adults, and Paul Schilder,[3] through his stimulating observations on the relationship between organic disease and psychologic reactions, paved the way for later investigators working with children. Strauss and Werner, with their co-workers, collaborated for a number of years at the Wayne County Training School in Michigan on the distinction between children who were mentally retarded because of some exogenous factor, as contrasted with those whose retardation derived from a developmental or endogenous basis. They made many contributions, particularly in the area of selective qualitative psychologic devices to test the characteristic performance of brain-injured children. These are well summarized by Strauss and Lehtinen.[4] Lauretta Bender, from her extensive experience with children at Bellevue Hospital in New York City, has published numerous discussions regarding the behavior and special problems related to organic factors in children.[5-8] Numerous reports on electroencephalographic findings in children with psychiatric problems, following the initial paper on this subject by Jasper, Solomon and Bradley in 1938, have been reviewed by Jasper[9] and have directed attention to neurophysiologic mechanisms which may influence children's behavior. Studies such as those reported by Levy and Lurie[10] and later by Annell,[11] on the relation of pertussis in infancy to later childhood problems; the work of Preston[12] and Rosenfeld and Bradley,[13] on the effect of early anoxia; as well as a comprehensive review of the effects of head injury on children's subesquent adjustment by Blau,[14] are examples of the interest shown in organic factors in the psychopathology of children.

Reference will be made to these publications subsequently. One significant observation runs through most of them: that, regardless of the original cause of organic brain damage, its immediate psychologic effects on most children coming to clinical attention are all very similar. While complications like mental retardation or sensory-motor handicaps may in some instances hinder recognition of this general similarity of symptoms, the resemblance to one another of behavior patterns of brain-injured children warrants careful study.

General Behavior Patterns

An understanding of psychopathology involves many considerations beyond the study of overt behavior. However, a description of the behavior of children whose adjustment is influenced by organic factors is apt to be the first information available to the clinician. Since, as has just been stressed, there is a pervasive underlying similarity in the outward behavior manifestations of brain-injured children, the problem is to pick out the essential characteristics from the welter of complaints and anecdotes which worried parents being to the doctor.

Behavior which appears to be the common heritage of brain-damaged children has been described in comparable terms by Kahn and Cohen,[15] Blau,[14] Rosenfeld and Bradley,[13] Strauss and Lehtinen,[4] Bender,[7-8] Bakwin[16] and others. The picture is that of a child who, compared to others of similar age and development, appears erratic, emotionally overreactive, hyperkinetic, has poor powers of concentration, is given to sudden rages, and is conspicuously impulsive. The erratic component has been variously described as "poorly integrated," "variable" and "incoordinated." The emotional overreactivity has been noted in terms of general anxiety and, in an analagous, if not strictly equivalent, characteristic described by Goldstein[2] as a tendency to "catastrophic reaction." The latter implies that the patient "goes to pieces completely" in frustrating situations with a degree of emotionality which seems out of all proportion to the situation evoking it. Hyperkinesis is mentioned by all workers in terms of "overactivity," "hypermotility," "hyperactivity" or "driveness." Poor power of concentration seems to have the same meaning as "distractibility" or "short attentions pan." Sudden rages might well be a manifestation of the emotional overreactivity just mentioned, but is frequently included as a special characteristic under the general term "irritability," which is often conspicuous. The impulsive aspect of the symptom complex, in terms of uncontrolled, abrupt, sudden shifting of behavior, comes nearest to summarizing the whole picture.

Perseveration, "the urge to continue what has been started whether or not it is appropriate," has also been noted. As a more patterned social reaction, it is described in terms of negativism, "refusal to give up" or shift an activity, particularly when this is the wish of someone other than the child himself. Special difficulty with number concepts[4] and arithmetic[13] has also been reported.

Strauss and Lehtinen[4] list "social inacceptability" as one of the characteristics of the brain-injured child. While this is hardly a mark of distinction, it is a handicap which very much enters into the total adjustment of such youngsters.

Naturally, parents and others who supply the clinician with information may not emphasize the particular points which have just been stressed, but the frequency with which the clinical history is replete with examples illustrating all of them is striking.

Psychologic Test Performance

The behavior described in the foregoing paragraphs is that which may be noted by parents, teachers and the general public in day-to-day life situations. In the special setting of the psychologist's office the child with an organic handicap may show additional distinguishing characteristics. These have recently been clearly summarized by Goldenberg.[17]

While the total scores on psychologic tests may reveal no unusual findings in terms of mental age or intelligence quotient, certain qualitative responses may be apparent on some items of commonly used tests like the Stanford-Binet, Wechsler Intelligence Scale for Children or the Arthur Point Scale. Drawing the diamond on the Binet Scale is usually carried out very poorly, as evidence of impairment in visual-motor performance. Bizarre and apparently erratic attempts to reproduce block designs on the Wechsler Scale may be similarly revealing. Other evidences of inability to reproduce designs efficiently may be conspicuous on the Bender-Gestalt test. Bender[3] has observed that the quantitative rating on the Goodenough Draw-a-Man test may give a mental age two years or more below that derived from other standard tests, although Goldenberg's observations do not confirm this. Strauss, Werner and co-workers, influenced in part by Goldstein's observations on brain-injured adults, have reported characteristic responses on a number of tests especially designed to distinguish retarded children with brain damage from those not similarly organically impaired.[4] They note difficulty in distinguishing the foreground figure from background details. This appears not only on tests utilizing direct visual stimulation but also on those testing tactile and auditory responses. Their "exogenous" children showed a confusion between foreground figures which would be quite conspicuous to most normal children when contrasted with background material—a sort of "confusing the forest for the trees" response. Their results are interpreted in terms of perceptual, rather than sensory, handicaps. In addition, these workers reported test evidence for perseveration as a thinking disorder.[4]

Goldenberg[17] notes that the many contributions of Strauss and his colleagues, which are well summarized in Strauss and Lehtinen's book,[4] have had undue influence on subsequent workers in the field. The fact that their work was done on mentally retarded children must be kept in mind in evaluating it in the present discussion, which, by and large, is focused on children without intellectual deficit. In Goldenberg' own work, a series of brain-injured children of good intelligence were compared with emotionally disturbed children and with "normal children" of comparable age and intelligence. He found the most sensitive distinguishing tests to be those involving copying of the Ellis designs[18] and the children's performance on the Strauss-Werner marble boards.[19-20]

Halpern [21] notes that "organic" children's Rorschach responses are frequently significant. Perhaps most important is distortion of body image, with displacement in the interpretation of the spacing and configuration of individual features as related to the whole figure. Poor control, perseveration, immature responses, greater interest in the chromatic cards than in the black and white reproductions, and many responses characteristic of anxiety (such as "midline responses") may be important.

An acquaintance with these detailed reports from the psychologist's laboratory, added to familiarity with the general behavior characteristics of brain-injured children, supply the clinician with a substantial background for understanding the influence of organic factors in childhood psychopathology.

PSYCHOPATHOLOGY

If we wish to understand any particular attitudes or behavior shown by a youngster with organic damage, it is necessary to take into account his total personality structure and the social milieu in which he moves, quite as much as the organic factors themselves. Whereas behavior such as that described above, which seems to be the direct result of cerebral trauma, may distinguish the child clinically from his noninjured brothers, sisters and playmates, and gives him a sort of kinship in our eyes with other brain-damaged chidren, it by no means accounts for all he does or everything he feels. Many would agree with Bender[7-8] that the child's own basic personality resources and the way he is accepted and supported (or rejected) by his family have a great deal more to do with his general adjustment than do the presence of organic factors alone.

A concept of primary and secondary symptoms is frequently useful in evaluating the manifestations of any psychiatric problem. In the case of the children under discussion, the *primary symptoms* are those which are the direct results of organic damage. The *secondary symptoms* represent behavior and attitudes which are the child's reaction to his handicap or the way he feels he is regarded by those with whom he comes into daily contact.

Primary Symptoms

As noted above, organic damage, regardless of its original cause, tends to result in a common pattern of behavior. The components of this are the primary symptoms of brain-injured children. They include the poorly integrated, erratic, variable behavior already described, as well as the extremes of emotional response, the hyperactivity, the distractibility and the tendency to "catastrophic" reactions to frustrating situations. In individual children, complicating signs and symptoms which are the direct outcome of more localized brain damage impairing special sensory or motor mechanisms may also be regarded as primary symptoms. They are not, however, the subject of our present discussion.

Secondary Symptoms

Secondary symptoms are far less uniform and may be harder to understand. They represent the youngster's personal reaction to his special handicap, as well as the fact that he is handicapped and is therefore "different" from other children. They may also represent his reaction to the way he feels he is being dealt with by those about him. While brain-injured children share with one another the handicap of similar crippling central nervous system impairment, they may differ a great deal in basic personality characteristics, family backgrounds and cultural surroundings.

The fact that a child has suffered cerebral injury does not immunize him to the possibility that other basic personality problems may also be present. One, therefore, may encounter organic factors in individuals whose fundamental adjustments are those of the potential schizophrenic, the psychopath, the epileptic, or those with other types of handicap.

Evidences of anxiety may be particularly prominent as a secondary symptom in brain-injured children. There would seem to be several reasons for this. Greenacre[22] has suggested that when the fetus or newborn infant is exposed to stress, particularly when this is accompanied by physical damage to the nervous system, physiologic patterns may be established which are the prototype of what we see in more mature individuals in times of tension. She suggests that this prenatal or neonatal anxiety prior to speech development presumably leaves "a kind of deepening of the organic stamp on the patterns of response" of the child—a sort of "predisposition to anxiety."

Bender,[8] noting the frequency of poorly patterned anxiety in brain-injured children, implies that it is related to the child's delay in motor maturation and that its origin, whenever apparently unrelated to a "reality situation," may be sought in a disorganizing disease.

Quite apart from these hypotheses, the frequent frustrations encountered by the brain-injured child and his parents are adequate reasons for anxiety, which is mutually contagious. The tendency of most young children of good intelligence to interpret their own illnesses and deviations from health in terms of punishment for real or fancied misbehavior heightens the likelihood that feelings of guilt and anxiety will present additional problems for brain-injured children.

Many intelligent children with organic handicaps appear emotionally immature or narcissistic. Frequent evidence of this may be their preoccupation with themselves and their own interests to the exclusion of those about them. Fenichel[23] and others quote Freud's observation that physical illness requires much "of the libido and mental attention of the person . . . which explains why being sick makes a person narcissistic." The psychoanalytic term "pathoneurosis" applied to such a situation may also "express the difficulties of the task of adapting oneself to the real (or imaginary) limitations set by the disease." This concept would seem to apply to brain-injured children as well as those who are ill in other ways. Moreover, satisfactions may be so difficult for a brain-injured child to find in his contacts with other persons that he may be encouraged to seek them within himself. In so doing he may give others the impression that he is narcissistic or emotionally immature.

Many other secondary symptoms represent the child's attempts to compensate for lack of success in day-to-day life. Refusal to comply with the wishes of others, whether this be called perseveration, negativism or something else, is a frequent mechanism by which all frustrated children seek to dominate and manipulate their elders. Aggressiveness, in terms of bullying smaller children, is usually a sign that the bully is failing to achieve a status of satisfaction by more socially acceptable means. Strauss and Lehtinen[4] note that brain-injured children often show "meticulosity." By this they mean preoccupation with details—a sort of pathologic interest in keeping things in a precise orderliness, representing the struggle of the disorganized child to keep himself and his belongings in a sensible and logically orderly "status quo" to compensate for his otherwise hectic and uncertain daily existence.

The reactions of parents and teachers to children with organic problems often produce situations which aggravate some of the symptoms mentioned above. Anxiety is particularly contagious within family groups. Parents' concern about the mysterious, unpredictable, unrewarding, frustrating activities of their brain-injured child is something which the younster himself may readily pick up and incorporate into his own outlook on life. Impatience and rejection by parents often stimulate negativism. This may take the form of delinquency, wherein by defiance of what is generally acceptable the youngster unconsciously fancies that he is striking back at the adult. On the other hand, if the child feels guilty, his delinquency may represent his attempt to seek punishment. By doing something he thinks is "wrong" and being "caught" and punished, he may feel that his "bad" personality has met with justice.

There are many ramifications to the ways in which the child's social milieu may stimulate and aggravate his own problems. Bender seems well justified in her observation[8] "that there are always other social and emotional problems in his life situation severe enough to account for the behavior disorder on a dynamic interpretation alone."

HYPOTHESES OF THE ORIGIN OF SYMPTOMS

Our basic understanding of the fundamental causes of the behavior that characterize the brain-damaged child is still in a theoretic stage. This is especially true regarding the more general symptoms, such as erratic behavior, overactivity, emotional overresponsiveness, distractibility and perseveration. Our comprehension of these phenomena is not to be compared with the assurance we have of the origin of more focal signs of cerebral damage, which may result in such conspicuous manifestations as hemiplegia, visual field disturbances, jacksonian seizures and other analagous symptoms. Hypotheses of the reasons for some aspects of the general symptoms come in part from the neurologist, in part from the physiologist, in part from the psychodynamically-oriented psychiatrist and in part from other areas of scientific interest.While their explanations have been neither crystallized nor organized into a proven body of fact, they do have some meaning and are worth mentioning.

Erratic, variable behavior, stemming from organic factors, may be more apparent than real. It must be remembered that the brain-injured child, on the basis of a perceptual disturbance (such as confusion of foreground figure and background detail), is reacting to surroundings which genuinely appear different to him from the way they look to his well-integrated companions. Granted that the reactions seem aimless to the observer, the patient may very well be responding to definite external stimuli which for him seem more compelling than they would be to someone else. The fact that at another time he is reacting to some other detail in the total setting, real enough in fact but not of equal pre-eminence in common opinion, at least explains the brain-injured child's response in terms of outside stimuli rather than completely disorganized and random neurologic intrapyschic structure. On the other hand, Jasper[24] and Bradley[25] have suggested an explanation for this type of behavior based on electroencephalographic observations. Since we know that electroencephalographic patterns vary from moment to moment, particularly in children who suffer from clinical disabilities such as convulsive disorders, the variability in behavior may actually reflect variations in synchrony of central nervous system elements. As Jasper puts it, "Any portion of the brain occupied by (epileptiform) discharge is lost to the individual for normal adaptive or integrative action of that area." Bradley[26] has noted daily variations in efficiency of school performance in a seizure-controlled epileptic boy which closely correlated with daily fluctuations in his electroencephalographic tracings. Whether erratic behavior and variability are best understood at a psychologic or a physiologic level of interpretation is, of course, not settled.

Extremes of emotional reaction have been explained in several ways. Strauss and Lehtinen,[4] Timme[27] and others imply that neurologically higher cortical controlling centers, which in the uninjured child contribute powers of inhibition, are functionally inefficient in the brain-injured organism. Deficient powers of inhibition permit greater extremes of emotional display. On the other hand, Bender[8] feels that all brain-injured children are particularly anxiety-ridden, and that extremes of emotional display are to be anticipated here as in other anxious patients. Greenacre's[22] hypothesis that early cerebral trauma may predispose to anxiety would tend to corroborate this. Goldstein,[2] based on observations of brain-injured adults, suggests that due to impaired organization and confused interpretation of the environment the patient is repeatedly threatened with frustrations when he encounters problems to which he sees no solution. As a result he "goes to pieces" in what Goldstein calls a "catastrophic" reaction. Whether this sort of interpretation is applicable to children injured in early life who have never experienced previous success in similar situations has yet to be demonstrated.

Hyperactivity resulting from organic factors has been interpreted in a variety of ways. Kahn and Cohen,[15] who coined the term "organic driveness," suggest that it results neurologically from brain stem lesions. Others feel it is presumably due to faulty inhibition of motor activity, resulting from damage to higher cortical controlling centers. Blau[14] in particular, suggests frontal lobe mechanism impairment. Bender[8] relates much of the overactivity to the constant attempts of very anxious children to seek meaningful and satisfying relationships with their surroundings, a quest which at times must seem endless to those handicapped by cerebral injury. The fact that the frustrated, unsuccessful and frequently unhappy brain-injured youngster, like patients whose maladjustments have other origins, remains emotionally immature and thus retains the excessive motor activity of a very young child is another plausible explanation. It is quite possible that in individual cases one or several of these hypotheses may be correct.

Distractibility and short attention span may be related to some of the foregoing characteristics. Strauss and Lehtinen[4] rightly point out that the brain-injured child is "so busy" paying attention to everything about him and responding to a variety of external stimuli in rapid succession that his powers of concentration, instead of being impaired, may be really "working overtime." His focus is determined more by the intensity of each external stimulus than by his own planned and motivated action. The general impression he creates, of course, is one of no sustained attention at all.

Perseveration may be a prominent characteristic of some brain-injured children. It is apt to be apparent in learning situations and may be interpreted by the teacher as negativism or stubbornness. It is possibly related to an uninhibited drive for continued action by the child with organic difficulties. It may also be thought of as a defense mechanism against the threatened frustrations of shifting to any new activity in which success is uncertain. In other words, the brain-injured child may feel more at ease continuing to respond in a manner which he has already started than by voluntarily shifting to something else.

The setting in which the child finds himself may have a great deal to do with the intensity, if not the very appearance, of some of these more general behavior responses which are related to organic factors. In many cultures, including that of most of the United States, children are commonly supposed to comply with standards which are set for those who are not handicapped. As compared with what is expected of adults, even in relaxed family and community groups children are expected to follow daily schedules of sleeping, eating, attending school, and the like, which are quite conventional and regarding which they have little personal choice. The fact that the majority of children are able to adapt to these regimes is a measure of the desire for acceptance and the wish to resemble one's peers, which is so prominent in childhood. The brain-injured child, however, is poorly equipped to fit into any predetermined schedule. The more rigid the system, the more conflict he encounters. Many of the general symptoms we have been discussing appear most prominent when such children are in stereotyped settings, such as the school room, the family dining room, or during the early morning rush of school days.

It is interesting to watch the diminution in intensity of some of these same symptoms as children grow older. To be sure, in many instances this may be a result of increasing maturity. However, it frequently seems more related to the wider latitude that the youngster enjoys as he grows older in selecting what he wants to eat, what he may wear, what hours he may keep and what occupation he may pursue.

Another factor which contributes to the particular expression of symptoms which are organic in origin is the particular developmental stage through which a child may be passing at the moment. Personality development may be described from a number of points of view. One that is currently of interest is that suggested by Erickson[28] and summarized by Witmar and Kotinsky[29] as represening the crystallization of child development opinion at the 1950 White House Conference on Children and Youth. Herein the child is described as being primarily concerned during successive stages with seeking to find the answers to certain general problems involving his personal satisfactions. For example, the infant spends the first part of his existence in becoming familiar with his surroundings, including the people about him. Out of this develops one of the foundation stones of personality— a sense of trust. Next, as he acquires skills in locomotion and communication and becomes less completely dependent on the maternal figure, his major task is developing a sense of self-sufficiency or autonomy. Numerous other similar problems are encountered in the process of developing an integrated personality. Since satisfaction at each stage requires as one of its essential ingredients acceptance and approval by parents, siblings and other contiguous persons, it is easy to envisage some of the problems encountered by the brain-injured child. Even in infancy the restlessness and extremes of emotional display exhibited by such an infant make consistent care and warm acceptance more difficult for even a patient mother. These are hazards to the baby in developing a sense of security and trust, as compared to the course of events for his more fortunate brothers and sisters. Later, in the process of trying to develop a sense of independence and autonomy, his erratic reactions to training, his frequent frustrations and their attendant emotional explosions may irritate parents and invite rebuffs and extremes of discipline. Satisfaction in terms of a sense of self-sufficiency takes longer for the brain-injured child than for those not handicapped. Projecting these problems into ensuing stages of personality development, it is easy to see why emotional maturity is slow of accomplishment and hazardous of achievement. As a result, the organically impaired child has more prolonged dependency needs than other youngsters. Very conscious appraisal of each child, not only in terms of *how* he reacts but *why he reacts so intensely* at each developmental stage, should enable the clinician to comprehend the true significance of organic factors. Not only is this essential for diagnosis, but its careful evaluation should point up very definite treatment needs in individual cases.

DIAGNOSIS

Establishing the fact that organic factors are present is an essential part of understanding the brain-injured child. Five considerations leading to an accurate diagnosis may be mentioned in what seems to this observer the order of their value to the clinician. These points, which will be immediately elaborated, are as follows: (1) The distinctive patterns of the brain-injured child; (2) his performance on judiciously selected psychologic tests; (3) evidence in the past medical history of a presumptive cause for organic impairment; (4) corroborative evidence of cerebral lesions on neurologic examination; and (5) electroencephalographic evidences of disordered cerebral physiology.

General Behavior Patterns

Evidence from all five of these areas should establish a diagnosis in a very convincing manner. Such completely correlated evidence, however, is not to be anticipated in the majority of brain-injured children. In many instances the general behavior pattern, if carefully evaluated, may be sufficient. Evidence from one or all of the remaining four categories may be conisdered as corroborative information.

The general behavior characteristics have already been discussed in sufficient detail to preclude the necessity of repeating them here. They are of diagnostic value when recognized as a symptom complex, a constellation of psychologic and psychiatric observations. They are significant when considered as a cluster of manifestations, of which no individual part is necessarily of prime importance. Since it is quite unlikely that several children in one family will have suffered from cerebral injury, the fact that this symptom complex is present in one child in contrast to what is noted in the rest of the family is often diagnostically helpful. Since the patient's problem is primarily a matter of his own general organization, it should be apparent in most social settings in which he is observed. Some evidence of his difficulty should date from the time he received his brain injury. Since the majority of children seen clinically appear to have been damaged early in life, their symptoms may well prove to be life-long in duration. Since his organic factor is a fixed and permanent factor, he will continue to show some evidence of its influence throughout childhood.

Diagnostic difficulties arise when the constellation of behavior characteristics is complicated or clouded by evidences of mental retardation or gross sensory or motor handicap. Equally confusing in certain instances may be the presence of pathologic fundamental personality patterns, such as those of autism or childhood schizophrenia. These not only intensify, but are intensified by, organic factors. When any of these complications are present the child's "organic" status can be properly understood only by comparing him with other patients of comparable age suffering from the same complicating factors, as well as with children having no major handicaps. In general, however, this core of quite definitely organically determined personality characteristics offers the clinician his most valuable criterion for diagnosis.

Psychologic Tests

Next to the general behavior pattern, a brain-injured child's performance on psychologic tests appears to give the most accurate information as to the fundamental nature of his problem. Tests will be of value only when selected and administered by a competent clinical psychologist who is sensitive to the special problems of the brain-injured child. Characteristic test performance has already been sufficiently discussed, and it is only necessary to repeat that total scores, in terms of mental age or intelligence quotient on standard tests, may give little clue as to the nature of the problem. On the other hand, special disabilities in reproducing geometric arrangements, presented as drawings or as marble board or block designs, may be most revealing, as may be Rorschach responses and discrepancies between the Goodenough Draw-a-Man score and the mental age as determined by other tests. The activity and distractibility of brain-injured children may make testing difficult. The ingenuity of the psychologist and his ability to observe and correlate behavior in the testing situation before it is recorded are very important.

Past Medical History

Interest in damage to the central nervous system as a cause of subsequent behavior problems in children was greatly stimulated by the world-wide epidemic of encephalitis which followed World War I. Here, perhaps for the first time in the annals of modern medicine, was wide-scale demonstration that changes in personality not necessarily complicated by intellectual retardation or sensory-motor handicap, could occur as the result of a specific illness in children who had been previously well adjusted. Many of the behavior changes which were observed followed the general pattern we have already discussed. They have beeen adequately summarized in many reports, such as those of Bond and Appel[30] and Bender.[6] Fortunately, no such extensive epidemics of any type of encephalitis have subsequently occurred. For a number of years, however, "post-encephalitic behavior disorder" was a term used as commonly as the current expressions, "organic factor" and "brain-injured children." Encephalitis of various types still does occur sporadically, and may in individual cases account for the role of organic factors in a particular child's problems.[7]

Other causes of permanent cerebral damage resulting in behavior difficulties in older children may be head injuries,[14] extensive body body burns[7] and, though less convincingly demonstrated, various forms of allergy.[16]

All the above, particularly when there is a definitely contrasting record of the child's preceding adjustment, may be helpful in establishing a diagnosis of brain injury as an important factor. However, all such evidence must be considered with due regard to the temptation of the general public and physicians alike to pin the explanation for behavior difficulties on some definite event. In the case of head injury the possiblity that the impulsive, overactive, erratic behavior of children in whom organic factors are already operating may have been a predisposing cause, rather than the result of trauma, must always be carefully considered.

Cerebral damage occurring during prenatal, natal and early postnatal periods appears at the present time, on the basis of clinical experience, to be a common origin of the organic factors which influence older children's behavior. The fact that events leading to these are remote in time, are not clearly understood, and are apt to be considered important only when their sequelae are highlighted by mental retardation or neurologic symptoms, makes it hard for many clinicians to accept their importance. So-called "birth injuries" on the basis of mechanical trauma or hemorrhage are particularly hard to evaluate because of the confusion in the minds of many informants as to just what happened during childbirth. Follow-up studies focusing on "organic" behavior patterns and special psychologic tests performance of children known to have suffered a rigorous birth experience are still far too few. There is considerable evidence that prematurity, unless complicated by the anoxia or hemorrhage to which premature babies are prone, is probably not a contributing factor to later organic behavior problems.[31] Many of the reports correlating definite organic behavior difficulties with early illness or injury have been made in retrospect by clinicians who are quite aware of the importance of cerebral damage and are impressed by the frequency with which potential traumatic experiences have occurred in the past medical history of their patients. Asphyxia in infancy[12-13] and the occurrence in infancy of diseases like pertussis, which may be complicated by either hypoxia or encephalitis[10-11] have been studied from this point of view.

Behavior symptoms related to progressive lesions such as brain tumors[16, 32] are difficult to evaluate. Here the relatively rapid changes in neurologic status, the frequent complicating effects of increased intracranial pressure, and the variable progress of the disease in each patient, are hard to assess.

With the exception of children whose behavior shows definite characteristic changes following known encephalitis or other injurious experience involving the central nervous system, diagnostic evidence for brain damage on the basis of a "positive" medical history is apt to be neither as clear cut nor as convincing as the general pattern of behavior or the performance of the child on judiciously selected psychologic tests. Eventually, behavior, test performance and definite evidence of preceding trauma must be correlated if we are to understand thoroughly the significance of organic factors. At the present time the clinician must rely heavily on what the parent and the psychologist tell him about the brain-injured child's present reactions.

Neurologic Findings

Neurologic evidence that cerebral insult has occurred tends to support a diagnosis of brain injury as a factor in a child's behavior problem. Such evidence may, however, not be present in many children in whom organic factors are obviously operative. Bender[8] rightly insists that in young, rapidly developing children a conventional neurologic

examination is of limited value. She stresses the importance of studying postural reflexes and the motility of the child as well as his manner
of relating to other individuals. Strauss and Lehtinen,[4] on the other
hand, point out that numerous conventional neurologic signs may be
helpful in confirming a diagnosis of cerebral trauma, particularly in
older children. Both points of view are valuable and the references
worthy of consideration. Neurologic examination has not always
played a major role in the study of children with psychiatric problems
in child guidance clinic practice. Moreover, relatively few pediatricians and neurologists who are experienced in detecting minimal signs
of brain damage are also thoroughly at home in evaluating children's
psychiatric problems and psychologic test performance. When both
of these approaches are more completely explored we may anticipate
greater contributions from neurology in arriving at a diagnosis of
organic factors in maladjusted children.

Electroencephalography

One further diagnostic procedure which must be mentioned is
electroencephalography. As was noted previously, numerous contributions dealing with electroencephalographic findings in maladjusted children have stimulated interest in its use as a diagnostic
technic This interest has resulted in a certain amount of unwarranted
diagnostic dependence on electroencephalography alone, particularly
by professional workers who are not acquainted at first hand with its
limitations. While the percentage of electroencephalographic abnormalities is statistically greater in children who are maladjusted than
is the case in adults, there is by no means a one-to-one correlation. An
abnormal electroencephalogram in the absence of organic behavior
patterns or psychologic test performance is of little significance as far
as specific psychopathology is concerned. On the other hand, many
children with convincing evidence that organic factors are influencing
their adjustment will show normal tracings. In individual cases, an
abnormal electroencephalogram may confirm other evidence of organic factors, and the procedure is best used as a part of any diagnostic
study with this in mind.

TREATMENT IMPLICATIONS

Since intelligently planned treatment normally follows an understanding of the psychopathology of the brain-injured child, it will be

discussed briefly at this point. Ordinarily organic factors themselves are not suspectible of removal or alteration. However, the brain-injured child has other resources which may be developed. The course of his adjustment will depend to a large extent on the acceptance and support he receives from parents and other persons. Attempts should therefore be made to develop and strengthen attitudes of acceptance and encouragement, particularly on the part of parents and teachers. A clear explanation to them about the nature of the child's handicap is a good starting point. This should be followed by adequate opportunities for discussion and free ventilation of doubts, misunderstandings and nonconstructive attitudes toward the youngster. If children's periods of infancy and dependency must be prolonged because of the nature of their handicaps, as is true in those with organic problems, it is wise to help parents see and accept this. "Overprotection," which is so easily derided by those who cannot comprehend what a dependent child really needs, may be a necessity for such children, but many parents will need external support to enable them to follow their own urges in this direction. Approval of a child's need to be dependent, up to a point where he himself begins to seek emancipation, can and must be encouraged. Lewis[33] and Bender[8] offer some excellent suggestions in this regard.

Teachers can contribute a great deal. Outlines of special technics for teaching, motivating and guiding the brain-injured child are competently described by Strauss and Lehtinen.[4] They stress many practical points, such as the elimination of as many distracting outside stimuli as possible, presenting material in ways that seem concrete and tangible to the child, and helping him slow down and organize the material with which he is dealing.

Meetings of parents and also of teachers who have been challenged by the special problems of children with organic factors should enable them to share and develop ideas coming from their practical experience, and later put them into use.

Even though the physical sequelae of cerebral damage cannot be eliminated, many of the psychophysiologic disturbances emanating therefrom may be neutralized to some degree in many brain-injured children by the judicious use of medication. While sedatives such as phenobarbital are frequently glibly suggested, careful inquiry as to their effects indicates that they increase, rather than alleviate, the child's daily problems. Greater irritability and decreased powers of concentration are a frequent consequence of their use. Some nonsedative anticonvulsive preparations, such as diphenylhydantoin sodium (Dilantin) and trimethadione (Tridione), have been advocated and may, in rare instances, prove helpful. The use of medication in the treatment of maladjusted children has been repeatedly reviewed by Bradley,[25, 34-35] who notes that of the presently available drugs the amphetamines (such as Benzedrine or Dexedrine) are most likely to be helpful. Under capable clinical direction their use in children may result in increased powers of concentration as well as a reduction in hyperactivity and erratic variability. This may be particularly valuable in learning situations where adequate achievement presents such problems for the brain-injured child.

Free interchange of factual information between clinicians, parents and teachers, as indicated above, combined with the sustained, long-term leadership of a physician who is thoroughly familiar with the problems of brain-injured children, assures a sound approach to the whole problem of effective treatment.

PROGNOSIS

Bender's[8] observations that the prognosis for children with organic problems depends on the way in which they are accepted and assisted, rather than upon the presence or degree of the organic factors themselves, is a point well taken. The psychodynamic reasons for failure and success in future adjustment may well outweigh other considerations. The possibility that some individuals sustaining cerebral trauma to certain areas in early life may, in the course of subsequent growth, develop compensatory skills and defenses which render the injury less devastating than if it had come at a later date also merits attention. An added favorable factor, not frequently mentioned, is the fact that in our culture, at least, older children, adolescents and adults have increasingly greater freedom than do little children in selecting their own way of life and are not expected by all concerned to fit themselves into the stereotyped and conventional patterns which are customary for those much younger. The brain-injured child, with his unconventional behavior, which easily irritates and frustrates those about him as well as himself, has to grow up "the hard way." Without greater parental and educational assistance than is available to most other children, he may not meet with success. If so, he may compensate for his inadequacies by withdrawing within himself or by striking out at persons and things about him, or by other devices through which he develops a personality and a way of life which he erroneously feels will bring him greater satisfaction and happiness. With adequate help, however, the prognosis for brain-injured children may be much more favorable than has been anticipated in the past. It is obvious that the outlook depends on factors which are not related to the organic handicap itself. It is on these other factors we must concentrate, if we plan to help brain-injured children meet the special demands of life.

REFERENCES

1. Cobb, S.: Biology of Health and Disease (Milbank Memorial Fund). New York, Hoeber, 1952, p. xx.
2. Goldstein, K.: The effect of brain damage on the personality. Psychiatry *15:* 245, 1952.
3. Schilder, P.: Brain and personality: Studies in the psychological aspects of cerebral neuropathology. Nerv. & Ment. Dis. Monogr. No. 53, 1931.
4. Strauss, A. A. and Lehtinen, L. E.: Psychopathology and Education of the Brain-Injured Child. New York, Grune & Stratton, 1947, 1955.
5. Bender, L.: The psychology of children suffering from organic disturbances of the cerebellum. Am. J. Orthopsychiat. *10:* 287, 1940.
6. ——: Post-Encephalitic Behavior Disorders in Children. *In* Encephalitis: A Clinical Study (J. Neal, ed.). New York, Grune & Stratton, 1942, pp. 361–384.
7. ——: Organic Brain Conditions Producing Behavior Disturbances. *In* Modern Trends in Child Psychiatry (Lewis and Pacella, eds.). New York, International Universities Press, 1945, pp. 155–192.
8. ——: Psychological problems of children with organic brain disease. Am. J. Orthopsychiat. *19:* 404, 1949.
9. Jasper, H. H.: Electroencephalography in child neurology and psychiatry. Pediatrics *3:* 783, 1949.
10. Lurie, L. A. and Levy, S.: Personality changes and behavior disorders of children following pertussis. J.A.M.A. *120:* 890, 1942.
11. Annell, A. L.: Pertussis in infancy as a cause of behavior disorders in children. Acta Soc. Med. Upsalien., suppl. 1, March 16, 1953.
12. Preston, M. I.: Late behavioral aspects found in cases of prenatal, natal and postnatal anoxia. J. Pediat. *26:* 353, 1945.
13. Rosenfeld, G. B. and Bradley, C.: Childhood behavior sequelae of asphyxia in infancy. Pediatrics *2:* 74, 1948.
14. Blau, A.: Mental changes following head trauma in children. Arch. Neurol. & Psychiat. *35:* 722, 1936.
15. Kahn, E. and Cohen, L. H.: Organic driveness: A brain stem syndrome and experience. New England J. Med. *210:* 748, 1934.

16. BAKWIN, H.: Cerebral damage and behavior disorders in children. J. Pediat. *34:* 311, 1949.
17. GOLDENBERG, S.: Some Aspects of Diagnosis of Cerebral Damage in Children. Seattle, University of Washington, 1953. (unpublished doctoral thesis)
18. HEALY, W., BRONNER, A., LOWE, G. M. AND SHIMBERG, M.: A Manual of Individual Tests and Testing. Boston, Little, Brown, 1932.
19. WERNER, H.: Development of visuo-motor performance on the marble board in mentally retarded children. J. Gen. Psychol. *64:* 269, 1944.
20. —— AND STRAUSS, A. A.: Causal factors in low performance. Am. J. Ment. Deficiency *45:* 213, 1940.
21. HALPERN, F.: A Clinical Approach to Children's Rorschachs. New York, Grune & Stratton, 1953, pp. 229–246.
22. GREENACRE, P.: The predisposition to anxiety. Psychoanalyt. Quart. *10:* 66–94, 610–638, 1941.
23. FENICHEL, O.: The Psychoanalytic Theory of Neuroses. New York, W. W. Norton, 1945, pp. 257–258.
24. JASPER, H. H.: Electroencephalography in Epilepsy. *In* Epilepsy (Hoch and Knight, eds.). New York, Grune & Stratton, 1947, pp. 182, 188.
25. BRADLEY, C.: Behavior disturbances in epileptic children. J.A.M.A. *146:* 436, 1951.
26. ——: Unpublished data.
27. TIMME, A. R.: What has neurology to offer child guidance? Neurology *2:* 435, 1952.
28. ERICKSON, E.: Childhood and Society. New York, W. W. Norton, 1950.
29. WITMER, H. L. AND KOTINSKY, R.: Personality in the Making. New York, Harper, 1952.
30. BOND, E. D. AND APPEL, K. E.: The Treatment of Behavior Disorders following Encephalitis. New York, Commonwealth Fund, 1931.
31. BENTON, A. L.: Mental development of prematurely born children: A critical review of the literature. Am. J. Orthopsychiat. *10:* 719, 1940.
32. LANGFORD, W. S. AND KLINGMAN, W. O.: Behavior disorders associated with intracranial tumors in childhood. Am. J. Dis. Child *63:* 433, 1942.
33. LEWIS, R. S.: The Other Child: The Brain-Injured Child. New York, Grune & Stratton, 1951.
34. BRADLEY, C.: Problem children: Electroencephalographic diagnosis and pharmacologic treatment. Connecticut M. J. *6:* 773, 1942.
35. ——: Benzedrine and Dexedrine in the treatment of children's behavior disorders. Pediatrics *5:* 24, 1950.

7

EMOTIONAL AND INTELLECTUAL CONSEQUENCES OF PSYCHOLOGIC DEPRIVATION IN INFANCY: A REVALUATION

By WILLIAM GOLDFARB, M.D., Ph.D.*

CLINICAL OBSERVATIONS AND SYSTEMATIC RESEARCH have confirmed the special significance of the child's nursery years. The supportive findings have been consistent and cumulative. An important source of evidence has been the study of children deprived of normal family rearing.

Our interest is in the family as a source of human impact on the growing infant and child. The family may be regarded as a psychologic climate as follows:

(1) The child is cared for by *specific* adults called parents. The parents are *warm* and *loving*. They minister to the child's innumerable needs with detailed understanding of what the child wants and with a sensitive personal intimacy.

(2) The child is in their presence for many hours during each day and for prolonged periods covering many months. The child's contact with the mother influence is thus *continuous* both in terms of daily routine and total life-span.

(3) The child experiences the mother as a source of safety and gratification. In the earliest months the mother magically brings release from physiologic tension and discomfort at the moment the baby wants this, and without effort on his part. She does this through a multiplicity of maternal operations such as cleaning, feeding, handling, fondling and rocking.

(4) Aside from the element of specificity and optimistic, pleasurable anticipation in the mother-child contact, the experience offers *con-*

* Director, Henry Ittleson Center for Child Research, Riverdale, New York; Associate in Psychiatry, Columbia University, Psychoanalytic Clinic for Training and Research, New York City.

stant stimulation. The loved ones come directly to the child. He is handled physically by them. He is talked to and sung to. He is encouraged by immediate recognition of any verbal or motor response which is indicative of growth. In sequence, he receives active encouragement, for example, to babble, make sounds and then words; sit up, stand, walk and climb. The physical surroundings are filled with numberless objects—toys, animals, people, household implements. The important fact is that natural and social processes are actively and abundantly made available for learning.

(5) Finally, the child's relationship to his parents includes a strong element of *reciprocation.* The baby is influenced to react to reality experiences in a way rewarded by the parent. Yet the child is given the opportunity to make decisions and to achieve pride in his capacity to regulate and order his enviromnent.

Children who do not have this type of family experience may be described as psychologically deprived. One does not normally set about depriving a child of the accepted mode of child rearing in our culture. However, there are infant institutions in which the psychologic climate offered the babies is the polar opposite of that in families. Usually these institutions are physically hygienic living units in which a single adult nurse cares for a large groups of babies. The adult-child ratio is small. Further, during each day up to three or four adults may be actively responsible for the child's care. Over a period of months there are frequent changes in the staff caring for the child. Thus, the child does not have a good opportunity for continuous, intensive or intimate contact with specific adults. Relationships are dim and fleeting. The opportunity for warmth and affection from the same adult person is minimal. Usually the sensory environment is less stimulating than in the family. Finally, the child has less possiblility for actively regulating his own life and activities. Group requirements and program needs dominate the individual child's own wishes and inclinations. There is less opportunity for assertive expression of what is unique in each child.

Table 1 summarizes the relevant differences between family and institution environments. We are interested in institutional care of infants because such care represents a specific type of prolonged psychologic deprivation. The two groups are described as high or low with reference to each other in the factors listed. This table confirms

TABLE 1.—*The Family Versus the Institution as Structural Models for Adult-Child Interaction*

Factor	Family	Institution
1. Number of children per adult......	Low	High
2. Continuity of adult-child interaction...............................	High	Low
3. Specificity of adult-child emotional response........................	High	Low
4. Warmth and intensity of adult emotional response.................	High	Low
5. Adult approval and reward........	High	Low
6. Gratification of tensions...........	Rapid, magical, achieved effortlessly	Unpredictable
	Influenced quickly by child's own demands	Determined by group routine
7. Richness of environmental stimulation...............................	High	Low
8. Stereotypy in environmental stimulation............................	Low	High

the complexity of the psychologic atmosphere that is made available to growing infants. There are great variations even in extent of simple perceptual experience. More important, however, are the qualitative and quantitative variations in the psychologic interactions in the primary rearing unit, whether family or institution.

In the past twenty years, a number of workers have studied the effects of psychologic deprivation in early childhood, most usually under circumstances of institutional rearing. The great majority have convincingly demonstrated conspicuous deviations in both intellectual and emotional response. Recently, in his World Health Organization monograph, Bowlby[2] summarized these deviations very carefully. Readers are referred to this unusual monograph for a clear and comprehensive summary of the considerable data. In the present paper I propose to consider some of our already published data in such a way as to bring out in relief the simultaneous and linked nature of the intellectual and emotional changes. These were controlled studies[5-13] in which we made a systematic effort to shed light on the problem of psychologic deprivation in infancy. Children reared until about three years of age in an institution and then placed in foster homes (institution group) were compared with children who had been reared continuously in families (foster home group). Both groups had been placed in substitute care in the early months of infancy. The institution group had been reared in an institution outstanding for its standards of physical hygiene. To prevent epidemic infection, babies below nine months of age were kept singly in separate cubicles. They had brief, hurried contacts with adults when they were cleaned and fed by the nurses. During the first year of life, therefore, each child lived in almost complete isolation. During the next two years, the experience was only slightly less impoverished. In these studies, care was taken to demonstrate that the foster homes of both institution and control family groups were equivalent in regard to children's facilities, economic status, cultural status, sociability, occupational status and educational status. In addition, the foster homes of both groups were equivalent in regard to such subjective aspects of family care as the over-all satisfactoriness of the families for each child and the degree to which the foster families had assimilated the child. Further, the true mothers of the institution children were superior to those of the foster home children in occupational, educational and mental staus. This tended to justify the conclusion, therefore, that differences in intelligence, emotionality and total behavior were a consequence of the differences in early life experiences of both groups.

The most thoroughgoing investigation was that of fifteen equated pairs of institution and foster home children at a mean age of about twelve years and three months and ranging between ten and fourteen.[7, 9] The institution group had entered the institution at about five months of age and had transferred to the foster home at a mean age of three years and eleven months. They had remained in the foster homes until studied. The two groups of children were individually studied by a long series of tests, experiments and ratings. We are grateful to Bowlby, who has carefully extracted some of the major differences between both groups. His tables of our own data are so clear that we are taking the liberty of reproducing them, with his agreement, along with some of our own (tables 2, 3, 4, 5).

In brief, the institution children were more retarded intellectually. Of great importance also was the finding that they were distinctly

TABLE 2.—*Differences between Children Who Had Spent Their First Three Years in an Institution and Controls Who Had Not (Abstracted by Bowlby)*

Function Tested Or Rated	Test or Rating Method	Results Expressed As	Results	
			Inst. Group	Cont. Group
Intelligence	Wechsler	mean IQ	72.4	95.4
Ability to conceptualize	Weigl	mean score	2.4	6.8
	Vigotsky	mean score	0.5	4.7
Reading	standard tests	mean score	5.1	6.8
Arithmetic	standard tests	mean score	4.7	6.7
Social maturity	Vineland Scale completed by caseworkers	mean social quotient	79.0	98.8
Ability to keep rules	frustration experiment	number of children	3.0	12.0
Guilt on breaking rules	frustration experiment	number of children	2.0	11.0
Capacity for relationships	caseworker's assessment	number of children able to make normal relationships	2.0	15.0
Speech		number of children up to average	3.0	14.0
Total Number of Children..............................			15	15

NOTE: In the case of all differences shown, p < 0.01.

impaired in conceptual ability. Indeed, they were inferior even to a group of known defective children in the Weigl Color-Form Test, while the foster home children were superior. It was felt that the institution children's impairment in categoric behavior and their characteristic "concrete attitude" was more than a reflection of low intelligence. There seemed to be a lack of differentiation and development of all aspects of personality. Most noteworthy was a generalized state of intellectual and emotional impoverishment and passivity. Along with the cognitive disability there were distinct emotional trends; chiefly, the absence of a normal capacity for inhibition. The institution group showed extremely difficult behavior with symptoms of hyperactivity, restlessness, inability to concentrate and unmanageability. Further, although indiscriminatingly and insatiably demand-

TABLE 3.—*Incidence of Problems in Children Who Had Spent Their First Three Years in an Institution and Controls Who Had Not (Abstracted by Bowlby)*

Problem	Rated By	Result Expressed As	Results	
			Inst. Group	Cont. Group
Unpopular with other children..	case-worker	number of children showing problem	6	1
Craving affection...............	"	"	9	2
Fearful........................	"	"	8	1
Restless, hyperactive...........	"	"	9	1
Inability to concentrate........	"	"	10	0
Poor school achievement........	"	"	15	1
Total Number of Children.................................			15	15

NOTE: In all cases but the first, $p < 0.01$. In the first case, it lies between 0.05 and 0.02.

ing of affection, they had no genuine attachments. They were incapable of reciprocating tender feeling, and their meager love potential was associated with the absence of normal tension in situations which would ordinarily arouse such tension. Similarly, there was an absence of normal anxiety following aggressive or cruel behavior. Finally, the institution children showed specific impairment in social maturity.

Bender's clinical experience with the so-called "psychopathic behavior disorder in childhood" is in remarkable agreement. Her clinical

TABLE 4.—*Frustration Experiment*

Function Tested	Result Expressed As	Institution	Foster Home
1. Spontaneous resumption after interruption.....................	mean score	2.5	5.6
2. Rise in tension..................	number of children	2.0	12.0
3. Aspiration influenced by competition..........................	number of children	0	13.0
4. Guilt on breaking rules...........	number of children	2.0	11.0
5. Apathy (absence of 2, 3, 4).......	number of children	11.0	0

NOTE: In the case of all differences shown, $p < 0.01$.

TABLE 5.—*Differences in Rorschach Responses between Children Who Had Spent Their First Three Years in an Institution and Controls Who Had Not (Abstracted by Bowlby)*

Significance of Response	Classification of Response	Result Expressed As	Results		p
			Inst. Group	Cont. Group	
Loose perceptions	W—	mean per-	47	19	0.05
poorly seen, arbi-	F+	centage	43	75	0.01
trary responses	O—	scores	91	20	0.01
Confabulations and	presence of DM	number of	7	0	0.01
poor organization	Beck's Z score	children	10	4	0.05
	below 20	showing re-			
		responses			
Lack of control over	at least 1 C	"	3	0	0.05
emotional responses	CF + C > FC	"	5	1	0.02
Diminished drive to	less than 3 popu-	"	10	3	0.01
social conformity	lar responses				
	original responses	mean per-	24	13	0.10
		centage			
		scores			

NOTE: Total number of children in each group is 15.

reports of this syndrome are the most important. I quote from one of them.[1]

There is an inability to love or feel guilty. There is no conscience. The unconscious fantasy material is shallow and shows only a tendency to react to immediate impulses or experiences, although there often are abortive efforts to experience an awareness of the ego or to identify the personality. Their inability to enter into any relationship makes therapy or even education impossible. There is an inability to conceptualize, particularly significant in regard to time. They have no concept of time, so that they cannot recall past experience and cannot benefit from past experience or be motivated to future goals.

We call attention to the startling multiplicity of altered responses shown by the institutionally deprived child. These findings cover both thinking and feeling. For purposes of study and discussion we ordinarily have separated intellectual and emotional trends. This separation is artificial and arbitrary. The children show behavior changes which involve the whole of their personalities. For example, can you separate low intellectual performance from restlessness, deficient concentration and apathy? In the frustration experiment, we explore the extent of ego involvement or apathy in situations of success or failure, the will or drive to achieve and to complete a given task, and the inclination to conform to direction. Are these merely facets of feeling and emotion? Do they not play a serious role in intellectual operations? In the Rorschach test the institutional children showed loose perceptions, arbitrary responses, confabulations and a lack of control such as is presumably seen in an overabundance of C and CF responses. Are these emotional or intellectual manifestations? Goldstein and Scheerer[14] have emphasized that in testing conceptual performance one is in effect evaluating the capacity level of the total personality. For example, the abstract attitude is represented in such activities as reasoning, hypothesis formation, self-critical awareness and the ability to account for one's behavior. It involves the ability to separate one's self from the immediate impact of outer or inner experiences. It includes the ability to plan ahead, to shift reflectively from one aspect of the situation to another, to grasp the fundamental essence of a whole, to abstract common properties. These abilities are essential for the appropriate adaptation to the demands of reality. Such adaptation is the special job of the regulative and coordinative aspects of self—often termed the ego. It is this psychic machinery which enables the human organism to act efficiently without damage and in accord with long-term needs. The individual is thereby in a position to act within the bounds of reality. It makes it possible for the person to distinguish between those needs which can be met immediately and those which realistically require waiting for gratification. It is the basis for purposeful, rational behavior. Apparently, the institution children who have been deprived of normal parental relationship in infancy are seriously impaired in ego formation.

Rado[17] presents a useful definition of levels of psychodynamic integration based on evolutional, as well as clinical information. Much in agreement with Freud's pleasure principle, at the lowest hedonic level, pleasure and pain act to alert the individual to what is safe and what is dangerous in his environment. The organism moves toward what is pleasurable and away from what is painful. Through this security system the organism possesses efficient machinery for evaluating environmental contacts and regulating its own responses. Pleasure tells one of coming reward, pain tells one of coming damage. As one moves upward in this hierarchically-ordered system of integration from mere hedonic to higher intellectual levels, the organism progressively acquires greater understanding of outer experience, with increasing capacity for abstraction and group cohesion. At the same time, the organism becomes more efficient in its adaptation. There is an expanding range of anticipation and foresight. The development of foresight is clearly a prerequisite for the forgoing of immediate pleasure in order to obtain ultimate advantage.

Again it is emphasized that the upper levels in this hierarchy of psychologic integration are expressed in the two qualities of planfulness and cooperation with the group. Planfulness is one aspect of conceptual thought. Group cooperation is psychologically rooted in the individual's capacity to feel tender emotion for others. These are exactly the qualities lacking in institution children. Another factor of significance is the importance to the individual of a capacity to delay action. This capacity to delay the immediate execution of motor impulse is the groundwork for conceptual thought and ability to act with purpose, efficiency and precision. The institution children are generally impaired in their capacity to inhibit response. This is shown in their aimlessness, short persistence and concentration, restlessness and the tendency to pay no heed to prohibitions.

This deficiency in inner controls is closely linked to a parallel failure in conscience so essential for group cooperation. Conscience refers to the individual's system of automatized self-restraint.[16] It is a psychic process based on an unconscious system of anticipations. Thus, anticipation of punishment leads to inner self-criticism and feelings of guilt, while the anticipation of reward leads to personal pride. Both guilt and pride are emotional aspects of conscience, though pride as a normal motivation in conscience needs to be stressed. Along with ego failure in the institution children, there is also failure in conscience.

Bowlby[2] makes the point that the institution children's impairment in abstract thinking explains in large measure the absence of normal ego and conscience (super-ego) development. At the same time, he says, "there remains the puzzle as to why deprivation should impair the capacity for abstract thinking." He offers the possibility that this thinking in itself can develop only if there is good ego development.

In summary, I should like to present a theoretical model which takes account of the major consequences of early psychologic deprivation.

THE FAMILY AS SOURCE OF THE SOCIAL EMOTIONS

The human infant has an unusually prolonged dependency. During this period, he is incapable of self-guidance, and it is clear that the mother-child union has an important security function for him. Independent adaptation requires well structured and efficient ego operations. The infant, therefore, is dependent on the mother for safety. Bowlby[2] interestingly describes the mother as the "psychological organizer" to which the unformed psyche must be exposed at critical periods for smooth development. Gradually, the child is encouraged to take over the regulating and control functions performed initially by the mother. This has been variously called identification, internalization or introjection. In any case, the family provides the setting for a necessary transfer of ego functions from parent to child. How does this occur?

The first need of the infant is to be maintained physiologically. Normally, this need is met by the mother. It is presumed that the baby's first image of the mother is that of a constant object who is continuously nearby, especially when a need for the mother arises. She is proficient in relieving physical tensions. She often gratifies cravings for movement and stimulation. Her entire presence or the presence of a part of her body (e.g., the breast) is associated with satiation and effortless physiologic release.

This maternal image soon merges with a more complex one of an individual whose psychologic presence alone is desired. The child has learned to love his mother; that is, he perceives her as a present or potential source of pleasure. By six months, specific attachments and related sentiments are quite definite.

When a baby is removed from his mother at this time, he characteristically suffers from a kind of psychologic shock. He becomes listless, withdrawn and unresponsive. Placement workers have always known this reaction, which has been systematically studied by Spitz and Wolf.[19] The separation reaction may be very prolonged. It is not quickly alleviated by the more satisfaction of hunger. A stable relationship with a mother-person has to be restored before the baby again reacts with its typical expressions of complacency or happiness.

Our studies also strongly confirm that if babies are entirely denied any opportunity for close contact with a mother, they show a singular inability to achieve close, reciprocating human relationships. In other words, they cannot love another person. They may cling, and they typically do so undiscriminatingly. Yet they do not love and cannot maintain enduring, deep attachments.

This is a most important finding. The ability to have tender feelings is apparently a derivative of social experience. More specifically, the family is uniquely suited to develop the capacity to love. It is believed that essentially one is not endowed with an inborn reservoir of tender affectivity which is then automatically piped out in quantitative terms to a series of human objects. The infant begins life with a potential disposition for loving, which is achieved only in an atmosphere of human warmth and reciprocal interaction.

IMPORTANCE TO CULTURE OF THE SOCIAL EMOTIONS

Kardiner[15] has most incisively developed the social and cultural values of tender affectivity developed in the family. Such affectivity includes a number of emotions—rooted in love—which he appropriately terms the social emotions. He stresses that these emotions are the basis for social cohesion and culture. Without such emotions there is only a system of mutual exploitation. The substitute for discipline on the basis of the social emotions is instrumental utilization of human relationships. This contrasts sharply with the family, for example, where the mother functions out of love and not mere utilitarian return to herself. In a social group in which the individuals are incapable of positive attachments, one may expect two dangerous outcomes: either anarchy or an ironbound dictatorial community regulated rigidly from without by external rules.

IMPORTANCE TO THE INDIVIDUAL OF THE SOCIAL EMOTIONS

Just as the social emotions are of central importance in social regulation, so are they primary in the individual's development of internal control and discipline. Almost from birth, the young infant is faced with a system of rewards and punishments. These are consciously and unconsciously engineered by his parents and other members of his primary group. He soon anticipates that certain of his actions will produce approval and others will bring punishment and disapproval. He then tends to repeat the desirable actions and to inhibit the undesirable actions. Simply viewed, the child gradually molds himself in the image of his parents (identification). In very subtle fashion he gradually assimilates and integrates into his own make-up the parental image (internalization). The wish to maintain parental love, therefore, would seem to be a most important stimulus for attainment of control, ability to delay impulsive responses, and to look ahead. Our studies in deprivation would tend to buttress these conclusions. The institution children show a defect in the inhibitory mechanism. It is presumed that this defect is causally linked to their apathy, their lack of differentiation and their inability to adapt along thoughtful, goal-determined, purposeful lines.

We have already developed the hypothesis that the individual's capacity to delay outward execution of impulse and to anticipate is the groundwork for conceptual thought. The following simple formula is offered:

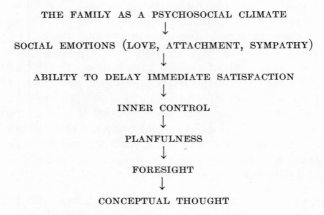

THE FAMILY AS A PSYCHOSOCIAL CLIMATE
↓
SOCIAL EMOTIONS (LOVE, ATTACHMENT, SYMPATHY)
↓
ABILITY TO DELAY IMMEDIATE SATISFACTION
↓
INNER CONTROL
↓
PLANFULNESS
↓
FORESIGHT
↓
CONCEPTUAL THOUGHT

For a moment, I should like to return to Bowlby's puzzlement over why deprivation impairs the capacity for abstract thinking.[2, p. 55] Does abstract capacity underlie ego functioning? Or can this capacity develop only if ego functioning develops normally? This is not unlike the question: Which develops first, the chicken or the egg? Yet we should like to refer to Zubin's considerations of the psychologic processes involved in the sorting tests.[22] He points out that the tasks ultimately make use of judgments of identity, equality, similarity and difference. He favors Stern's[21] theory of the genetic development of thinking. In this theory, the self and its awareness are crucial in the early development of inductive reasoning. Thus, the grasp of identity is derived from the sense of the continuity of self—despite change—transferred on to external objects. The judgments of equality and similarity, too, are personally referred. Similarly the judgment of difference is presumed originally to be a feeling of disruption of the personal situation. (Perhaps this occurs first when the infant becomes aware of his mother's absence when she is out of sight.) These judgment activities are eventually separated from the concrete personal experiences which provoked them, and become abstract. The reference to the self is forced into the background. This theory offers an explanation of why inadequate awareness of self would lead to an inability to make the elementary judgments called upon by tests of conceptual thought. We go one step further, and hypothesize that psychologic deprivation blocks the development of normal apprehension of self. For example, the sense of continuity of self may itself be impossible to achieve, except in relation to a specific, same adult with whom the infant is in continuous interaction.

At this point we should like to stress the special role which maternal reward and gratification plays in early personality development. The infant's experience of gratification and predictable release from tension leads to a hopeful attitude and a sense of pride and confidence in the ability of the self to attain pleasurable gratification. Hopefulness, pride and confidence are themselves elements which compose the independent attitude. The infant also looks forward to what it enjoys. Its earliest anticipations are of this nature. Kardiner[15] has suggested that the sense of time is an offshoot of the child's activities in looking forward to pleasurable gratification.

He also offers an interesting theory of artistic creativity as it relates to the present discussion. In the mother-child relationship, the child is stimulated to move away from a mere concentration on the self. He begins to be interested in the mother and then expandingly to other people and finally to the outer world of nature and natural processes. The interest in nature causes its idealization, the root of artistic creavity and imagination. In contrast to these qualities, a persistently depriving or nonrewarding infancy leads to qualities of resignation, apathy, clinging dependence, lack of pride, an exaggerated interest in the self, absence of interest in the outer world, meagerness of imaginative fantasy and artistic creativity, and a deficient time sense.

In conclusion, most workers have been impressed with the family as a source of tension. One is sometimes even led to ponder how a child can survive the turbulent, troublesome by-products of family living. Indeed, an important body of facts and theory, such as that of psychoanalysis, has been preoccupied with the pathologic vicissitudes of the child in a family setting. Studies of children deprived of family-type rearing, therefore, do an essential service. They shift our awareness back to the positive values of the family climate, both to the individual and the community.

REFERENCES

1. BENDER, LAURETTA: Psychopathic Behavior Disorders in Children. *In* Handbook of Correctional Psychology (Lindner and Seliger, eds.). New York, Philosophical Library, 1947.
2. BOWLBY, J.: Maternal care and mental health. World Health Organization Monograph No. 2, 1951.
3. BRODBECK, A. J. AND IRWIN, O. C.: The speech behaviour of infants without families. Child Development *17:* 145–156, 1946.
4. Gesell, Arnold and Amatruda, Catherine S.: Developmental Diagnosis. Normal and Abnormal Child Development (ed. 2). New York, Hoeber, 1947.
5. Goldfarb, William: Infant rearing and problem behavior. Am. J. Orthopsychiat. *13:* 249–265, 1943.
6. ——: The effects of early institutional care on adolescent personality: Graphic Rorschach data. Child Development *14:* 213–223, 1943.
7. ——: The effects of early institutional care on adolescent personality. J. Exper. Educ. *12:* 106–129, 1943.
8. ——: Infant rearing as a factor in foster home replacement. Am. J. Orthopsychiat. *14:* 162–166, 1944.
9. ——: Effects of early institutional care on adolescent personality:Rorschach data. Am. J. Orthopsychiat. *14:* 441–447, 1944.
10. ——: Psychological deprivation in infancy and subsequent adjustment. Am. J. Orthopsychiat. *15:* 247–255, 1945.
11. ——: Effects of psychological deprivation in infancy and subsequent stimulation. Am. J. Psychiat. *102:* 18–33, no. 1, 1945.
12. ——: Variations in adolescent adjustment of institutionally-reared children. Am. J. Orthopsychiat. *17:* 449–457, 1947.

13. ——: Rorschach test differences between family-reared, institution-reared, and schizophrenic children. Am. J. Orthopsychiat. *19:* 624–633, 1949.
14. GOLDSTEIN, KURT AND SCHEERER, MARTIN: Abstract and concrete behavior. An experimental study with special tests. Psychol. Monogr. *53:* no. 2 (whole no. 239) 1941.
15. KARDINER, ABRAM.: Social Stress and Deprivation. *In* Beyond the Germ Theory (Galdston, ed.). New York, Health Education Council, 1954; and personal discussions.
16. RADO, SANDOR: Emergency Behavior. *In* Anxiety (Hoch and Zubin, eds.). New York, Grune & Stratton, 1950.
17. ——: Hedonic Control, Action-self and the Depressive Spell. *In* Depression (Hoch and Zubin, eds.). New York, Grune & Stratton, 1954.
18. SPITZ, RENÉ A.: An inquiry into the genesis of psychiatric conditions in early childhood. I. Hospitalism. Psychoanalyt. Stud. Child *1:* 53–74, 1945.
19. —— AND WOLF, KATHERINE M.: An inquiry into the genesis of psychiatric conditions in early childhood. II. Anaclitic depression. Psychoanalyt. Stud. Child *2:* 313–342, 1946.
20. —— AND ——: The smiling response: A contribution to the ontogenesis of social relations. Genet. Psychol. Monogr. *34:* 57–125, 1946.
21. STERN, WILLIAM: General Psychology from the Personalistic Standpoint. New York, Macmillan, 1938.
22. ZUBIN, JOSEPH AND THOMPSON, JANE: Sorting tests in relation to drug therapy in schizophrenia. New York, N. Y. State Psychiatric Institute, 1941.

8

EARLY ENVIRONMENT—ITS IMPORTANCE FOR LATER BEHAVIOR

By WILLIAM R. THOMPSON, Ph.D.*

T HE MAIN THESIS I would like to develop in this paper is that the early environment in which an organism grows up is a crucial determinant of later behavior. When stated in such broad terms, perhaps the truth of this proposition may seem obvious. Every layman, from his own experience and from common sense, thinks he knows this already, and thus may regard research on the subject as a waste of time. In fact, it is not. Not only is the area a most important one, but it is one in which the answers are by no means self-evident. That they appear to be so is due to the nature of what we call common sense. This may need some explanation.

Common sense is often regarded as the body of knowledge that everybody has except psychologists, who achieve it only after great effort. This may be true. But as a well-known psychologist recently pointed out in an interview with a popular magazine, common sense is notorious in that it can maintain two completely contradictory propositions at the same time. Such propositions are generally put in the form of aphorisms or proverbs; for example, "More hands make light work," and its opposite, "Too many cooks spoil the broth." A social psychologist studying the efficiency of committees of varying sizes, after spending a great deal of time and money, may eventually settle tentatively near one of these polarities. Let us say he concludes that under such-and-such conditions, larger groups are more efficient than smaller. A newspaper account of his work may then appear, headlined, "Professor X's ten-year research program proves that 'more hands make light work'." Quite naturally, this startles no one.

The problem to be discussed in the present paper is of much the same type. Everyone knows that "blood will tell." Equally true, "as

* Department of Psychology, Queens University, Kingston, Ontario, Canada.

the twig is bent, so is the tree inclined." Psychology itself has, in fact, swung from a galtonian stress on heredity to a watsonian stress on environment, and is only now finding a middle point. Consequently, we should be prepared to forgive the lay public if it shows no surprise at any conclusion we may reach. It has already known it for some time.

Be this as it may, when the basic proposition that early environment is important is put into more specific and operational terms, questions arise that might even confound the layman. For example, it is a matter of conjecture as to whether all or only some events occurring during the early part of life have any effect. It is equally uncertain as to what kinds of events have an effect and how intense they must be to do so; whether such events will affect all target organs equally; at what developmental ages the effects are maximal for different functions; and finally, whether the effects in the various cases endure for a long or only for a short time. All these are *bona fide* scientific questions, and the answers to them are not obvious.

In this paper, I will not attempt to tackle all of these problems. I will confine my discussion, instead, to several major issues. First, I will deal briefly with the important problem of prenatal factors in influencing psychologic development, stressing, especially, the need for more experimental research in this area. Secondly, I will present some of the evidence available on the effects of early postnatal restriction on later behavior, including the work that some researchers at McGill have been doing on the problem. Thirdly, I will speculate a little on why early environment is so important, and on the role of sensory stimulation as a determinant of normal psychologic development.

The Influence of Prenatal Factors on Psychologic Development

The possibility that the prenatal environment may be important as a determinant of later behavior has been stressed by Sontag (1941) and Montagu (1950) among others. It is true that the fetus, suspended in the amnion of the uterus, leads a fairly sheltered life, for the most part free from mechnical strains and pressures and from severe temperature changes undergone by the mother. However, although there is no direct neural connection between the mother and the fetus, there is an indirect one. The fetal circulatory system is separated from the maternal circulatory system in certain areas only by a cell wall. Through this, nutritive materials can pass in, and waste materials pass out. More important in the present connection, many maternal endocrine products, such as acetylcholine, ephinephrine and adrenalin can also be transmitted through the placental barrier from mother to fetus. These can then directly affect the nervous system of the fetus. Indeed, even postnatally, such substances can have very profound effects, not only psychologically, but physiologically. As Graham has pointed out recently (1953), there is an antagonism between growth hormone and increased activity of the adrenal cortex, an antagonism reflected in the importance of emotional disturbances in modifying the growth of children. This being so, it seems probable that the same substances will have even greater effects on the prenatal organism.

There is, in fact, plenty of experimental and clinical evidence to indicate that many severe congenital defects may be produced in the young organism by various stresses undergone by the pregnant mother. These defects, as well as others caused by purely genetic factors alone, or by genetic factors in combination with environmental influences have been reviewed by Fraser and Fainstat (1951) and Wilson (1954). Such agents as trypan blue, hypoxia, cortisone and many dietary deficiencies may produce, when administered to the mother, a number of gross aberrations in a wide variety of different organs or organ systems. The exact mechanism by which many of these produce their effects is not clearly known, as Fraser and Fainstat have pointed out (1951). Cortisone, for example, has many complex physiologic actions. It may interfere with embryonic development by disturbing the mother's hormonal balance and causing a flow of metabolites, abnormal in kind or amount, across the placental barrier; or again, it may act by damaging the placenta itself, or, finally, by producing certain catabolic effects which act directly on the embryo.

In view of the ease with which such gross somatic abnormalities as, for example, cleft palates, absence of cranial bone, blindness and other defects may be produced, it is not unreasonable to suppose that psychologic changes in the fetus may occur even more readily as a result of stress experienced by the mother. As Fraser et al. (1953) have suggested by inference from the action of cortisone, it is likely that any kind of stress that causes the mother's adrenal cortex to release excessive amounts of corticoids may seriously affect the developing fetus. Psychologic stress, arousing strong emotion or anxiety in the mother, can produce these effects just as readily as other agents. The precise manner in which the fetus will be affected is a matter for conjecture. It seems likely, however, that the primary target system may be the fetal autonomic nervous system. Possibly its threshold of reactivity will be lowered, or its balance changed. Perhaps particular organs, crucial in the system, such as the adrenal glands, will be structurally altered. There is clearly a rich field for experimentation here.

While little basic information on the subject is available, there does appear to be considerable clinical evidence to show that neuroticism and autonomic overactivity often occur in infants whose mothers underwent severe emotional stress during pregnancy (Sontag, 1941; Montagu 1950). Neuroticism is defined here by many symptoms such as hyperirritability, excessive crying, gastrointestinal disorders and regurgitation. Sontag and co-workers (1941) have found that maternal emotion or fatigue, even while they are occurring, produce a marked increase in fetal activity, "probably as a result of increased adrenaline level in the maternal and therefore the fetal blood." Studies relating amount of prenatal activity to behavior characteristics of the neonate have shown the following: (1) Very active fetuses tend to be light and show a minimum of fat storage, due possibly to the burning by activity of sugar which would otherwise be stored as fat. (2) The motor development of fetuses which have been active during the latter half of pregnancy tends to be more advanced during the first postnatal year than that of inactive fetuses, as indicated by the Gesell Schedule at six and twelve months. Sontag suggests that this may be due to the fact that activity increases myelinization of motor nerves which, in turn, accelerates motor development.

Accordingly, it is clear that available evidence tends to confirm the hypothesis that maternal experiences can influence the behavioral development of the fetus, and hence of the child. What was once a belief, accepted explicitly in many exaggerated forms, then later rejected outright, now appears to contain some degree of truth. Indeed, the effects of prenatal experiences on the growing organism may be much more widespread and enduring than has been suspected. We do not suggest, of course, that the child whose mother was frightened by a cat during pregnancy will show a phobia for cats. At the same time, as Sontag has indicated (1950), it is not unreasonable to assume that even so-called basic intelligence may be affected, and that an unsatisfactory prenatal hormonal environment may serve to lower the IQ below the level it would otherwise have had. In view of the great plasticity of the developing organism and the potency of neurohumoral factors, such a possibility is entirely reasonable. At the same time, the limitations of the existing evidence must be clearly recognized. For example, it is entirely possible that mothers showing a high incidence of emotional distress during pregnancy—a stressful period at the best of times—may be genetically disposed in this direction. Consequently, the neuroticism of their offspring might as well be ascribed to genetic make-up as to intrauterine influences. In addition, mothers who are emotionally unstable during pregnancy, may also be emotionally unstable during and just after birth. This may seriously affect their treatment (e.g., handling) of the neonate. What is badly needed is a large-scale program of animal experimentation employing refined technics and careful controls. Only in this way will any definite conclusions be established.

THE INFLUENCE OF EARLY POSTNATAL FACTORS ON PSYCHOLOGIC DEVELOPMENT

Compared to the relatively calm and stable environment of the uterus, the world into which the nine-month-old fetus is suddenly plunged is fraught with hazards. From the standpoint of sheer survival, the neonate is probably quite well off, since most of the basic physical structures and functions which keep him alive have reached the full complexity of their development. Psychologically, however, he is particularly vulnerable. For it is during this early period of life, while a large part of the brain is still developing, that the bases for all the complex psychologic processes of learning, perceiving, remembering and emoting are laid down. Although conditions must be rather drastic for these to develop abnormally, such conditions can occur, and when they do, the results, as I shall show, are correspondingly drastic. Under normal circumstances, however, the neonate is far more vulnerable to another kind of danger. Having learned to perceive and remember in the usual way, the child becomes capable of undergoing stressful experiences and, more important, of retaining them in memory. As Hebb has indicated (1946), fears often arise when a familiar perception appears in slightly distorted form. A disembodied limb may produce severe emotion in an adult chimpanzee as well as a human being, though it will probably have no effect on a young chimp who has not lived long enough to build up a stable perceptual world. Similarly, a child who has known love and affection of parents will be seriously disturbed by even a temporary separation from them. Normalcy brings many advantages, but it also brings some disadvantages.

My argument is simply this: If a specific function is to develop normally, whether it be walking or perceiving, it must have ample opportunity to function in a variety of situations. More than this even, the evidence indicates that the organism actually *needs* the environment in a very real sense. Inadequate environmental stimulation early in life can produce serious deficiencies. The same kind of restricting conditions imposed later on in life, however, do not result in such widespread effects. But they probably will produce emotional stress. Thus, there appear to be two kinds of unfavorable early experience: in the first, the organism is prevented from functioning; the harmful effects are primarily cognitive. In the second, the organism is prevented from functioning *in the manner it is used to*; and here the effects are primarily motivational and emotional. I will now discuss each of these in turn.

The Effects of Restricting Experience in Early Life

The experimental evidence on early restriction that has accumulated over the years is considerable. While it may be categorized in a number of ways, it will be considered in the present paper under three headings: first, restriction of specific motor functions; second, restriction of specific sensory modalities; and third, general restriction. In view of a recent review of the literature in this area (Beach and Janes, 1954), only a few representative experiments under each category will be considered.

In the case of specific motor functions, the deleterious effects of restriction have been known for some time. As early as 1875, Spalding found that the flying of young swallows could be impaired by restricting their incipient flight movements from an early age. Dennis

(1941), repeating this experiment with buzzards, obtained even more serious effects. Matthews and Detwiler (1926) restricted the swimming movements of *Ambystoma* by the use of paralyzing solutions of Chloretone (chlorobutanol). Immersion in the solution beyond a certain critical period (seven or eight days) resulted in definite retardation. Metfessel (1940), in an interesting variation of the restriction experiment, found that roller canaries, brought up in soundproof cages, were able to develop the species song which they had never actually heard; but this could be altered so as to incorporate vibratos of varying frequencies (e.g., seven pulses per second), presented by an electric oscillator while the birds were still young. An ingenious series of studies on the effects of restriction on the maternal behavior of the rat has recently been reviewed by Riess (1954). In one of these, Birch used a large rubber collar to prevent animals from smelling or licking their own genitalia during the period from birth to sexual maturity. The maternal behavior of these restricted rats was later found to be characterized by a complete absence of suckling, cleaning or licking their young. In another experiment, females were raised in cages that contained no movable objects of any kind. Unlike normals, the isolated rats made poor mothers, showing no nest-building and decreased retrieving and suckling of their young. Evidently, such a complex function as maternal behavior in the rat requires previous experience in early life, with a number of special stimulating conditions, if it is to develop normally.

On the sensory side, changes just as drastic may be produced by early restriction. Riesen (1950), for example, in a now classic experiment, reared chimps in almost total darkness for the first sixteen months of life. The extreme incompetence shown by his animals in a number of visual tests led the author to conclude that " . . . the postponement of light exposure for too long can result in making the development of normal visual mechanisms extremely difficult if not impossible." Similarly, Nissen, Chow and Semmes (1951) restricted the tactual, kinesthetic and manipulative experience of a young chimpanzee by placing cardboard cylinders on its extremities for from four weeks to thirty-one months. Marked tactual–motor deficiencies resulted. In addition, the experimenters made the interesting observation that the animal apparently obtained great pleasure from tactual–pressure stimulation, even when this was sharp enough to be painful for normal animals, and, much more than normal chimps, solicited all kinds of scratching and tickling, to which it responded with "pleasure-panting."

The above experiments have dealt with the restriction of special functions or senses. However, a general restriction of the early environment, involving both motor confinement and a deprivation of varied sensory stimulation, can have much more widespread effects. This appears to be true even in insects. Faure (1933) has shown, for example, that Rocky Mountain locusts may be transformed into the migratory form (*gregaria*) by raising them in crowded conditions in a small cage. Locust nymphs raised in isolation, however, assumed nonmigratory morphologic characteristics. In mammals, severe deficits in rat learning, arising as a result of early restriction, have been shown by a large number of workers (Wolf, 1943; Hebb, 1947; Forgays and Forgays, 1952; Hymovitch, 1952; Bingham and Griffiths, 1952). On the other hand, enrichment of the rat's early life, raising it in a kind of "rat playground," improves its maze-ability well beyond that of animals reared in the usual kind of rat-cage. It is interesting, as I have pointed out previously (1954) that the extent of change that can be induced in rat intelligence by manipulating the early environment is as great as that obtained by selectively breeding for brightness and dullness in a maze. This point is illustrated in table 1.

With dogs, a higher species with a wider and more complex behavior repertory than rats, the changes that result from restriction for the first eight months of life are extremely marked. A preliminary experiment done at McGill University several years ago (Clarke et al., 1951) indicated effects on intelligence, temperament, social behavior,

TABLE 1.—*A Comparison of Hereditary and Environmental Effects on the Intelligence of Rats*

	Error Score on Hebb-Williamson Maze*
Hereditary Dull..............................	279.5
Environmental Restriction.................	238.2
Hereditary Bright...........................	142.8
Environmental Free.........................	137.3

* The environmental scores are based on data of Forgays and Forgays (1952) and Hymovitch (1952); the heredity scores on data of Thompson (1954).

emotion and motivation. Continued experimentation has tended to confirm these early conclusions.* I will now describe some of the changes that occur.

Details of procedure have been presented elsewhere (Thompson and Heron, 1954a-b). In general, restriction was imposed on half the dogs

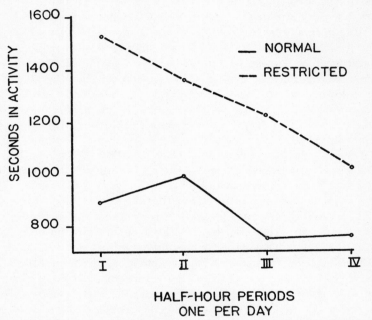

FIG. 1.—A comparison of the activity levels of normal and restricted dogs over four daily half-hour tests.

of each litter by rearing them for the first eight to ten months of life in rather small cages or boxes with opaque sides. Some light was permitted to enter through the tops of these cages. The littermates of the restricted animals were raised normally, as pets either in private homes or in the laboratory.

The most notable characteristic of the restricted dogs after they

* The research reported here was supported by a grant-in-aid from the Rockefeller Foundation. It was carried out in the psychology department of McGill University.

have been removed from restriction is hyperactivity. In many cases, this has lasted several years or more. It takes the form of a clumsy and puppy-like playfulness, frantic nuzzling and hand-licking, and sometimes even a curious whirling-type of behavior which starts during restriction and continues for some time later. Whirling consists in* rapid tail-chasing movements, accompanied by yelps, barks and growls. It may last for several minutes. Although it has not yet been examined carefully, it seems to be set off by some change in stimulating conditions, such as the introduction of a food dish, or the daily cage-cleaning operations. The difference between the normal and restricted animals in their activity level has been measured in several experimental situations. The results of one such test are shown graphically in figure 1.

In this test, the animals were allowed to explore, one at a time, a small empty room for four daily half-hour periods. The time spent by each animal in activity was recorded. It is clear from the graphs presented in figure 1 that the restricted dogs were much more active than the normals.

In social behavior also, the effects of restriction are apparent. For example, the restricted animals tend to be definitely submissive when put in a competitive situation with a normal dog. Two restricted dogs, presented with one bowl of food, are also inclined to share it rather than fight for it. Normal animals rarely share. In a group situation, the restricted often provoke aggression by their high activity level and clumsiness, but are inept in defending themselves because of their submissiveness.

Emotionally, the restricted dogs appear to lack the differentiated reactions of a mature, normal animal (Melzack, 1954). Strange objects, such as a rabbit, an umbrella or a toy snake, generally provoke fairly definite aggressive or fearful responses from normal dogs. But they produce only generalized excitement in the restricted subjects. This difference also shows up in the dominance tests mentioned above. A restricted animal does not usually behave aggressively towards a normal animal competing with it over the possession of a bone. But it does not behave fearfully either. Undifferentiated excitation is the most common response. This finding on emotional behavior is supplemented by another equally interesting and important observation. Restricted dogs do not seem to react to painful stimulation as much as normals. One restricted animal, for example, would continually approach and make contact with a lighted match or cigar without showing any definite signs of pain or distress. This observation is now being studied more carefully in a larger sample of restricted animals.

A final effect of early restriction, perhaps the most crucial one, is on intelligence or problem-solving capacity. Restricted dogs are clearly retarded in this respect, as shown by a variety of different tests, including delayed reaction and an open-field maze. A summary of these results is presented in table 2. The intellectual deficit appears to be fairly enduring, showing up in dogs that have been out of restriction for as long as three years.

In general, the restricted dogs present a picture of retarded psycho-

TABLE 2.—*Differences Between Normal and Restricted Dogs in a Number of Tests of Problem-Solving*

PRELIMINARY TESTS

Test		Mean Errors or Times	
		Normal	Restricted
Orientation	Test I..............	0.30 err.	8.10 err.
	Test II.............	1.86 err.	4.30 err.
Barrier	Test I..............	3.25 err.	7.60 err.
	Test II.............	29.40 sec.	72.10 sec.

DELAYED REACTION TEST

	Median Delay Period Reached in Seconds	Median Number of Trials Required
Normal...............................	240	230
Restricted.............................	0	300

OPEN-FIELD MAZE TEST

	Mean Errors for 18 Problems
Normal....................	237
Restricted.................	344

logic development. In almost every way, their behavior is more like that of puppies than of mature dogs. It is difficult to say, at present, how restriction of early experience produces these effects. There would seem to be three possibilities: in the first place, restriction might have ill effects on the health of the experimental animals. However, our observations show that it does not. The restricted dogs were always just as healthy and heavy as their normally-reared littermates. In fact, visitors to the laboratory commonly mistake the restricted dogs for normals, on account of their liveliness and excellent physical appearance. Secondly, restriction might exert its effects solely through limitation on the motor activity involved. This certainly may be an important factor, but it is still probably a secondary one. With rats, Wolf (1943), was able to produce deficits in learning ability by restricting perception alone, and not motor activity. Further, Hymovitch (1952) and Forgays and Forgays (1952) found that motor restriction by itself did not usually produce as severe effects as perceptual restriction. A third possibility is that restriction retards development simply by limiting early perceptual experience. This appears to be the most likely explanation of the effects in the experiments just described. Undoubtedly, the restriction of visual perception was the most important factor. But restriction of other modalities —in particular, the tactual–cutaneous sensory channels—may also have contributed. Not only were the restricted dogs in the McGill experiments visually depreived, but they were tactually deprived, insofar as they received a minimum of handling for the first eight to ten months of life. Riesen's chimps, however, which apparently did not show such gross general retardation, received little light or pattern stimulation, but did get considerable handling during the period of restriction. This suggests that cutaneous stimulation may well be of great importance. Indeed, as Montagu (1953) has pointed out, not only the fact that it has a large representation in the brain, but also a growing body of experimental evidence lends support to this idea.

At a purely observational level, it has been known for some time by animal breeders, laboratory workers and others concerned with the care of animals that young rats, mice, guinea pigs and other mammals depend on tactual stimulation from the mother in order to excrete normally. Without maternal licking, or some reasonable facsimile, young animals cannot usually survive. Even with adult animals, Hammett found many years ago (1922) that "gentled" rats—that is, rats which had been petted and stroked—were much more likely to survive surgery than rats which had not been handled. He observed, in addition, that ungentled rats were irritable and tense, while gentled animals were friendly and relaxed. Hammett's findings have recently been confirmed and extended by Weininger (1954). This experimenter subjected gentled and nongentled groups of rats to stress by immobilizing them on their backs without food and water for forty-eight hours. The animals were then killed, and autopsy performed. It was found that the nongentled rats had suffered considerably more cardiovascular and gastrointestinal damage than the gentled animals. In addition, the adrenals of the nongentled were significantly heavier than those of the gentled, a difference which Weininger attributes to stimulation of the adrenals by increased ACTH output under stress. Bernstein (1952), in a brief discussion of some previous experiments on early experience, has called attention to the action of another factor—"rapport" between experimenter and experimental animal. Although Bernstein regards this as something different from purely sensory stimulation, he nevertheless defines rapport operationally, in terms of handling. King, in a preliminary unpublished experiment, has found some evidence that young guinea pigs reared with any adult animal develop more rapidly and have a lower mortality rate than those raised in isolation. (The experimenter bottlefed and induced defecation in both groups.) This result is not easily explained. It may have been due in part to cutaneous stimulation of the young animals supplied by the adults. It may also have been due to the fact that an adult animal provides, for the young, visual stimulation which evokes motor activity, providing, in turn, further kinesthetic stimulation.

Thus, animal evidence does suggest that cutaneous sensory stimulation plays some definite part in normal development. It is interesting that observations made with human subjects, of necessity rather ambiguous in this area of research, are perhaps less ambiguous on this particular point. The importance of tactual stimulation in the care of newborn infants has been strongly emphasized by Ribble (1944). Briefly, she has argued that the infant requires three types of sensory experience for adequate development: tactile, auditory and kinesthetic, which are most readily supplied by a mother who holds the child, massages or fondles it and talks to it. According to Ribble, infants lacking such "mothering," may show negativism, regression, and even shock-like states requiring quite radical treatment. Although her claims may be exaggerated, and her evidence slim, as Orlansky (1949) has pointed out, nevertheless, her basic thesis that "the nervous system of the infant needs some sort of 'stimulus feeding' " does seem to agree with the animal experimentation cited above. There is clearly a need for further research on the early restriction of cutaneous stimulation.

In general, all the evidence on early experience reviewed above seems to point to the same important conclusion: varied sensory stimulation of all kinds is essential to the growing organism. This may be provided through any one of the sense modalities, though the visual and the cutaneous are probably most important. The evidence also indicates that restriction of such stimulation must occur early in life to have the effects described. Both Wolf (1943) and Hymovitch (1952) found, with rats, that late restriction causes no appreciable change in learning ability. This conclusion is also supported by the greater severity of early, as compared to later, brain damage, as Hebb (1949) has pointed out. At the same time, late restriction may have other effects, which I shall now discuss.

The Effects of Restricting Experience Later in Life

While restriction of experience occurring early in life definitely retards normal development, it is not in itself stressful, if stress is taken to refer to some sharp change of the stimulus situation. To a dog which has never known any other environment, confinement and lack of association with other dogs and with people is not emotionally upsetting. On the contrary, the first stress such a dog encounters—and this is clear, observationally—is on leaving restriction. On the other hand, as Scott (1950) has pointed out, dogs are seriously upset by isolation, even for a few hours, once they have become used to a normal environment. Thus, the effects of restriction later in life are primarily emotional, rather than functionally retarding. Any radical change in a fairly well-structured environment will usually produce a strong affective reaction.

This line of reasoning may partially explain the interesting clinical observations made by Bowlby et al. (1952), Spitz (1952) and others on children separated from their parents at an early age for the purpose of medical treatment. Such children, according to Bowlby (1952), go through three phases of emotional response, which are described as *protest, despair* and *denial*. Often, the children, on leaving the hospital, apparently reject the mother and mothering in general. Because of the traumatic character of the experience, it has been ascribed considerable importance in the etiology of mental illness. This may well be true. But complex psychoanalytic interpretations of such an event are probably unnecessary. As Orlansky (1949) has implied, the child may be a much more naive creature than Freud and his followers imagined. A more economic explanation of the separation experience can be made as follows: By the age of two, the child has built up a general perceptual framework at the center of which are his parents. Through them, the young child retains contact with his familiar world whenever he ventures into strange territory. Accordingly, his entrance into a hospital is not alarming to him as long as his parents are with him. Their departure and prolonged absence, however, will produce strong emotional reactions. The crucial traumatic factor may be regarded as the "loss of a love-object"; it may equally well be regarded as the loss of a familiar preceptual framework. This may seem to be a quibble over terminology. But it is more than this. If the wealth of clinical data collected on early experience is to prove scientifically fruitful, it is essential that it be described and reported in simple and economic language. The separation experience in the human infant, while it may have unique features, does not appear to be too remote from the "spontaneous fears" described by Hebb (1946) in chimps and by Melzack (1952) in dogs. If they are similar, there is no reason why they should be kept in separate psychologic compartments merely because of a difference in terminology. Both the clinician and the experimentalist have much to offer each other.

While the effects of restriction in later life may be primarily emotional, there is some evidence to show that they may be secondarily cognitive. Some recent experimentation (Bexton et al., 1953) indicates that a drastic reduction in sensory stimulation for periods as long as five days can produce in adult subjects lowered motivation and problem-solving ability, distortions in the "body-image," and even hallucinations. These effects are not so severe as those produced by early restriction, of course, and are presumably not enduring.

A final question of great importance in the present connection is whether the emotional changes caused by restriction and other stressful experiences are permanent. There is probably no simple answer to this problem since many variables are involved—age of the subject, his genetic make-up and the intensity of stress being a few. Stress probably has a greater effect on the infant than the older child or adult in a somatic sense, through not in a psychologic sense. That is to say, a traumatic experience may permanently alter structural characteristics of the autonomic nervous sytem (e.g., the adrenals) of the infant more readily, but it will be retained as a definite and particular conscious experience less readily. With increasing age, the stability of the autonomic system as well as the stability of memory and habits increases. Accordingly, the effects of stress also change. The importance accorded to early trauma by psychoanalytically-oriented psychologists is perhaps justified, but in a general rather than a particular sense.

Having presented some of the empiric evidence on restriction, both as a retarding influence and as a stressful experience, I shall now suggest briefly some reasons why early life is such an important period.

THE IMPORTANCE OF EARLY EXPERIENCE

The importance of early life rests on the nature of the young organism. During this time, the individual is a highly fluid and dynamic system. Every function and structure is changing, each growing at different rates, and each affecting the others. Furthermore, the number of fully differentiated parts is smaller than it ever will be again. In the words of the late Kurt Lewin (1946), "the life-space of the newborn child may be described as a field which has relatively few and only vaguely distinguishable parts." This statement holds true both at the psychologic and, in many ways, at the physiologic level. In almost every respect, the individual is functionally more of a whole than he ever will be again. Precisely because of this fact, environmental factors can affect not only one aspect of the organism, but many others as well. We may add to this the fact that any particular function or organ, while in the process of growth, is much more susceptible to change by external agents than it will be once it is fully formed. To take an obvious example, it is not difficult to influence height at an early age by nutritional or hormonal variation; but it is virtually impossible to affect it once the individual has completed his development. The same applies to the basic psychologic functions. There is no doubt that an individual continues to learn and perceive throughout his lifespan; but it is probable that he learns to learn and perceive quite early, and that once these basic capacities are fully developed, they cannot be changed very much. It also seems true that there are certain periods in early life when a particular function or structure is maximally susceptible to change. Their importance has been stressed by McGraw (1946) and Scott (1950). It is probable that the length of these critical periods, as well as their time of occurrence, varies considerably with different functions and structures. For example, Warkany and Schraffenberger (1947) have found that x-irradiation of mother rats produces cleft palates in the young if applied between the tenth and sixteenth day of gestation, and maximally on the thirteenth day. On the other hand, to produce a deficit in dog intelligence, a period of restriction lasting several months may be necessary.

The previously presented evidence clearly supports the view that the young organism is highly susceptible to change. But more than this, it points to a real need on the part of the developing individual for a moderate amount of varied sensory experience, if excessive change is to be avoided. How such sensory stimulation acts to aid normal development is a most complex problem.

Physiologically speaking, it is noteworthy that any type of sensory stimulation is projected to the cerebral cortex by two different neural pathways. One is specific and follows particular nuclei to a fairly well circumscribed cortical locus. The other is a diffuse system, the reticular activating system, projecting to almost all parts of the cortex. Sensation may thus have specific and nonspecific effects. It is possible that in development, both of these are of utmost importance and act in concert (as Jasper (1952) has suggested) to produce normal cerebral integration. The *sine qua non* for the achievement of such integration must be the continual firing of both systems by varied sensory stimulation. In this manner, the randomness of neuronal connections in the cerebrum is reduced and gradually replaced by organization. The exact role of each of the two systems in bringing about normal development is at present unknown. Following Hebb's ideas (1949), however, it seems likely that patterns of neuronal firing are probably established over fairly wide areas of the cortex through the specific sensory pathways. These patterns, which may be "cell assemblies" or "phase sequences," constitute the neural basis of integrated, purposeful behavior. Restriction of perceptual experience will, of course, reduce the chances of such patterns being built up, with the result that behavior will be much less purposeful and much more random. The part played by the diffuse projection system is even more problematic, but there are some grounds for believing that it may be of great importance to normal development. In the very young animal, sensory stimulation seems important in a general as well as in a specific way. The massive stimulation supplied by handling or "mothering," for example, may serve not only to build up patterns of central neural firing, but may also contribute to the general physiologic well-being of the infant through some kind of priming action via the reticular activating system. Indeed, in the adult brain, there is reason to believe that sensory stimulation has this double function. That is to say, it can have a specific cue function, distinct in form from other types of stimulation; and it can also have a general arousal function by which the brain is kept in an alert state. The first of these functions is probably subserved by the specific, the second by the diffuse projection system. Thus, early restriction, besides limiting the growth of organization in the brain, may also have the effect of dampening the arousal function. It is important to note in this connection that stimulation, in order to maintain arousal, must be varied. The reticular activating mechanism apparently adapts quickly to repetitive stimulation and loses its arousing properties (Sharpless, 1954). Uniformity of early environment can thus have as serious effects as complete sensory deprivation.

In summary, it does not seem beyond the realm of possibility that sensory stimulation has an important dual role in development, and that this functional duality corresponds to a physiologic duality in the sensory system. Though such a hypothesis goes far beyond the data available at present, it would appear to be one worth exploring. Its implications undoubtedly have enormous theoretic and practical significance.

REFERENCES

BEACH, F. A. AND JANES, J.: Effects of early experience upon the behavior of animals. Psychol. Bull. *51:* 239–263, 1954.

BERNSTEIN, L.: A note on Christie's "experimental and experiential naivete." Psychol. Bull. *49:* 38–40, 1952.

BEXTON, W. H., HERON, W. AND SCOTT, T. H.: The effects of decreased variation in the sensory environment. Canad. J. Psychol. *7:* 70–76, 1953.

BINGHAM, W. E. AND GRIFFITHS, W. J.: The effect of different environments during infancy on adult behavior in the rat. J. Comp. Physiol. Psychol. *45:* 307–312, 1952.

BOWLBY, J., ROBERTSON, J. AND ROSENBLUTH, DINA: A two-year-old goes to hospital. Psychoanalyt. Stud. Child. *7:* 82–94, 1952.

CLARKE, R. S., HERON, W., FEHTERSTONHAUGH, M. L., FORGAYS, D. G. AND HEBB, D. O.: Individual differences in dogs: Preliminary report on the effects of early experience. Canad. J. Psychol. *5:* 150–156, 1951.

DENNIS, W.: Spalding's experiment on the flight of birds repeated with another species. J. Comp. Psychol. *31:* 337–348, 1941.

FAURE, J. C.: The phases of the Rocky Mountain locust (*Melanoplus mexicanus*). J. Economic Entomol. *26:* 706–718, 1933.

FORGAYS, D. G. AND FORGAYS, J. W.: The nature of the effects of free-environmental experience on the rat. J. Comp. Physiol. Psychol. *45:* 322–328, 1952.

FRASER, C. F. AND FAINSTAT, T. D.: Causes of congenital defects: A review. Am. J. Dis. Child *82:* 593–603, 1951.

——, FAINSTAT, T. D. AND KALTER, H.: The experimental production of congenital defects with particular reference to cleft palate. Neo-natal Studies, vol. II, no. 2, 1953.

GRAHAM, B. F.: Neuroendrocrine components in the physiological response to stress. Ann. New York Acad. Sc. *56:* 184–199, 1953.

HAMMETT, F. S.: Studies of the thyroid apparatus. Endrocrinology *4:* 221–229, 1922.

HEBB, D. O.: On the nature of fear. Psychol. Rev. *53:* 259–276, 1946.

——: The effects of early experience on problem-solving at maturity. Am. Psychologist *2:* 306–307, 1947.

——: Organization of Behavior. New York, Wiley, 1949.

HYMOVITCH, B.: The effects of experimental variations on problem-solving in the rat. J. Comp. Physiol. Psychol. *45:* 313–321, 1952.

JASPER, H. H.: Electrical activity and mechanisms of cerebral integration. Twenty-Seventh Annual Conference, Milbank Memorial Fund, 1952, pp. 226–240.

LEWIN, K.: Behavior and Development as a Function of the Total Situation. *In* Manual of Child Psychology (Carmichael, ed.). New York, Wiley, 1946.

MATTHEWS, S. A. AND DETWILER, S. R.: The reactions of amblystoma embryos following prolonged treatment with chloretone. J. Exp. Zool. *45:* 279–292, 1926.

McGRAW, M.: Maturation of Behavior. *In* Manual of Child Psychology (Carmichael, ed.). New York, Wiley, 1946.

MELZACK, R.: Irrational fears in the dog. Canad. J. Psychol. *6:* 141–147, 1952.

——: The genesis of emotional behavior: An experimental study of the dog. J. Comp. Physiol. Psychol. *47:* 166–168, 1954.

METFESSEL, M.: Relationships in heredity and environment in behavior. J. Psychol. *10:* 177–198, 1940.

MONTAGU, M. F. A.: Constitutional and prenatal factors in infant and child health. *In* Symposium on the Healthy personality (M. J. E. Senn, ed.), 1950, pp. 148–175.

——: The sensory influence of the skin. Texas Rep. Biol. & Med. *11:* 291–301, 1953.

NISSEN, H. W., CHOW, K. L. AND SEMMES, JOSEPHINE: Effects of restricted opportunity for tactual, kinesthetic and manipulative experience on the behavior of a chimpanzee. Am. J. Psychol. *64:* 485–507, 1951.

ORLANSKY, H.: Infant care and personality. Psychol. Bull. *46:* 1–48, 1949.

RIBBLE, MARGARET A.: Infantile Experience in Relation to Personality Development. *In* Personality and the Behavior Disorders (J. McV. Hunt, ed.). New York, Ronald Press, 1944, vol. 2.

RIESEN, A. H.: Arrested vision. Scient. Am. *183:* 16–19, 1950.

RIESS, B. F.: The effect of altered environment and of age on mother-young relationships among animals. Ann. New York Acad. *57:* 606–610, 1954.

SCOTT, J. P.: The relative importance of social and hereditary factors in producing disturbances in life adjustment during periods of stress in laboratory animals. Proc. A. Research Nerv. & Ment. Dis. *29:* 61–71, 1950.

SHARPLESS, S. K.: Habituation of the Arousal Mechanism (a paper). Read before the Eastern Psychological Association, New York, April 1954.

SONTAG, L. W.: The significance of fetal environmental differences. Am. J. Obst. & Gynec. *42:* 996–1003, 1941.

——: The genetic of differences in psychosomatic patterns in childhood. Am. J. Orthopsychiat. *20:* 479–489, 1950.

SPALDING, D. A.: Instinct and acquisition. Nature *12:* 507–508, 1875.

SPITZ, R. A.: Psychiatric therapy in infancy. Am. J. Orthopsychiat. *20:* 623–633, 1950.

THOMPSON, W. R.: The inheritance and development of intelligence. Proc. A. Research Nerv. & Ment. Dis. *33,* 209–231, 1954.

—— AND HERON, W.: The effects of early restriction on activity in dogs. J Comp. Physiol. Psychol. *47:* 77–82, 1954.

—— and ——: The effects of restricting early experience on the problem-solving capacity of dogs. Canad. J. Psychol. *8:* 17–31, 1954.

WARKANY, J. AND SCHRAFFENBERGER, E.: Congenital malformations induced in rats by roentgen rays. Am. J. Roentgenol. *7:* 455–463, 1947.

WEININGER, O.: Physiological damage under emotional stress as a function of early experience. Science *119:* 285–286, 1954.

WILSON, J. G.: Influence on the offspring of altered physiologic states during pregnancy in the rat. Ann. New York Acad. Sc. *57:* 517–525, 1954.

WOLF, A.: The dynamics of the selective inhibition of specific functions in neurosis: A preliminary report. Psychosom. Med. *5:* 27–38, 1943.

Discussion of Chapters 5–8

By LESLIE R. ANGUS, M.D.*

EACH OF THE WRITERS has explored thoroughly the field he has undertaken to review, each has carefully collated and correlated his data, and each has documented his observations meticulously. Conclusions have been drawn sparingly and judiciously, and expressed with moderation and due regard for the possibilities of other interpretations, though certainly not without conviction. The evidence has been painstakingly accumulated and classified, and it remains only to evaluate it in terms of practical application to clinical problems.

Perhaps the most striking feature of these papers is that, with the exception of Dr. Goldfarb's, no systematic attempt has been made to explain psychopathology in purely psychologic terms. In contrast to the semiphilosophic theories which seem to bulk so large in much modern psychiatric thinking, we have in Dr. Thompson's presentation the results of controlled laboratory experiments on animals; in Dr. Benda's, the findings of the neuropathologist and from Dr. Bradley a survey of clinical neurologic observations. Psychopathology is thus considered as involving the organism as a whole rather than being exclusively an aberration of the postulated intangible organ system known as the psyche. The multiple approach of these papers has been well summarized by Dr. Terhune[1] who states that "the anatomy, physiology, and pathology of the human body, influenced by environment, provide the basis for, and the only logical explanation of, behavior; psychology and psychopathology are evidence of the functioning of the nervous system and its correlated systems in health and disease."

A second important point of agreement lies in the emphasis each author has placed on external or environmental factors as contrasted with those of heredity or constitution. In spite of the known occurrence of genetic factors in some specific situations, the consensus of our authors is clearly that the overwhelming preponderance of the causes

* Director, Child Research Clinic, Woods Schools, Langhorne, Pennsylvania; Instructor in Psychiatry, University of Pennsylvania, Philadelphia.

of psychopathology are to be found in the environment, rather than inherently in the individual. This concept is, of course, not new. The idea that the events in which a developing organism is involved early in life are important to that individual in later life is so generally accepted even by the laity that it is regarded almost as axiomatic, requiring no demonstration.

Dr. Thompson points out, however, that this general proposition is not as simple as it seems, and that it is of no practical help unless we know, further: whether *all* events are significant, or only some; the relative values to be assigned to those which are effective in producing a change; the intensity of application which is necessary to produce the effect; the time relationship in regard to the development of the organism at which the maximum effect is produced; and the degree of permanence of the effect once it has occurred.

These are legitimate questions in considering the psychopathology of childhood, and they are questions to which today's speakers have attempted to supply some of the answers. Admittedly, in the present state of our knowledge these answers are not complete, and it should be borne in mind that the over-all design of the program for this symposium has precluded the present group from trying to cover the entire field. Conditions such as schizophrenia are explicitly excluded, since their discussion has been reserved for later sessions, and the present purpose is to consider basic principles of psychopathology rather than to go in minute detail into every aspect of the problem.

One set of answers to the questions raised by Dr. Thompson comes from Dr. Goldfarb, who has shown that if children are deprived of the usual sensory and emotional stimuli in the first three years of life, definite and apparently predictable changes in behavior and intellectual development occur, which, in his series of cases, persisted to the age of twelve, and showed no indication of altering at that time. Dr. Goldfarb evidently believes that these results are closely associated with the separation from the emotional warmth and personal attention of the parents, or of adequate parent substitutes. Whether this view could be brought into harmony with that expressed by Dr. Thompson on the basis of animal experiments, which appears to suggest that it is the sensory stimulation which is important rather than the emotional rapport implied in the parent–child relationship, is a point which has not been clearly settled.

At least it appears that the sort of stimulation which seems to be required to bring about normal development is found most commonly in the family circle, and Dr. Goldfarb has done a real service in bringing this fact to attention. As he says, we have been so preoccupied with the family setting as a source of psychopathology in the child, that it is well to be reminded that the situation has its constructive side. Dr. Goldfarb's comments on the relation existing between intellectual and emotional maturation, and his theoretic formulation of the integration occurring during mental development, is a study which would seem to merit further investigation.

Dr. Bradley has dealt with a different problem; namely, that of demonstrable brain damage in infancy or at least in early life, which likewise results in a fairly well-defined psychopathologic entity in the form of a behavior pattern. He is careful to point out, however, that the pattern in any particular case is greatly influenced by various factors in the environment, and states explicitly that the purpose of making a diagnosis is not to decide whether the case is "functional" or "organic"—as if these were mutually exclusive—but to determine the proportions in which the various contributing factors are mixed, with a view to rational prognosis and treatment.

Dr. Bradley's comments on the limited value of electroencephalographic findings are particularly appropriate when so much emphasis is being placed on these by the public. All of us in the field are exposed almost daily to demands for EEG studies by parents, whose attitude toward these studies amounts often to superstitious reverence.

His separation of symptoms into primary and secondary groups is a useful concept both from the point of view of treatment and outlook.

Mental deficiency traditionally has been regarded as belonging outside the realm of psychiatry, or indeed of medicine. Interest in intellectual retardation as a problem in psychopathology is of comparatively recent origin, but already the studies have proved that, far from being a homogeneous entity, intellectual limitation may be a symptom of many fundamentally different conditions. As a result of the investigations made thus far, the emphasis on heredity as an almost universal cause is being discounted, and is being replaced by an increasing awareness of the importance of environmental factors, particularly those occurring in the prenatal or early postnatal stages of life. Experiments with developing animal embryos have demonstrated that the growing organism is particularly susceptible to stimuli and vulnerable to various noxious agents. Injuries due to mechanical interference are naturally more common at and after birth, while those due to hormone disturbance, toxins and infections may occur either pre- or postnatally. The effects of such damage tend to be more extensive when the pathogenic factor has acted early in the development of the organism.

Dr. Benda believes that in order to study a condition adequately it is essential to know its pathology, and the present paper presents a careful investigation of the changes demonstrable in autopsy examinations of the brains of a series of cases clinically diagnosed as mentally deficient. He classifies the cases on this basis into those in which the damage has occurred in the prenatal, paranatal and postnatal periods of life, and those of the third group include instances in which the age of onset was as high as eleven years. Those occurring in later childhood are almost invariably associated with trauma or infection, while in earlier life toxins and hormonal disturbances seem to be more frequent causes. In this connection the work of Dr. Hans Selye on the hormonal influence on the psyche would seem to offer some suggestive leads.

In the cases presented by Dr. Benda genetic factors seem much less significant than those due to environment. Indeed, Dr. Benda suggests that the common concept of "endogenous" and "exogenous" causation is of less value for practical diagnosis than a grouping based on the period in the life of the individual at which the noxious agent produces demonstrable results. He points out that in some diseases, well-established as hereditary, pathognomonic signs may not occur until relatively late in life.

A little reflection makes it obvious that the cases which come to autopsy in an institution for the retarded are not typical of the whole field. Many cases of mild or moderate retardation do not get into such institutions at all, and of those who are admitted, probably relatively few reach the laboratory of the neuropathologist. This mild and moderately retarded group is known to show a higher proportion of genetic factors than the group discussed by Dr. Benda, so that it is not altogether fair to minimize heredity as a causative factor in mental deficiency on the basis of his report. Dr. Benda has demonstrated, however, that genetic or constitutional factors are not the universal or nearly universal determinants they were sometimes considered.

Earlier in this discussion, reference was made to the absence of a purely dynamic concept of psychopathology in these papers. Certainly this apparent omission should not lead to the conclusion that psychologic studies are considered by the authors to be of no value. The contributions of dynamic psychiatry are too well known to be discounted, and the impetus they have given to therapy is fully recognized. These papers demonstrate the well-known but often overlooked fact that as an all-embracing theory of psychopathology, dynamic concepts are somewhat less convincing, particularly when the observed phenomena can be explained satisfactorily on the basis of the relatively well-established sciences of physiology, pathology and anatomy. It is good to be reminded (as we were by Dr. Kubie[2]) of Freud's statement that instincts have biochemical and neural components as well as a complex psychic superstructure. Our speakers today have emphasized these biochemical and neural factors, knowing that later sessions of this meeting will afford a fuller opportunity to discuss the psychic superstructure.

The importance of physiologic and anatomic considerations in psychopathology lies not only in their theoretic aspects but even more in their practical corollaries.

One of the most obvious of these implications is that psychiatry, including child psychiatry, is a branch of medicine. This statement may seem so self-evident as to be trite, but observation of the attitudes of some of our recently trained psychotherapeutically-oriented graduates shows the presence of a somewhat disturbing tendency to seek and accept psychodynamic explanations of symptoms without investigating the patient, by even so elementary a medical procedure as a routine physical examination.

Fundamentally, we who are responsible for the care of children with psychiatric disorders are doctors, and the duty and responsibility of the doctor is the study and treatment of the whole patient. Neglect of this fundamental principle in the past has succeeded in some instances in making us ridiculous in the eyes of our professional brethren. Of infinitely more serious significance than mere embarrassment, however, is the possibility of errors in diagnosis and treatment which may have disastrous consequences for those under our care.

A second implication of the papers is the note of moderate optimism resulting from the emphasis on environmental factors which are presumably modifiable, as contrasted with those genetically determined which for all practical purposes are unalterable. Increasing knowledge of the nature of the environmental factors involved should lead to the development of technics designed to eliminate the undesirable or noxious stimuli and to foster the constructive elements. Application of these principles might be expected to reduce the number of cases showing pathologic manifestations.

A third implication of the significance of physiologic and anatomic factors in psychopathology is the urgent need for more research and investigation of the many problems still unsolved.

Contributions to the knowledge of psychopathology may come from many specialties, of which pediatrics, neurology, psychiatry, internal medicine, psychology and the experimental laboratory are a few of the more obvious. The value of the multidimensional approach has been demonstrated so often in other fields that its technics should not be neglected in the field of psychopathology. Extension of the cooperative investigations illustrated in today's papers, and now being made in many parts of the country, is clearly indicated, and should accomplish not only an increase in academic knowledge but an object of even more significance; namely, the improved treatment of children suffering from various forms of psychopathologically-determined incapacity.

REFERENCES

1. TERHUNE, WILLIAM B.: Physiological psychiatry. American Journal of Psychiatry, vol. 106, no. 4, Oct. 1949.
2. KUBIE, LAWRENCE S.: Instincts and homeostasis. Psychosomatic Medicine, vol. 10: 15, Jan.-Feb. 1948.

9

Presidential Address

PROBLEMS OF PREVENTIVE PSYCHIATRY IN WAR

By DAVID McK. RIOCH, M.D.*

IN THE COURSE OF WORLD WAR II psychiatric concepts of both prevention and treatment underwent pronounced changes, almost amounting to reversals in policies. Whereas, at the beginning of the war it was widely held that, by proper selection of men on the basis of their personality characteristics, neuropsychiatric casualty rates would be reduced, and that emotional breakdown was an illness re-requiring evacuation, it was learned "the hard way" that, within limits so broad as to be almost negligible, selective screening fails, and that the majority of psychiatric casualties return to satisfactory duty following very brief treatment and rest. The same painful lesson was learned in World War I, but, for reasons still unknown, was lost sight of in the intervening period— a phenomenon which might well repay historical research. In the Korean War psychiatric "selection" of inductees was abandoned, excepting personality problems manifest to "the man on the street," and the best methods of treatment developed in World War II were institutionalized in the Army in Korea within a few months of the start of hostilities.[4] The static position during the last two years of the war favored further study and testing of the principles both of prevention and treatment in military psychiatry with steadily improving results.[10]

It is proposed in this paper to consider certain of these principles, with particular reference to preventive measures. They contribute to the elucidation of basic problems of interpersonal transactions and relationships, and may be of very practical value in current and anticipated problems of planning for civil defense. Consideration of data

* Director, Neuropsychiatric Division, Army Medical Service Graduate School, Walter Reed Army Medical Center, Washington, D. C.

from a number of sources suggests that a preliminary, but consistent, description of certain important aspects of the problem of prevention may be given; though it is clearly not yet possible to formulate an adequate rational basis for preventive psychiatric measures. The combat zone—or any "disaster" zone—still has "to be seen to be believed," and for a truly sentient belief it must be seen at the time of the action. This is not because the observer observes any particular event or series of events, but rather because it permits the observer to realize the change in his capacities for perceiving, to "feel" the automatic change in his value system and in his concepts of the relevance of separate parts of the events, and to experience his capacities for distortion, both under the circumstances and also when he is later reporting the event in retrospect.

Valid data on acute situational stress, i.e., the *changes in the form* of personal interaction with the environment, and of interpersonal transactions and relationships, are very difficult to obtain. Direct observation, which must necessarily be by participation, leads only to one consistent conclusion; namely, that the participant observer suffers changes himself which distort or sharply limit his perceptual and conceptual capacities. In part, such limitation represents personal reorganization to withstand the load which the environment imposes and, in part, the limitation of the participant observer results from the inherent inability of the human nervous system to deal with new information at the rate at which it is supplied in combat or in disasters. Our concepts of acute and subacute situational stress must, therefore, be inferred, preferably from sources utilizing different methods.

In August and September, 1952, and in May and June, 1953, I had the opportunity of visiting Korea under the auspices of the Army Medical Service Graduate School. The objective of these visits was to attempt to define problems in preventive psychiatry susceptible to investigation under the circumstances, and to initiate research projects for their solution. I was virtually the guest of the Neuropsychiatric Section of the Medical Corps in the Far East Theater, and the hospitality and assistance accorded me in Tokyo was only exceeded by that of the Division Psychiatrists in the field. Besides supplying the practical needs of living and traveling, this gave intimate contact with the psychiatric work in progress, and also provided introductions to officers and men of all other services, particularly the combat services. Considerable opportunity was thus provided for direct observation and discussion of many of the aspects of life and work in the combat zone. Due to the short time I was there and my lack of previous experience, however, I feel that I came away with a number of impressions which require validation, rather than with reliable data. The conditions of the tour, with no responsibilities for practical problems, permitted more attention to subjective phenomena than would otherwise have been possible. It may be useful to record certain of these in conjunction with other observations later in this paper.

The question as to whether investigations of psychiatric problems, preventive measures, psychologic and physiologic stress and fatigue can be carried out in the field may be definitely answered in the affirmative. There is a general recognition by officers and men in all echelons of the need for more knowledge of the human factors in warfare, particularly that involving modern weapons. A number of studies in these areas have been carried out during the past two years. The Army Medical Service Graduate School has sent workers to the Far East Medical Research Unit, attached to the 406th Medical General Laboratory, to investigate a variety of problems which occur only in the combat zone and cannot be duplicated in the laboratory. Maj. John Howard, M.C., (Reserve) found, while engaged primarily in studying shock, that 17-ketosteroid excretion was not increased under ordinary conditions of combat on the main line of resistance, but that under certain acute situational stresses it might be raised to the levels seen in severely wounded men. Capt. Roger Little, M.S.C., carried out a study of the informal social structure of a rifle company on the line and in reserve through the winter of 1951-53. Under the command of Maj. F. G. Harris, M.C., the Psychiatric Research Team, including M/Sgt. Herman A. Becker, psychiatric social worker, and Cpl. Joseph Mayer, psychologist, made an extensive survey of neuropsychiatric casualties, of various factors inducing stress, and of possible statistic indices for strain in an infantry division. The survey included combat and the immediate postcombat transition period. The Team, under Lt. Col. Vincent J. Cassone, M.C., with M/Sgt. Becker and Pvt. Yehudi Cohen, anthropologist, surveyed similar problems in a Regimental Combat Team stationed in Okinawa during the spring and summer of this year. The Operations Research Office of the Johns Hopkins University sent a group of physiologists and psychologists to Korea in the autumn of 1952 to make observations on water balance, adrenal cortical function and a number of other functions, including perceptual and conceptual abilities. Throughout these studies the investigators have received warm collaboration in the field and every assistance the units they worked with could offer.

An extensive study on human factors in infantry tactics and on the relations between men and their weapons was initiated early in World War II by Brig. Gen. S. L. A. Marshall (Reserve) and has been continued through the Korean War. General Marshall was an infantry officer in World War I, a Colonel in the Historical Section of the Army assigned first to the European and then to the Pacific Theaters in World War II, and in civil life is a correspondent for the *Detroit News*. Besides numerous reports to the Army on men and weapons under various conditions of combat he has written a number of books, of which "Men Against Fire"[7] and "The River and the Gauntlet"[8] are probably the best known. I was fortunate to have the opportunity of accompanying General Marshall on several occasions in June, 1953, when he was collecting data on small unit actions. He has developed a remarkably effective technic of group interviews which not only provides a detailed account of the action under study but also supplies a great deal of personal information on the performance of men in acute situational stress. The method of interviewing has been described in "Island Victory."[6] General Marshall emphasizes the importance of having as many of the participants in the action as are available together at the same time for interviewing. This permits cross checks between one and another and frequently reveals the extraordinary degree of distortion and limitation of awareness under stress as well as the well-known intervals of amnesia which men suffer. Another important principle is to hold interviews as soon after the action as possible, preferably as soon as the group can be collected on their arrival in an area just behind the front. The difficulties of early interviewing are more than compensated for by the greater accuracy of the critical details in the information obtained. With the passage of time and change in the environment, not only is information lost, but that which is recalled is modified by current needs and purposes. This reconstruction of memory data, particularly that concerning personal attitudes and subjective phenomena, has been one of the greatest hindrances to the development of an operational concept of acute situational stress. General Marshall's studies, though undertaken for the purposes of improving infantry training and tactics, provide important material for consideration by all workers in preventive psychiatry.

One of the commonest examples of errors in formulation by persons far removed from the events is the very common statement that combat stress, or acute situational stress in general, results from fear—"instinctive fear of death" or of mutilation. Now the concept of "fear of death" is either merely a conventional form of expression or else a very complicated concept which only a very exceptional person would have time to think of in combat. Usually, it is the former, and is used in conventional situations to refer to at least three things: unpleasant feelings under stress for which, at the time, there was no name; the need to give this subjective experience a name; and the need to express a strong desire not to return to the stressful situation. It seems fairly certain that everyone under acute situational stress suffers decrease in competence to a greater or lesser degree. The response of different people—and of any one person at different times— to acute situational stress varies widely, with a corresponding variety of subjective phenomena. Such feelings as exhilaration, increased alertness, joy of action, and so forth, are not uncommon. An undefined "tension" or tense alertness, "absence of feelings" are probably more frequent. Apprehension, neurotic anxiety, somatic pain and incipient terror are more rare. However, all these subjective reactions seem to have a common characteristic which may be described as "queer" or "awesome," and which is apparently related to the decrease in competence of function. This "queerness" differentiates the experience in acute stress from closely related subjective phenomena which occur in secure situations, such as an examination, an athletic contest, or, in general terms, situations in which the course of the event is under the control of the group, and the response of the environment will most probably coincide with patterns already culturally learned. General Marshall[7] refers to such a universal feeling in combat as the "lonesomeness" of the battle field and the threat of isolation. Harry Stack Sullivan[15] attempted to limit the definition of the term "anxiety" to this sense, emphasizing that it referred to a phenomenon of *interpersonal insecurity*. Both Marshall's and Sullivan's concepts are derived from explicit statements and implicit meaning in verbal communications—

as well as from inferences from the overt behavior—of persons suffering stress. Thus, for example, a man will proceed to certain death or mutilation with little disturbance of motor coordination or autonomic function, provided the situation is culturally structured and he is playing his role in the group life; and further, the great preponderance of defenses against breakdown in acute situational stress concern the development and reinforcement of group cohesiveness. Although Freud's concept of the death instinct[2] has been interpreted in a number of ways, it seems likely that it basically refers to these same phenomena. "Death" carries the implication of the sense of doom and separation. The concept of instinct in nineteenth century biology was used to define transactions of living organisms in terms of the end-state probably attained if the transaction was completed.

Quite apart from any disturbances of intrapsychic function, decrease in human competence in acute situational stress is probably inevitable, due to the limitations imposed by the time constants of the central nervous system. Adequacy of performance in the course of interaction requires time for analysis and organization of sensory input. Accuracy of perception and adequacy of conception appear to be functions of anticipatory preparation for the analysis of new information. Acute situational stress, however, is characterized by massive sensory input; sudden, unpredictable, drastic change; lack of time in the rapid progress of events; and impossibility of immediate control of the adverse forces. The problems of preventive psychiatry, therefore, must center around improving the defenses against inordinate breakdown rather than obviating the stress.

It may be useful to digress briefly at this juncture to consider a characteristic of the mammalian nervous system which has possibly not received the attention it deserves. This characteristic is its virtually fantastic resistance to disorganized function. Probably the rarest observation in neurophysiologic studies is that of clearly random activity. Sherrington[11] has emphasized the absence of "confusion" in the spinal cord. He found that the transition from one reflex to an antagonistic reflex might be accompanied by some "hesitation" of one or two seconds' duration, but that there was no disorganization or random activity. Convulsive phenomena, e.g., due to strychnine, which at first glance appear as disorganized behavior, are seen to follow organized patterns on closer observation. Coordinated participation in the total pattern by definite forebrain systems in the spasms evoked by tetanus toxin has been demonstrated by Spiegel.[12] It appears that if random transmission of impulses occurs at all through central nerve nets, it does not spread and is transient. The overt manifestation is either one of loss of the functions subserved by the affected structures or is an expression of the organized activity of unaffected systems.*

Similarly, destruction or injury of parts of the nervous system are followed by loss of function of other parts and/or reorganization of function of the surviving structures. Similar conclusions have been arrived at from careful observations of neuropsychiatric clinical material over long periods. Demonstrably random activity in schizophrenic panic states is rare, and then only of very short duration, if it occurs at all (H. S. Sullivan, personal communication). Weinstein[16] has demonstrated in a series of recent studies that symptoms resulting from brain injury which are often classified as "confusion" and "loss of memory" actually represent well integrated, though simplified and stereotyped, patterns.

It appears that similar principles operate in the changes in behavior induced by acute situational stress. With the impairment of the more complex functions, such as those of scanning a large number of factors in a situation and exercising long-term foresight, there is a reorganization of the person with the environment in one or another simpler, more stereotyped pattern. Certain of these simpler patterns not infrequently improve a man's efficiency for carrying out particular missions under the circumstances. A characteristic example is the by no means rare report, "I was not afraid. I worked smoothly. *Everything was shut out except* what I had to do immediately in front of me." However, whatever the compatibility with the needs of the situation, each of these patterns, in addition to indicating impairment of functional capacity, represents a positive or, if you please, a "purposeful" or-

* That localized abnormal—though not necessarily random—activity may result in temporary loss of a complex function is illustrated by the aphasia accompanying electric stimulation of cortical speech areas described by Penfield.[9] The maintenance of organized function in parts of the nervous system while other parts are involved in abnormal, although organized, seizure patterns is illustrated by the only slight modification of posture, facial expression, etc., during petit mal attacks.

ganization, with its own inherent resistance to further breakdown and its own potentialities for adjustment to the course of events. In addition, short of complete panic, human transactions under stress include functions designed to reduce the stress, chiefly by increasing group cohesiveness. In this regard the importance of interpersonal relations and group organization can hardly be overemphasized.

In other words, the phenomena commonly referred to as the symptoms or signs of stress are not merely disorganization of normal behavior. They represent, rather, loss of the more complex functions and reorganization of human transactions so as to resist further breakdown and reduce stress by strengthening interpersonal and intragroup relations.

The tactical situation in Korea allowed an observer to proceed rapidly and with minimal discomfort from ordinary civilian life to forward areas in the combat zone. With exercise of reasonable care in selecting the time and place of forward visits or work, the danger of injury was about the same as that from traffic accidents in the U. S. However, a number of characteristics of the culture and life of the combat zone were impressive in contrast with life at home. Things, places and particularly people assumed an immediate importance which is seldom felt under other circumstances. The spatial and temporal horizons were markedly narrowed, and there was increased alertness to specific features of the particular area, such as the roads, bunkers, trenches, ridges and streams. "The war" became, as it were, the action in the company sector today, since yesterday was in the distant past and tomorrow did not yet exist. The political and broad ideologic reasons and purposes of the war were irrelevant to the situation and were never mentioned. It was clear that there were other companies on the flanks, but only occasional reference was made to them. The other regiments of the Division were vaguely recognized and rarely mentioned. Divisions in some other part of the line seemed as distant as another continent, and as strange as another culture. Together with this sense of immediacy, I found a very rapid development of a sense of "belongingness" with the unit I was with. A number of psychiatrists with experience at the front have commented on this phenomenon, particularly from the standpoint of the very warm, almost insistent, hospitality shown to the newcomer the moment it is established he has definite, favorable purposes. I was not infrequently embarrassed at the extent to which men and officers would undertake additional work in order to assist me, but found invariably that whatever was done was done with pleasure and without implication of obligation. Other investigators have had the same experience. I do not wish to leave the impression that hospitality supersedes business. Rather, one receives complete attention during the time available in the succession of events, not partial attention concurrently and in a manner to interfere with routine duties.

The constriction of the horizon, particularly as regards time, probably is the clearest evidence of decrease in capacity for effective performance. The difficulties become emphasized in the function of planning. I found that even in the rear areas of the combat zone I had considerable trouble assessing problems which had come to my attention, and planning their study. In the forward areas the most I accomplished was to make observations on predetermined questions, or to make note of unanticipated phenomena, for future consideration. Problems of "research design" were limited to questions of shelter, transportation, equipment, previous military training, and so forth, which a potential investigator would require and could expect. I left the planning and direction of my visits forward entirely in the hands of officers who accompanied me, other than indicating the situations I wished to observe. It was quite clear I had neither the "know-how" nor the physical stamina to move about independently with any ease. Parenthetically, I may note that fatigue, even the brief effects of a short, steep climb, was more disruptive of intellectual processes than I have previously experienced. The difficulties of planning, exercising judgment and using foresight under stress are widely recognized. One officer, in discussing this with me, emphasized the problem by stating it somewhat facetiously He said, "Up here if a man can think five minutes ahead, we make him squad leader. If he can think half an hour ahead we make him sergeant. But if he can think all of two days ahead we make him battalion commander." It appears that occasional men can sometimes, though not always, make plans and use judgment on fairly complex problems even in acute situations. A good man is one who can be relied on under stress to put predetermined plans or previously-learned operations into effect. One not infrequently hears of decisions on the basis of "hunch" or "intuition," but, except as these relate to forgotten training or experience, it would appear that effective results follow only fortuitously. That is, one does not hear of hunches or intuitions which miscarried.

The problem of time is emphasized not only by the value of a predetermined plan of action, but also by the importance of having a known mission. The selection of a mission is considerably more difficult than is decision on the plan for attaining the objective. It seems one reason for this is that the mission carries with it the connotation of the relationship of the local group or unit with the larger group of which it is a part and thus, by extension, with the home community. The structuralizing power of a mission to coordinate group activity over a period of time is very much a function of the usefulness of the results to the larger community, and the genuine prestige value of the objective to be attained. There is little so demoralizing as effort and/or sacrifice for ends that are not well esteemed. The only question which I was asked on several occasions concerned the attitude of the people at home toward the war—was the war news of front-page importance? General Marshall points out another relationship of mission to the organization of time in "Men Against Fire." He found it occasionally happened that with the completion of a task, group organization broke down, and it required a strong stimulus to initiate coordinated action for attaining a further objective, even though reasonable safety depended on it. It would appear that the accomplishment of the interim mission temporarily destroyed all anticipation of anything further happening.

One may be justified in speculating that the current sense of continuity of time is determined by the course of the transaction between the organism and its goal. For humans, however, distant time is fixed by verbal symbols. Every man I asked in Korea knew exactly the number of points he had with respect to the time for his rotation home. Even men who by preference extended for weeks or months kept count of their points. This system not only set a maximal necessary period, and so relieved the anxiety of uncertainty, but it also provided a system of symbols in which a wide variety of feelings could be expressed without being named. Thus, in the discussion of points, one could hear simple pleasure at returning home, bitter recrimination against the system, guilt at leaving comrades or uncertainty as to fitting into life in the home town. Thus, the same concrete symbol could be used for intimate communication between men of widely divergent points of view, and provided a useful bond.

In "Men Against Fire" General Marshall has summarized volumes of data which demonstrate the fundamental need for direct human contacts through sight or voice as defense against group disorganization and the consequent psychologic strain of isolation. Consideration of the organization and methods of combat psychiatry provides equivalent evidence obtained by observers working independently with therapeutic rather than investigative methods. In the first place, the fact of rapid diagnosis, treatment and return to duty of men with tolerable symptoms itself represents a significant communication to the group as a whole. In addition to demonstrating the serious consideration the Army has for the soldier's personal welfare, this policy establishes the importance of the individual to the group by the unequivocal implication that his presence and effort are more highly valued than comfort. That this policy—with the information it conveys regarding the relationship of the individual soldier to the group structure—represents a positive support and is not merely an inhibitory threat is indicated by the fact that reduction in the rate of evacuation for psychiatric and psychosomatic causes has not been accompanied by a compensatory increase in other categories. The policy is "tough" in the sense that it assesses the personal worth and abilities of men at a higher level than many have been confident they could maintain. It is by no means "tough" in the sense of expressing personal disregard and contemptuous punishment for failure.

It is not proposed in this paper to discuss the developments or method of combat psychiatry in detail, since this subject has been presented in a series of publications by Col. Albert Glass, M.C.[5] and members of the Neuropsychiatric Section of the Medical Service who collaborated with him in the work in Korea. I would like, however, to summarize certain generalizations which I think may be justifiably deduced from the data. The effectiveness of modern combat psychiatry is attested to by the fact that in Korea approximately 80 per cent of neuropsychiatric casualties were returned to duty by the division psychiatrists, and better than 75 per cent were returned to duty from the neuropsychiatric installations in the rear areas. Only about 10 per cent came back to the division psychiatrist. Colonel Glass[3] in a follow-up study of neuropsychiatric casualties returned to duty from forward treatment installations in the Italian theater during the winter of 1944–45, found that slightly more than half performed effectively in combat and that about a quarter of the "ineffectives" were able to remain in some capacity in the division. Maj. Harris and the Psychiatric Research Team carried out a follow-up study of neuropsychiatric casualties treated and returned to duty in the combat zone. Data on the men's performance was obtained chiefly from company and platoon sergeants who had personal knowledge of the men. According to their estimates, between 55 and 60 per cent of these men returned to duty and, remaining with the company, proved themselves to be average to superior soldiers. An additional 30 to 35 per cent were below average but still useful in some capacity. Approximately 10 per cent were regarded as liabilities, although remaining on duty. A control group consisting of minor medical and surgical casualties, treated and returned to duty, and men who had not been casualties were estimated as approximately 95 per cent average or superior and less than 1 per cent liabilities. In summary, more than three-fourths of the neuropsychiatric casualties treated and returned to duty in the combat zone are enabled to complete their tour as limited, but still useful, or as average to better soldiers.

It seemed to me that the major factor in securing these extraordinarily good results was the relationship of the psychiatrist to the division as a whole. In contrast with the civilian psychiatrist who too often considers himself as a genus apart, the military psychiatrist has become a member of a group with a definite and important mission. It is his job to keep as many men active as possible, using a different technic, but in no sense a different principle from every other officer. The basic problem of the neuropsychiatric casualty is not what happened to him in his childhood. That is without doubt a very interesting problem for ontogenetic research. The trouble, rather, is that he is a failure, he does not know how this has come about, he does not know what he needs at the time, but he does know that he is no longer a member of the group to which he owes allegiance, and he is convinced that he cannot regain the group and his own respect. If he is evacuated, his failure is confirmed and treatment becomes more difficult, particularly if he is subjected to hospitalization for any considerable period of time. His sense of failure may, in fact, be confirmed by two or three questions into life history, inevitably implying that the doctor thinks he has some long-standing weakness inherent in his character. The treatment that makes sense is the careful consideration of (1) the precipitating events and of (2) what the man is experiencing during the period of treatment. The psychiatrist has to take the responsibility of deciding on the man's further course. Undue delay, ambiguous statements, procrastination are fatal. A large number of men after two or three days spontaneously say, "Well, I guess I'm ready to go back up now." Others get ordered back, occasionally bitterly resentful. However, if the psychiatrist has come to the conclusion that the man can make it, this is the only way to say so really convincingly. It is worthy of note here that none of the psychiatrists to whom I spoke had found the resentment at their decisions lasting for any length of time. Instead, there were not infrequent letters of appreciation for having enabled the man to finish his tour in his job. It is also to be noted that the neuropsychiatric casualties returned to duty either have trouble again in the near future and again come to the psychiatrist—some 10 per cent, as mentioned before—or have no further symptoms which are recognized as requiring psychiatric treatment. The psychiatric problems (chiefly psychotic in nature) which appear amongst men in the transports on the way home, or shortly after their return to the States, are entirely separate problems and affect a different group of men.

The importance of belonging to the group by contributing to the accomplishment of the group mission is emphasized in the negative by consideration of the neuropsychiatric casualties who had to be evacuated to rear areas or to the States. Maj. Harris investigated a number of these cases by visiting the companies from which they had come. In every case he found that these were men who, from the day they arrived, had not become contributing members of the squads to which they were assigned. Almost invariably they showed a psychotic reaction, and were usually referred to the division psychiatrist within a matter of days. In a considerable number of such cases the psychotic reaction would clear shortly after return to the rear area. Such cases would "break" again promptly and more severely if returned to the culture of the combat zone—regardless of the degree of real danger. Many could complete their tour of duty effectively and honorably in jobs which involved danger, but where the culture did not demand the intense, direct intimacy which is demanded of every man in the groups at the front.

Another area in which the relationship of the combat psychiatrist to the military group is highlighted is the area of "crime," particularly the minor types of deviant behavior which characterize the men colloquially referred to as "eight-balls." Here it is useful to keep in mind the operational definition of crime as discussed by George Dession in the preface to his textbook, "Criminal Law Administration and Public Order."[1] Dession approaches the problem from the standpoint of cultural values, and conceives "crime as a distinctively experienced subclass of deviational or value-depriving behavior; and the role of criminal sanctions as the economical use of value deprivation to achieve a net value gain." The criminal is, therefore, one who, while apparently a member of the group, actually disrupts the system which maintains the integrity of the group. The problem is a group problem, and is not a medical problem, and the responsibility is that of the accepted or established group leaders, not of the physician. The reason for these statements becomes more apparent when we consider that in dealing with crime it is necessary not only to provide for the protection of the integral solidarity of the group but also to provide for relieving the anxieties of the group when this solidarity is threatened. If the psychiatrist assumes the role of executive, lawmaker and judge simultaneously, his usefulness as a member of the group is lost and, regardless of his technical ability, he is pushed aside as an impractical dreamer. Very shortly thereafter, those men in command positions who wish to avoid their own responsibilities will attempt to use the psychiatrist as a means of getting rid of individuals who are administrative headaches. As Col. D. B. Peterson, M.C., remarked to me, "The psychiatrist is treated as though he were a sink for getting rid of dirty water." Respect for the psychiatrist as a medical specialist is thereby lost, and it becomes impossible for him to return men to duty, even in cases in which such return is therapeutically indicated. The group will not accept the judgment of a physician who does not respect the primary needs and responsibilities of the group, and they will not accept back into their ranks men that such a physician returns to them. On the other hand, uncompromising return of administrative problems to the responsibility of the administrators not only establishes the psychiatrist as a person who respects his own limitations, but, by implication, also increases the self-respect of the administrators as being recognized as capable of exercising judgment and authority.

In the above I do not mean to say that antisocial behavior is *not* an area for psychiatric investigation. The combat zone— that is, the period of acute and subacute situational stress—is not the place for instituting projects divergent from the mission of the group at the time.

A final factor in modern combat psychiatry must be mentioned: the improved communication between the division psychiatrist and the battalion surgeons and line officers. In Korea it was routine for the psychiatrist to visit battalion aid stations during relatively quiet intervals, and thus become personally acquainted with the surgeon and company commanders. This permitted discussion of particular cases and the problems they presented to their units and officers. It also enabled the psychiatrist to learn by personal observation how men who did not break down dealt with stress; and further, it gave the psychiatrist better appreciation of the mixed feelings of the unit for the man who could not be counted on to carry his weight. By such informal contacts and information both the treatment of casualties and the recommendations for their assignment on return to duty could be carried out on the basis of personal knowledge and interest—as necessary for the satisfaction of the psychiatrist in his work as it is for the effectiveness of the treatment.

That there is a reciprocal relationship between stress and communication may be taken as self-evident. Indeed, there is a good deal of descriptive evidence that communication, broadly defined as the acquisition and clear transmission of reliable information, may be the best measure of the intensity of psychologic stress in a group. For example, in discussing postcombat interviews, General Marshall pointed out to me that certain characteristics of the form in which the group participated proved to be good indicators of the status of effectiveness for further action. Effective groups were characterized by freedom to contribute relevant observations, and interest in resolving the inevitable discrepancies which arise from the distortions of the sense of time which men suffer under stress. With "poor morale," participation flagged. The relationships between group organization, formal and informal communication, and individual effectiveness are well illustrated in "The River and the Gauntlet."[8] Although infrequent messages and tenuous formal lines of communication are sufficient when no rapid changes are occurring, they do not suffice when the situation suddenly alters. Disintegration of organization, disruption of communication, distrust of the reliability of information and deterioration of the capacity of individual persons to receive and transmit information proceed more or less equivalently. An organized group may thus disintegrate into a crowd or a mob. It is to be noted, however, that a mob does not represent total disorganization. It always has a common, ultimate goal, and there is active, immediate communication—of very short-term reliability—from each person to those adjacent. This is far from panic. The term "panic" should probably be reserved for those states in which the presence of other persons is either not perceived or is conceived as an additional threat.

The term "reciprocal relationship" is used here to indicate two aspects of the total phenomenon. The first is that acquisition of information relevant to the situation increases the likelihood of development toward improved organization and personal capacity. Reciprocally, improved organization or personal capacity increases the acquisition of information. The definition of relevant information still needs a great deal of study, as to both its content and its implication. Thus, no more than the sound of the voice or the sight of the combat leader may be necessary for an infantry skirmish line under fire,[7] implying the reliability of coordination with other units. During training, however, content of verbal communication becomes much more important. The second aspect of the phenomenon we are considering, which the term reciprocal relationship refers to, is the impossibility at present of determining which are causes and which are effects in the great majority of instances. Occasionally, factors extraneous to the group may be identified as causes. Thus, the destruction of field telephones and radios by a barrage may initiate disorganization if communication is not or cannot be maintained at the necessary level by the slower method of runners and messengers. Also, disorganization may "start" due to pathophysiologic factors in individual men, such as embarrassment of cerebral circulation accompanying physical overexertion. By and large, however, the concepts of determining cause and effect relate more to establishing innocence and guilt *post hoc*, or to the common human wish for a magical panacea *ante hoc*. We will learn more about the problems of stress in both civilian and military life as we learn to observe carefully without being encumbered by threats of praise or censure.

Apart from the problems of the formal transmission of tactical information, it should be noted that informal verbal communication undergoes modification in acute situational stress. I was impressed by the simple directness of conversations with and between men in the combat zone. On the one hand, questions, answers and discussions related to immediate needs and actions—why was I there, what was I doing, what did I want to know, did I need a bunk, and so forth. The fact that data being collected by psychiatric and psychologic investigators would only be useful in the (distant) future was accepted as self-evident and without urgency. On the other hand, topics such as politics, race, creed, etc., which disunite groups in the zone of the interior, were automatically excluded in any contentious sense. The importance of "your being for me" and "my being for you" completely superseded any past differences. It has seemed to me that the feeling of intensity I had in the course of numerous apparently casual conversations about the weather, the food, the point system, and what not, was primarily related to the implication of the *fact of having a conversation*, namely, that we are together. In this face-evident fact may be condensed a large number of further inferences of commonality of purpose, mutual support, personal interest, and others. However, under stress, the question of attitude *for* me versus *against* me urgently demands an all or none, black or white answer. There are no shades of gray, any more than there are shades of gray in killed, wounded or missing in action.

I also realized in conversations, particularly in the forward areas of the combat zone, that the use of language changed with the other aspects of the culture and reflected both the greater immediacy of attention and the increased need for human contact. This showed in the greater concreteness in the use of words. We did not talk of carbines, bunkers, families, homes—in general. It was this carbine, my family, your home—in particular. However, together with the greater concreteness of language there was a condensation of one or several personal needs and attitudes in the symbol. Thus "my carbine" not only referred to the particular gun, but also implied my need for a weapon for aggression or defense, my problems maintaining it in working order, my pride in my outfit and/or others. The cohesiveness of the group seemed particularly related to the common understanding and acceptance of these tangentially expressed personal concerns. Another illustration of the shift in language to the more concrete was the infrequency of use of conventional adjectives to describe feelings. Instead, the desired or anticipated action was described. Thus, I occasionally heard expressions such as "I felt like getting out of there. I guess I was scared," or "I felt like shooting him. I must have been mad" in the course of comments on recent episodes. Current feelings were never clearly referred to. "This gets you," depending on the situation and the tone of voice and accompanying gesture, could imply a nameless thrill or a nameless threat of the combat zone. In addition, it is to be noted that the fact of verbal reference to personal feelings itself implied several aspects of the relationship between the speakers. In part this form of expression of feelings seems related to the fact that under stress a man's performance of his role in the group is crucial, but how he feels about it is functionally irrelevant. A more important factor is that during stress, for the most part, one does not know what one feels. In discussing these subjective phenomena with friends recently, I have found myself using a number of terms such as "absence of feelings" during certain definite activities, "exhilaration" at the time of accomplishment, "apprehension" coming on while sitting and waiting, and so forth. These, however, are more reconstructions than retrospective descriptions. Certainly these terms do not convey the sense of the episodes. I have speculated on one other possible reason for the avoidance of conventional terms for feelings. The use of language in large part is to orient the speaker for action. It may be that under stress there is danger that the use of a conventional term might precipitate equivalent behavior; that is, the conventional definition of an emotional role might lead to the carrying out of that role in its conventionally conceived form. Needless to say, such a result would be undesirable or even disastrous under the circumstances.

Many other phenomena of inter- and intrapersonal and group processes and relationships in acute situational stress have been described by various observers, but it is not feasible to review them here. A more serious omission has been data on the disruptive effects of discrepant information and attitudes (transactions). Investigation of such phenomena requires careful documentation to be of value, as very frequently the initial difficulties are thoroughly obscured in the later reports. In this regard, attention should be called to the analysis of the phenomenon of "acute excitement" by Stanton and Schwartz.[13-14]

Preventive psychiatry, as it applies to the problem of relatively large groups under acute stress, is a recent development, but has acquired considerable impetus from the needs of Civil Defense. As in preventive medicine, in which physicians, zoologists, entomologists, engineers, bacteriologists and many other specialists have learned to collaborate and talk a common language, so we can already recognize in preventive psychiatry the participation of a variety of disciplines. The development of a common language which requires a generally understood operational frame of reference is now proceeding more rapidly, but there is still much to be done in the theoretic field. On the practical side, a number of acute problems require serious study. These include such divergent questions as: What information is relevant to the various parts of a community before disaster occurs? What are the minimal requirements for recuperation during prolonged action under stress? What are the varieties of structure of informal channels of communication which are adequate for monitoring the formal channels in organized groups? Recent developments in social psychiatry, the social sciences, information theory and philosophy have indicated ways in which such problems may be investigated and formulated. This is not to say either that the methods and terminology previously used are insignificant, or that there is any magic in scientific technic which will replace the human. Rather, the experience and information collected by men in situations requiring the solution of practical problems are now sufficient to permit more rigorous handling; and scientific laws and technics can provide useful guides and tools for further exploration of human capacities.

REFERENCES

1. DESSION, GEORGE H.: Criminal Law Administration and Public Order. Charlottesville, Va., Michie Casebook Corporation, 1948.
2. FREUD, SIGMUND: Die endliche und die unendliche Analyze. Internat. Ztschr. f. Psychoan. *23:* 209–240, 1937.
3. GLASS, ALBERT, J.: Effectiveness of forward neuropsychiatric treatment. Bull. U. S. Army M. Dept. *7:* 1034–1041, 1947.

4. ——: Psychiatry in the Korean campaign. U. S. Armed Forces Med. J. *4:* 1387–1401, 1563–1583, 1953.
5. ——: Psychotherapy in the combat zone. Am. J. Psychiat. *110:* 725–731, April 1954.
6. MARSHALL, S. L. A.: Island Victory. Washington, D. C., Infantry Journal, 1944.
7. ——: Men Against Fire. New York, William Morrow, 1947.
8. ——: The River and the Gauntlet. New York, William Morrow, 1953.
9. PENFIELD, WILDER AND JASPER, HERBERT: Epilepsy and Functional Anatomy of the Human Brain. Boston, Little, Brown, 1954.
10. PETERSON, DONALD B.: The psychiatric operation: Army Forces Far East (with statistical analysis). Am. J. Psychiat. *112:* 23–28, 1955.
11. SHERRINGTON, C. S.: The Integrative Action of the Nervous System. New York, Scribner, 1906.
12. SPIEGEL, E. A.: Streifenhügel und Körperhaltung. Klin. Wchnschr. *3:* 1568–1570, 1924.
13. STANTON, ALFRED H. AND SCHWARTZ, MORRIS S.: The management of a type of institutional participation in mental illness. Psychiatry *12:* 13–26, 1949.
14. —— AND ——: Observations on dissociation as social participation. Psychiatry *12:* 339–354, 1949.
15. SULLIVAN, HARRY STACK: The Interpersonal Theory of Psychiatry. New York, W. W. Norton, 1953.
16. WEINSTEIN, E. A. AND KAHN, R. L.: Denial of Illness: Symbolic and Physiological Aspects. Springfield, Ill., C. C Thomas, 1955.

10

CULTURAL PRESSURES AND ACHIEVEMENT MOTIVATION

IRVIN L. CHILD, Ph.D.* and MARGARET K. BACON, Ph.D.*

I N OUR SOCIETY, when people are troubled, it is sometimes found that one focus of their concern has to do with strivings for achievement. Indeed, so far as adult life is concerned, the layman is very much aware of the fact that strivings for achievement are a source of frustration and worry, for this is an area of human life in which we are able to be relatively frank with ourselves. The layman, thinking of achievement in adult terms of occupational success and social prestige, may be much less aware of the seriousness of such concern in children. The clinician working with children, however, has ample opportunity to see that here, too, problems connected with achievement strivings may be a serious element in psychologic dysfunctioning. Stephen Doe, for example, was once referred to one of us for a psychologic examination. He was failing badly in prep school, and his teachers suspected that it was a question of inadequate intelligence; the boy himself appeared to be completely convinced of his own stupidity. The results of an individual intelligence test, however, indicated an intelligence quotient of at least 135. That a boy of such superior ability could appear to himself and his teachers to be stupid seemed clearly related to the high level of intellectual attainment of his family, and especially to the fact that he had been preceded throughout his schooling by an outstandingly brilliant older brother. Wherever he had gone he had been met with, "Oh! you are Robert Doe's brother!" His reaction to his constant expectation of failure in the face of such formidable competition had been such as to prevent his performing at anything like his own very superior level.

We feel that to attain a thorough understanding of this element in human adjustment, it is essential to obtain better knowledge of the way strivings for achievement are established or influenced by pres-

* Department of Psychology, Yale University, New Haven, Connecticut.

sures from the child's social environment. To be sure, specific social pressures toward achievement are not the whole story. Conflicts about achievement may often be basically conflicts about other and possibly less conscious motives, as when success in competition functions primarily as a form of aggression or as a means of obtaining love. Even here, though, environmental pressures play an important part in determining whether basic motives are expressed in achievement strivings or in some other form. In addition, it seems to us that environmental pressures may sometimes be responsible for rather severe conflicts concerned quite directly with achievement strivings, as when the environment strongly encourages the individual to orient himself toward specific goals of high attainment which he is incapable of reaching. For these reasons, we have felt that some practical aim might in the long run be served by indulging our curiosity about the ways in which social pressures influence achievement motivation.

In speaking of achievement motivation, we mean essentially the same as Murray (1938) and McClelland et al. (1953), and would particularly stress that behavior here is oriented toward a goal which involves evaluation of the individual's performance in terms of some standard of excellence. Cultural pressures toward achievement striving would include any customary treatment of children likely to lead them to evaluate, and to be concerned about possible evaluation, of their behavior in terms of standards of excellence. Often, though not necessarily, competition with others is stressed, and the pressures include the promise of special approval or other rewards for the individual who attains the highest standard. Thus, the child who is urged to get high grades in school, and the two-year-old whose mother brags about how many words he has in his vocabulary are both being subjected to pressure for achievement. The responses to such pressure are, of course, manifold. If the child is gifted with natural competence and versatility he may completely internalize the achievement pressure and stand at the head of his class, eventually graduating from college magna cum laude, the captain of the football team and "most popular man in the class." A less-gifted child, of course, experiences failure to the degree of the pressure on him to reach the very highest level of achievement. Some such children may compensate for failure in one area by achievement in another. Some may accept a mediocre level of performance with resignation. Others may give up and negativistically perform at a level far below their real capabilities. But in all these cases there is a common thread of orientation toward standards of performance, an orientation which, while sometimes carried out directly and effectively, sometimes directly but without success, and sometimes reacted against, is in these instances ever present as an underlying influence upon behavior.

What we have attempted thus far, in studying this aspect of human motivation, is to survey relevant features of child training practices in a considerable number of human societies for which anthropologists have given us a record of how people bring up their children. We have at the same time been surveying other features of child training, too, but will confine ourselves here to training in achievement striving.

The main point which emerges thus far from our cross-cultural comparisons is one that is no novelty to readers of Margaret Mead or other anthropologists who have already drawn explicit contrasts between our society and some of the societies they have studied. It is, however, a point which we feel can hardly be repeated too often for those who wish to understand the origins of behavior in our own society: that is, that there is a very wide variation among human societies in the extent to which children are trained to strive for achievement.

Should we begin, perhaps, with our own society? Upon reviewing anthropologists' reports about child training in a number of other societies, we are quite sure that the degree of stress upon achievement in our own child training is very high indeed. This might be most strikingly illustrated by the fact that achievement pressures are in a sense exerted even at an age when they cannot possibly have an effect, as in praising a young baby for his birthweight or his liveliness, or at an age when their effect can hardly be other than detrimental, as in the very early imposition of severe demands for achieving cleanliness. Mothers in the park compete over teething schedules, time of rolling over, sitting up, smiling, etc., and anxiously consult publications which give developmental norms. This competition between parents (often in the presence of the children) continues through the preschool years with regard to nearly every aspect of motor and verbal development. Happy the parents whose child weighs nine pounds at birth, sits up at four months, walks at nine months and seems to utter a sentence at 13 months! With the beginning of school, the pressure for achievement becomes more serious and is brought to bear more directly on the child. Children are divided into several reading groups according to their speed of learning. Stars are given for excellence of performance. Papers are graded on a scale of perfection, and marks are sent home on a card at regular intervals. As children progress through school the emphasis on achievement becomes more elaborate and extensive, and even penetrates the area of recreation. There are real rewards for the child who shows athletic prowess. There is competition for the leading role in dramatic productions. Status in the Boy Scouts is definitely a function of various forms of achievement. There are even prizes for pinning the tail on a donkey at birthday parties.

But strenuous demands for achievement striving are by no means confined to our own society, nor are they confined to any larger segment of the industrialized world alone. Various North American Indian tribes provide notable examples of a high degree of achievement training in a relatively simple society. One such society, for which a good picture of child training has been provided by Morris Opler (1946) is the Jicarilla Apache. The training of Jicarilla Apache boys involves marked emphasis on achievement. Babies are given amulets to wear which are believed to help in the development of various skills. As soon as they are old enough that instruction and advice are likely to be effective, a persistent process of training and correction is begun. At four or five, a boy is given a small bow and arrows. He is taught to use a sling and urged to throw stones. He is made to throw big rocks until he is tired. He is forced to get up before sunrise to run long distances. At six or seven he is told to run after horses. Parents are much concerned over the conduct of their children. They are ashamed if a child's behavior falls below a certain standard expected. Each boy tries to make arrows better than those made by others. His progress in hunting is marked by formalized procedures. At six to eight he goes on a hunting expedition with his age-mates for the purpose of killing small animals. Approval is expressed in terms of the number of animals killed. The goals of a boy are physical strength, speed and endurance and courage. Parents encourage them to compete with their age-mates. Their games emphasize competition and the acquisition of skill, and they are constantly urged on to higher accomplishment and ridiculed for failure.

As we have already implied, there are other societies which stand in direct contrast to the two we have described with respect to the degree of achievement striving expected of children. Among the Wogeo, for example, as described by Hogbin (1946), there is little emphasis on achievement and a minimum of anxiety over failure to achieve. The Wogeo baby is not allowed to crawl and is discouraged from walking until nearly two years of age. Up to the eighth year children are usually left to amuse themselves four out of five days. They play games, but competitiveness is almost never in evidence. Children participate in adult life apparently as they wish. They are often given part of a garden but are not expected to work in it. They help with gardening and fishing willingly, at first as a form of recreation. Much praise is given for their efforts but a precocious child is never held up as a model. Everyone believes that physical disaster would result from an immature person's working really hard. Boys climb trees when they are four or five but are dissuaded from going too high.

The Mountain Arapesh, who have been studied by Margaret Mead, (1935), also demand little of their children in the way of achievement. They have a long and sheltered infancy in which they are carried in bags by the mother, or else on the father's shoulders. They are not asked to perform tasks that are exacting or difficult. There is little pressure on children to grow up or to acquire skills. They do not play games which encourage aggressiveness or competition. Children characteristically play oppossum, sing, and watch adults dance. They learn to be passive and accepting and to follow when others lead.

What implications are we to draw from this fact of great diversity with respect to the stress laid by various societies on achievement striving, in the upbringing of their children? There is of course, first of all, a certain interest in being able to see our own behavior in a universal perspective. To us, acting as parents, concerned that our child should do better than he is in his school work or in athletics, or wishing that we could be less concerned, or perhaps being gratified that our child is doing so well, it is of real interest to know that we are markedly different from participants in some other cultures. In comparison with some other groups, we are different not only in the specific content of our concern—that is, that achievement in use of the English language, in study of American history, in playing baseball and football is what we are concerned about—but also in the very fact of having much concern at all about the standard of excellence our child is attaining. It is of interest, in short, to know that while we in this country are by no means unique in having such a concern, this concern does not arise directly out of our inborn nature as human beings but rather out of our particular cultural traditions.

The more important practical implication, however, has to do with the effects of these variations in mode of upbringing. It has to do with the notion that variations in pressures toward achievement exerted in child training are effective in producing lasting differences in the extent to which people will be motivated to strive for achievement. We hope eventually, in the cross-cultural work we are doing, to provide some evidence on this notion, by determining whether differences in achievement stress in child training are correlated with other and quite different kinds of stress on achievement in the general adult culture of the same societies; for example, by determining whether stress on achievement in child training is associated with preoccupation with themes of achievement in the folktales of the same society. This notion has already been strongly argued for by other writers, on the basis of intensive analysis of single cultures. In some instances, the systematic training of children to orient themselves toward outstanding achievement has been seen as part of the way children are prepared to act effectively as adults in a society where earnest striving for personal advancement or competitive success is expected. Contrariwise, the absence of training in achievement orientation in certain other societies has been interpreted as preparation for a pattern of adult life in which competition and striving for personal advancement are not valued and indeed would be disruptive of a social system smoothly functioning under the guidance of other motives and goals. If we grant that it is at least highly likely that differences of this sort in child training do play an important part in bringing about differences in the role of achievement strivings in the later life of a person, then implications of some practical consequence follow.

In the first place, this tells us something about the general meaning of the social setting in which we are all raised, with respect to its probable effect on the development of achievement striving in us as individuals. It is that we live in a society which in general places very strong pressures on children in the direction of orienting themselves toward achievement goals, and that this background of pressure

toward achievement should be taken into account in trying to understand the part played by such strivings in the life of any individual.
At the same time, this general cultural background of members of our
society is not one which would be expected to lead simply to a strong
and unconflicted motive to do well. In this same cultural background
there are sources of potential conflict. One such source is the very real
possibility of failure in achievement strivings. The goals which we hold
up even to school children are often ones which by their nature can be
achieved only by a limited number; where the goal is not merely to do
well in relation to one's own capabilities, but to do outstandingly well
in relation to others, it becomes of necessity impossible for everyone
to succeed. Thus, the possibility of failure as well as the possibility of
success looms up in a person's future as a possible influence on his
present striving. Sometimes failure can be avoided by not striving for
success in the first place. The boy who is a poor speller may not be
able to avoid getting poor grades in his spelling class, but he can at
least choose not to go out for spelling competitions as an extracurricu-
lar activity. In some people the avoidance of failure is highly generalized, so that a dominant motive may be that of protecting oneself
against failure at the cost of withdrawing from a great variety of activities in which failure is a possible outcome.

In addition to conflicts between desire for achievement and desire
to avoid failure, our culture is not altogether unconflicted even about
success itself. Various elements in our political and religious traditions
may come into conflict with strivings for achievement. Traditions of
political equality and of humility can be so stated, and are on occasion
so stated, that they would tend not only to interfere with the achievement strivings which are encouraged by other aspects of our culture
but even to make a person feel positively guilty if he had been outstandingly successful in such strivings. Here, then, is another source
of conflict about achievement which our cultural traditions might
lead one to expect to occur on occasion. It is complicated by the fact
that the outstandingly successful achiever may earn the hostility of
his less successful contemporaries. The taunting cry of "mother's boy,"
"teacher's pet," or the like, is on occasion a reflection of the fact that
one person's achievement is not necessarily pleasing to everybody,
and that the immediate social environment provides some realistic

motivation which is in conflict with the desire for outstanding achievement.

A second general implication is that if achievement strivings and conflicts about them are, in a broad sense, a product of certain uniformities in our culture, this very fact leads us to expect variations in them from one individual to another, within our society. For this is not an aspect of behavior for which cultural rules dictate any absolute uniformity. If we may rightly say that our child training practices do generally place a very heavy stress on the development of achievement motive, it is also true that we find considerable variations within our society in the extent to which such a stress is made in the life of individual children. And if it is reasonable to attribute the generally great concern of adults in our society with achievement, in considerable part, to this aspect of the way they have been reared, then it seems reasonable to suppose that differences among individuals in their concern with achievement may have been greatly influenced by differences among them in this aspect of their background—differences, for example, in the extent to which orientation toward achievement and success in achievement was in their childhood made a condition of parental love or at least an occasion for especially conspicuous parental approval, differences in the extent to which they have been able to succeed or have instead failed in trying to achieve various standards of excellence, differences in the extent to which they have been reproved for unseemly enjoyment of their successes, and so on. In seeking to understand the individual fully, we must recognize that other factors deserve at least equal attention. Constitutional factors, for example, may play an important part in influencing achievement strivings and reactions to them; this is most apparent in the case of gross physical defects which set limits on possible performance, but it seems quite likely that constitutional factors play a much more subtle role too. And, as we have said before, problems which seem superficially to have to do with achievement may turn out to be merely symptomatic of other problems unrecognized by the individual, and in this case the background of his training in relation to achievement has relevance only in understanding the choice among alternative symptoms rather than in understanding the origins of the problem. In relation to such other factors, our point is simply that we feel the individual's specific background of training in relation to achievement merits rather more, and more explicit, attention than it has at times received.

Our point here could also be supported by evidence from psychologic studies of individual differences in achievement-oriented behavior as a function of differences in background factors (for review of such studies, see Child, 1954). But although we are psychologists, not anthropologists, our concern in this paper and in the research on which we are currently engaged is rather to draw particularly upon anthropologic data for evidence pertinent to the common interests of the two fields. With this aim in mind, then, there is a further contribution of anthropologic thought relevant to the individual differences we find in our society in achievement motivation. It is that a part of this variation from one person to another is not entirely idiosyncratic, not entirely dependent upon the purely individual heredity, family experience and accidents of life in each single person, but is to a very appreciable extent itself a product of cultural pressures.

The cultural pressures to which we refer here are, of course, ones associated with membership in the narrower groups which make up our society, pressures which vary from one group to another because of a certain degree of general variation in culture among groups within our society. Positive encouragement of a strong motive to achieve may vary from one group to another; so may the development of motives which would lead the individual to fear or avoid outstanding achievement; so also would the more specific conditions tending to produce success and failure in various kinds of activities which tend to be evaluated with respect to excellence of achievement. These variations associated with the customs of specific parts of our society, then, may be an important part of the influences creating differences in achievement-oriented behavior among individuals.

Thus far the study which best brings out these facts, we believe, is the analysis of life histories of a number of Southern Negro adolescents by Davis and Dollard in their book, "Children of Bondage" (1940). For the community they were studying, they call attention to several cultural differences between the lower-class and the middle-class which seemed to have an important influence on the achievement-oriented behavior displayed in school. One fact, for example, is that middle-class parents characteristically took a great interest in their children's report cards, responding favorably to high grades and unfavorably to low grades, whereas lower-class parents often took little or no interest in report cards and, in extreme cases, did not even see them. Another relevant fact is that the middle-class child, looking at his parents as identification models, sees them engaging in activities in which they are making use of the skills he is acquiring at school to a much greater extent than is true of the lower-class child; thus, the powerful motives involved in the identification process—presumably the same motives and perhaps of essentially the same strength in the two class groups—are to a much greater extent in the one group than in the other enlisted in support of achievement-oriented behavior. Such differences in cultural pressure may be characteristic of class distinctions within American communities generally, and there may be subcultural variations of similar character associated with regional, ethnic and religious distinctions within our society. As a specific example of such a difference we would cite the respect for scholarship, and the encouragement of children in learning, which seem to be associated with Jewish cultural traditions.

One final point we would like to make. To say that an important motive in our society is culturally determined, that it is a strong motive only because we make it so, is sometimes taken as implying a sort of criticism of that motive and of the conditions giving rise to it. This interpretation is perhaps particularly likely if the motive is one that is so clearly a source of problems in the individual life history, as is the striving for achievement. It seems to us that anthropology is at this point a sound ally of common sense in guarding us against too easy a criticism of whatever causes problems in our daily life. Anthropologic study, if it does give us increased perspective on our own ways and allows us to see their relativity, also suggests that a culture, like a personality, is to a considerable extent a genuine functional whole, any part or aspect of which may be playing a role of unsuspected importance in the maintenance of the whole. In the case of the training of children to strive for achievement, indeed, we do not think the importance of this aspect of our culture in the functioning of our culture as a whole goes entirely unsuspected. It is likely that much of this training, as performed by parents and teachers, is quite consciously motivated by the intention of preparing children to take effective parts in the life of contemporary American society, in which motives for achievement in adults play so important a part. To be quite lacking in motive for achievement might be even more maladaptive in American society than to have an overly strong and compulsive need for achievement which is expressed in inappropriate ways. Respect for the importance of achievement training to our society, then, simply gives us more reason for looking with a critical eye at the details of this training, seeking to understand where and how it is exerted successfully, where unsuccessfully, and with what effects on general mental health.

REFERENCES

CHILD, I. L.: Socialization. *In* Handbook of Social Psychology (Lindzey, ed.). Cambridge, Addison-Wesley, 1954.

DAVIS, A. AND DOLLARD, J.: Children of Bondage. Washington, D. C., American Council on Education, 1940.

HOGBIN, H. I.: A New Guinea childhood: from weaning till the eighth year in Wogeo. Oceania *16:* 275–296, 1946.

McCLELLAND, D. C., ATKINSON, J. W., CLARK, R. AND LOWELL, E.: The Achievement Motive. New York, Appleton-Century-Crofts, 1953.

MEAD, M.: Sex and Temperament in Three Primitive Societies. New York, Morrow, 1935.

MURRAY, H. A. ET AL.: Explorations in Personality. New York, Oxford, 1938.

OPLER, M. E.: Childhood and Youth in Jicarilla Society. Los Angeles, The Southwest Museum, 1946.

11

CHILD AND FAMILY PSYCHOPATHY: PROBLEMS OF CORRELATION

By NATHAN W. ACKERMAN, M.D.* and
MARJORIE L. BEHRENS, M.A.†

O NE CONSPICUOUS STUMBLING BLOCK to further progress in the
understanding of psychopathologic states in childhood is the
difficulty of establishing definitive correlations at each stage of the
child's development between the behavior of the child and that of
the family. Essentially, this is a question of interrelating the growth
processes of childhood with the developmental processes of the child's
emotional integration with his family group. It is the interaction and
merging of these biologic and social factors, stage by stage, which
mold the characteristics of personality. But it is essential to view these
dominant modes of behavior in the growing child as being shaped by
the total psychosocial configuration of the family, rather than by the
child–parent relationship in isolation. What is implied here is the need
to define parental role functioning and child–parent interaction in the
broader context of the psychosocial pattern of the family as a whole.

In this paper, we propose to consider some of the difficulties intrinsic
to a fuller comprehension of this problem, and to explore some fresh
paths by which to investigate the phenomena of interconnection of
child and family. It is hoped that a new look at this basic problem with
the introduction of some broader perspectives may bring some added
insights.

Up to now, the continuing efforts to establish psychodynamic formulations for the relation of emotional disturbance in a child with
his family environment can claim only partial success. A frank examination of current concepts must bring the quick admission of serious
deficiencies. Much has been learned of child–parent relations, but this

* Associate Clinical Professor of Psychiatry, Columbia University, New
York City.
† Research Assistant, Henry Ittleson Center for Child Research, Riverdale,
New York.

is a far cry from systematic elucidation of the total range of child–family interaction. Relatively little is yet known concerning the group dynamics of family life, the relations of family structure to child-rearing and the multiple determinants of parental role functioning influenced, on the one hand, by individual personality and, on the other, by the interpersonal patterns of family life and the surrounding culture. Despite an unprecedented growth of knowledge in the fields of child development and child psychiatry, there is an impressive lag in our capacity to revise and modernize obsolete concepts concerning the correlations of child and family psychopathy.

Knowledge of child psychiatry has tended to accumulate in fragments, rather than in integrated wholes. Readily understandable has been the inclination to concentrate studies in child psychiatry on partial phenomena, where the variables are few and conveniently restricted. But the scientific cost of conveniences which rest on an arbitrary separation of the part from the whole may prove prohibitively expensive, if what begins as an attempt at simplification ends in distortion of the findings.

It is easy to discern some of the factors which have thus far deterred a clearer understanding of the relations of child and family psychopathy. The scope of this research problem is virtually global: it includes the individual, the family and wider community; it necessitates the consideration of multiple and overlapping variables, difficult to control and analyze; it requires training in the technics of social science as well as in psychiatry; it requires a formula for integrating the biologic and social factors in the development of personality, defining the interplay of intrapsychic and interpersonal events, and relating the emotional life of the individual to the dynamics of the family group. The complexities of the phenomena of family life make it difficult to reduce these processes to the level of an operational definition, which can then be systematically correlated to the emerging personality of the child. For these reasons and more, the task of clarifying the dynamic connections of child and family psychopathy has lagged.

The validity of current theories regarding the emotional relations of child and family rest in large part on empiric wisdom which has accumulated from psychotherapeutic experience. Such formulations depend mainly on the acuity and skill of the clinician. Truly amazing sometimes is the astuteness of the psychiatric clinician in drawing cogent, useful and, within limits, reliable dynamic interpretations. But, the fact remains, such conclusions are usually fragmentary and selective. Beyond the sphere of a few central correlations, interpretations of the emotional interaction of child and family become progressively vague, and eventually reach the point of sheer conjecture. In the end, this tends to become a delightful exercise of the imagination, a form of pleasurable fantasy-play unchecked by facts. The insufficiency of ordered objective data soon becomes critical and makes it impossible to judge which dynamic interpretations are right and which wrong.

The main emphasis in such formulations has been on the correlation of specific types of reactions in the child with specific parental attitudes: rejection, harsh or inconsistent discipline, overindulgence, overprotection; and also the relation of specific body behavior in the child —oral, anal, genital, etc.—to specific anxieties in the parent. Some correlations are made with regard to the child's reactions to rivals for the exclusive possession of the mother's love, and his reactions to the punishing authority of the parent. Finally, conflict in the child is related to conflict between child and parent, or between the parents.

Needless to say, psychodynamic investigations concerning the interrelations of child behavior and family experience have been given tremendous impetus through the discoveries of psychoanalysis. Psychoanalysis has pointed a beacon light to the basic needs of the child and their role in emotional development, the integration of psyche and soma, the role of unconscious conflict, the relations of id to the body, and ego to the environment. It has placed in bold relief the psychic bond of child and mother, the child's fear of abandonment and loss of love, his struggle with parental authority and the critical role of the balance between satisfaction and frustration. The freudian theory of the psychosexual development of the child related the processes of socialization to the child's biologic drives, and illuminated the role of anxiety and the mechanisms of conflict in the emergence of personality. Freud conceived the child organism as being dominated by biologic urges, emerging in a universally predetermined sequence, and organized mainly by unconscious mental processes. Social experience was interpreted mainly as setting curbs on the unrestrained release of the biologic urges. In this sense, the child is forced to renounce the pleasure of immediate impulse release and must accept the painful necessity of frustration in order to meet the requirements of the social environment.

In a recent lecture, Anna Freud* emphasized the inevitable role of frustration and conflict in the emotional development of the child. She pointed out that the child must always experience some "delay and rationing" in the satisfaction of his needs; this is the background for the continuing struggle between pleasure and pain. She indicated that in the search for causes of neurotic development in the child, early emphasis on the father as the authority figure and the source of the castration threat has given way to increasing recognition of the importance of the mother as the parent who disciplines through the power of deprivation. There has been a strong backward push in time from a first emphasis on oedipal conflict as the core of neurosis, to a more recent and sharper emphasis on pre-oedipal conflict, from the father who denies the child sexual pleasure, to the mother who denies the child oral pleasure. According to Anna Freud, together with this shift of emphasis from oedipal to pre-oedipal levels of conflict, there came another shift from an early attitude of sheer optimism concerning the possibility of preventing neurosis in the child to one of increasing pessimism. She explained that there are some mothers who are continuously rejecting, some intermittently rejecting, some who reject the child for accidental reasons, and some whose very devotion is interpreted by the child as rejection. She made the point that the child reacts with anxiety both to the parent who is punitive, and to the parent who is permissive. In other words, a child requires parental control to feel protected; without it, he feels abandoned and insecure. Obviously, then, optimal child-rearing involves a modicum of satisfactions, some inevitable frustrations, and an appropriate quality of social control exercised through the authority of the parent. Whatever the level of conflict, it is the ego that continues to mediate the struggle between pleasure and renunciation. The ego takes its cue from the environment, said Anna Freud. But here, curiously enough, she dropped the curtain on her discussion. She went no further in interrelating the emerging ego functions of the child with the social patterns of the family as a whole. But under what conditions does

* "Psychoanalysis and Education," New York Academy of Medicine, May 5, 1954.

parental control mean protection to the child, and under what conditions does it become a threat? This is the very heart of the matter: how and by what processes does the growing child internalize the significant psychic content of its family environment? What is the dynamic correlation of ego and the social interaction patterns of the family? If these processes were better understood, we might have a more solid foundation for approaching the critical issues of prevention of mental illness, and be less prone to erratic waverings of mood between optimism and pessimism.

From one point of view, psychoanalysis has created more problems than it has solved. Yet, in a paradoxic sense, this may be the very measure of its lasting worth. At the present stage of development there are critical obstacles in the way of implementing psychoanalytic contributions in the building of an integrated theory of adaptation, within which it is possible more adequately to interpret the child's emotional integration with his family environment. Freud's formulation of the psychosexual stages of the child's development, valuable as it is in its own right, fails to provide a satisfactory scheme. A critical difficulty emerges from the tendency of Freud's psychosexual theory to dissociate the biologic and social determinants of behavior. When a psychoanalyst alludes to a given psychosexual level—oral, anal, or genital—this generally carries a dual connotation: (1) a specific level of instinctual organization, and (2) an implied level of ego maturation or total personality organization related to the dominant patterns of instinctual drive. This two-fold meaning is ambiguous and confusing. The reference to level of ego maturation is vague and ill-defined, and the dynamic relations of instinctual drive to total personality organization and to the dominant mode of adaptation to environment are not clearly established. This is by no means to discount the value of the psychoanalytic contribution, but merely to point to some of its present limitations.

The recognition of the basic drives of the child does not compel the uncritical acceptance of Freud's theories regarding the libidinous and destructive instincts. Anthropologic evidence shows us that these body needs of the child may be differently organized in different cultures, depending on the specific content of requirements for social adaptation. It seems evident, therefore, that the need arises for reformulating stages of development of child personality in an adaptational frame, which would allow a clearer correlation of progressive stages of bio-social maturation with the processes of social interaction between child and family. There is, of course, the further requirement that definitive criteria be evolved for evaluating the psychosocial functioning and mental health of the family group.

In psychoanalytically-oriented formulations, certain selected patterns of interaction are suggested between the child's unconscious needs and particular elements of parental behavior, or between the overt actions of the child and the unconscious wishes of the parent. Clearly, such correlations are partial in nature; they hypothesize a relation between a piece of the child and a piece of the parent. This piece of the child—usually a set of conflicting unconscious needs— is not defined in its proper relation to the whole child, nor is the whole child seen in an accurate perspective with regard to the whole parent, or to the full breadth of the relationship between the parents, or to the psychosocial configuration of the family as a whole. Unfortunately, these partial patterns of interaction are not viewed in the appropriate psychosocial context. Often, parental behavior is defined incompletely and with selective prejudice, and, accordingly, the interpretation of the child's presumed response is rendered suspect. The determinants of parental role functioning are multiple. They derive partly from individual personality, but are otherwise influenced by the parent's interaction with the child, the other parent, the family and community structure. In addition, parental behavior, multiply-determined in these ways, may undergo significant shifts at different stages of the child's development. It is self-evident that an accurate definition of the interrelation of child and family requires that a part of the child's emotional life be viewed in relation to the total personality of the child, and its total pattern of adaptation to the family environment.

Despite the monumental contributions of psychoanalysis, critical gaps in understanding still persist. These gaps derive from several sources: the incompleteness of current theories regarding the progressive stages of emergence of the child's personality, the inadequacy of present criteria for evaluating parental behavior and family life, and the lack of a systematic frame of reference within which to examine the phenomena of adaptation at each successive stage of maturation. Until greater precision of definition is achieved in these areas, the issues of interaction of child and family must continue to remain unclear. Of particular importance is the need to specify the changes in mode of adaptation, as the organism moves from the postbirth vegetative phase, to the preobject symbiotic phase, and finally to the differentiation of a separate self and the establishment of object relations. At each of these stages, we need to discern how the child internalizes into its psyche experience derived from the family relationships, and how it establishes, step by step, the structure of a separate self.

It is well to be reminded in this connection of the paradoxic feature which is intrinsic to this process of maturation; namely, that success-full separation of the child's intact self from the mother is contingent on a continuing satisfactory experience of psychic "togetherness." As soon as the quality of "togetherness" is impaired, the process of separation of self is instantly placed in jeopardy. The level of emotional communication between child and parent is a central feature of this process. According to Ruesch,* the earliest phase of communication is mediated through the language of the body, then language expressed in action, and finally, the child achieves the verbal level of communication with the parent. It is along this path that we may illuminate the processes by which interpersonal experience in the family molds the emerging homeostatic mechanisms of child personality.

In the context of the child's struggle to adapt to his environment, it is necessary to mark out concretely the discrepancies between conscious and unconscious strivings, illuminate the interplay between specific components of pathologic motivation and total personality organization, and also to show the interplay between these pathologic units and the totality of the child's social interaction with his environment. Last, and by no means least, there is the need for a psychosocial definition of the family environment itself. Insofar as the family constitutes an integrated social system, a change in the functioning of any one part will affect every other part. This is reflected in the interdependence and reciprocity of the various family roles—husband and wife, father and mother, parent and child—and in the tangible influence which a change in one family pair exercises upon

* Jurgen Ruesch: Psychiatry and the challenge of communication. Psychiatry, vol. 17, no. 1. Feb. 1954.

another family pair. Bearing in mind the relative fluidity of family organization, it is easy to see that over the span of time, and at different levels of the child's maturation, the family may exert a changing influence on the child.

Some of the inadequacies of present-day conceptualization are dramatically illustrated in clinical practice and in the teaching of child psychiatry. Certain features of the method of psychiatric examination of a child may sometimes predispose to error in the initial evaluation of the child's pathologic condition. Diagnostic impressions of child personality based exclusively on psychiatric examination of the child in isolation from the parents may prove misleading. The behavior of a child in a first interview with a psychiatrist may contrast strikingly with the same child's behavior in the presence of a parent or other family member. The quality of emotional contact and communication achieved with the child may vary with the presence or absence of family members, also with the sex and interview technic of the psychiatrist. Changes in the interpersonal situation may produce critical shifts in reactivity of the child, so that what might appear to be a malignant psychoneurosis or even a psychosis, may prove actually to be only an acute, transitory disturbance reactive to current family trauma. Errors in the opposite direction can also be made. On initial examination the child may appear to show "normal" emotional reactivity, whereas actually the dynamics of the interpersonal experience between child and psychiatrist failed to mobilize the pathogenic conflicts of the child. Such examples could be multiplied many times. This qualifying feature of the examinational situation seems to account for some initial errors in evaluating child psychopathy.

For these reasons, the senior author has made a practice of checking the evaluation of the child's condition, derived from an examination of the child in isolation, against parallel data observing the child in an altered interpersonal situation, i.e., the child interacting with mother and other family members. He has similarly instituted a procedure for a check of observations obtained in office interviews against parallel observations of the child's interpersonal reactivity in the familiar surroundings of family and home. For this purpose a special technic of home visits by a professionally qualified observer is required.*

* The contribution of home visits to the study of "Family Diagnosis" will be the subject of a separate report to be published in *Social Case Work.*

The same difficulty of evaluating the child's interaction with family may be illustrated another way. When the clinical history of a child is presented, certain components of the child's behavior are judged to be "reactive" to the family environment. But, reactive to what in the environment? As soon as one demands concreteness in such allegations, it is seen that the isolation and definition of specific pathogenic features of the family environment is no easy task. Often, conclusions as to these pathogenic elements and their influence within the frame of the child's total family experience remain vague. Furthermore, one finds often that only a loose distinction is drawn between the components of the child's behavior presumed to be "reactive" to current environment, and those other components of personality conceived as rooted in fixed intrapsychic mechanisms and shaped by past experience. Past and present determinants of behavior are thus intermingled in an unclear way.

Still another manifestation of the same problem is to be seen in the way in which the data of a child's history are organized. One section of the history deals with onset of symptoms, a separate section with the child's development, and still another deals with family background. The social data on the family and the psychiatric data on the child's personality are often inadequately assimilated. The two sets of data tend to emerge in a dissociated way. It becomes difficult therefore, to discern the relevant connections, stage by stage, between the emergence of deviant behavior and the child's interactional experience with family.

Teaching experiences have revealed all too convincingly some of the limitations of our present ability to make correct surmises as to the relations of child and family psychopathy, especially where only a part of the relevant data is known. In teaching, the senior author has tested the validity of current concepts concerning the interaction of child and family by experimenting in the following way: starting with the clinical demonstration of a disturbed child, all aspects of the child's present behavior are elucidated—the onset of symptoms and the child's development. The members of the class are then challenged to predict from this the probable configuration of the parental personalities, and the family relationships. The same experiment was carried out in the opposite direction; namely, presenting first the family picture and then challenging the class to predict from this the probable pattern of the child's pathologic manifestations. The ensuing discussion is useful in delineating the unsolved problems of correlation of child and family psychopathy.

In recognition of the existence of these problems, we took a new departure in the study of this problem, hoping that a fresh examination of the relevant phenomena would shed some additional light. We undertook a long-term study of "family diagnosis,"* one phase of which deals specifically with the correlations of child and famly psychopathy. This is an on-going research, which includes up to the present an extensive study of 50 families in which the child and one or more additional members of the family have been or are in psychiatric treatment. The objectives of this broad research are to establish criteria for family diagnosis, and a classification of the psychosocial functioning and mental health of families. Through this, it is hoped that a more dependable method may be evolved for tracing the dynamic relations of an emotionally disturbed child with the psychosocial structure of the family. This study is essentially a qualitative exploration, an attempt to develop ways of observing and describing family dynamics, and a quest for new hypotheses concerning the relations of emotional illness in one family member with the mental health of the family as a unit.

For purposes of our study of the integration of an emotionally disturbed child with the psychosocial structure of the family, we made the following assumptions: the homeostasis of personality is relative; the homeostasis of child personality is substantially less than that of adult personality. Therefore, there is no true autonomy for the child's personality; his individuality is incomplete. The emerging personality of the child can be best understood in terms of specific patterns of biosocial integration with his significant personal environment; and these processes are best defined in an adaptational context. The basic needs of the child must be evaluated in the frame of the total pattern of emotional reactivity of the child and the social interaction patterns of the family.

The unconscious tendencies of the child, in particular, need to be

* N. W. Ackerman and R. Sobel: Family diagnosis. Am. J. Orthopsychiat., vol. XX, no. 4, October 1950; and "A Study of Family Diagnosis" by N. W. Ackerman and Marjorie Behrens, presented at the annual meeting of the American Orthopsychiatric Association, March 1954.

defined both in the context of the total self-structure and in the context of social interaction. With this conceptual orientation we hope to avoid the pitfall of dichotomizing the biologic and social determinants of behavior and also the error of failing to view unconscious urges in the frame of conscious organization of experience.

Taking into account the fact that heredity predetermines physical type, intellectual potential, temperament, affectivity and motor patterns, we attempt to view stages of child development in terms of progressive levels of biosocial integration with the environment. We regard personality, family, social structure and culture patterns not as separate and independent entities but as interrelated and interacting parts of a whole, which change and shift over time.

The effort to achieve more precise correlation of child and family would therefore seem to require the following:

(1) An integrated system of psychiatric appraisal of child personality.

(2) A theory of development of child personality, specifying the stages in terms of levels of the child's biosocial integration with the environment.

(3) A system of evaluating specific pathologic units of behavior of the child in the context of total personality organization and patterns of social adaptation.

(4) Definitive criteria for the psychosocial status and mental health of the family group. This must include an evaluation of the family's internal organization and external adaptation to the community; criteria for evaluating the mental health of salient family relationships, parental behavior, and the integration of personality into family roles.

In our study of family diagnosis we have attempted to pursue these principles, and also to meet relevant methodologic requirements. We have made use of a system of psychiatric diagnosis of child personality based on the system of Brown, Potter and Pollak, but modified to include dynamic and etiologic considerations.* We have evolved a tentative scheme for analyzing the family as an integrated social unit, defining the family both as to its pattern of internal

* Psychiatric Disorders in Children—Diagnosis and Etiology in Our Time. *In* Current Problems in Psychiatric Diagnosis (Hoch and Zubin, eds.). New York, Grune & Stratton, 1953.

organization and external adaptation to the community. We have set up a series of principles for evaluating parental behavior, integration of individual personality into the parental role and the reciprocity of parental and marital roles. We have tried to find means for evaluating the child's interaction with mother, father, and with parents as a couple and with the family as a whole. Also we have considered indices for the evaluation of the mental health of the significant family relationships—marital, parental, and parent–child. Finally, we have endeavored to reformulate stages of development of child personality in the frame of the child's biosocial integration with family environment. We conceive these principles as tentative conceptual instruments for exploring some of the uncharted territory of the dynamic interrelations of child and family psychopathy.

This method of approach is specified in the following:

(1) A reformulation of the stages of personality development of the child in the frame of adaptational theory.

(2) A guide for the organization of data leading to family diagnosis.

(3) A guide for the evaluation of the psychosocial structure and mental health of the family, including criteria for the integration of personality into parental role, and the reactions of the child to family experience at each stage of maturation of the child's personality.

(4) Tentative procedures for the correlation of child psychopathy with family psychopathy.

For purposes of definition, the child's emotional development is divided into stages. Each stage is conditioned by the previous stage and merges imperceptibly into and overlaps with the next stage. With maturation from one stage to the next, the processes intrinsic to the previous stage do not cease but become less prominent and are differently integrated into the dominant patterns of the succeeding stages. These stages of development, loosely ordered on a temporal scale, are best identified in terms of the characteristic trends of adaptation.

(1) The immediate postbirth stage reflects mainly a vegetative adaptation. The organism feeds, sleeps, cries when hungry. The integration of nervous system functions is incomplete; perceptual responses are crude, relatively unorganized and do not leave permanent psychic residues. In the first weeks, it is not yet possible emotionally to condition the infant's nervous reactions.

(2) The second stage is one of primary "togetherness" with mother. Though physically separated from the mother at birth, the infant is totally dependent for survival and development on the symbiotic union with the mother. It requires nourishment, tender warmth, touch contact and stimulation, and protection from danger. The omnipotent behavior of this stage is conceived not as a function of the child's individuality but rather as an expression of the child's psychic union with mother. The child commands, the mother obeys; the mother commands, the child obeys. The child cannot distinguish the mother's self from his own self. The mother functions not only as the source of love and security, but also as the perceptive and executive agent of the child, conveying through her own behavior her affective interpretation of the prevailing realities, and also devices for dealing with them. In this stage, premature withdrawal of the mother induces in the child feelings of helplessness, panic, fear of loss of life, and outbreaks of agression precariously controlled.

(3) The third stage is one of gradual separation of the infant's self from the mother's self. As the child matures, there is progressively less panic and less aggression on separation. The child begins to assert its separate self more strongly. This is accelerated as he becomes ambulatory, develops the power of speech and greater physical control over the environment. As the original psychic unity with the mother lessens, omnipotent behavior gives way to an increasing measure of real control and progressive testing of reality. Along with these trends, social discipline of the child assumes increasing importance; the child must come to terms with the social standards of his parents, which will vary with family structure, social and cultural patterns. The mother's care and control of the child, which is the core of early socialization, does not occur in isolation but is influenced by the quality of her relations with the father and other family members. As the child submits to early phases of parental discipline, he begins to internalize social standards, at first depending on the parent as an "external conscience," but gradually incorporating these standards into his own personality.

(4) The fourth stage reflects the child's differentiation of the two parents according to sex, a redirection of the child's love needs to the two parents in accordance with the recognition of sex differences and the pattern of relations between the two parents. In a parallel process,

there emerge corresponding distinctions in identification with each parent. There is a deeper internalization of the functions of conscience, now influenced by the distinction between male and female parent and the emerging sexual identity of the child. The further stages of submission to parental discipline are differentiated accordingly.

(5) The fifth stage is one of expansion of the emotional and social sphere of the child's interaction with his environment beyond the confines of his immediate family, testing of social reality and learning in the context of wider contact with peers and parent substitutes. This is a period of broadened social growth, education and preparation for adolescent maturation.

(6) The sixth is a stage of pubescent growth, bringing in its wake the struggles of adolescent adaptation. Differentiated sex drives emerge and there is reorganization of the lines of identification, realignment of group allegiances and roles, anticipation of and preparation for the tasks of adult life.

GUIDE FOR THE ORGANIZATION OF DATA LEADING TO FAMILY DIAGNOSIS

I. *Identifying Information*

    A. Child
        1. Sex, age, position in family
        2. Behavior described by mother, observed by examiner (note discrepancies in information between parent and examiner and between parents)
    B. Family
        1. Composition of family: age, sex of family members, other persons living in home
        2. Income, occupation, religion, education of parents, ethnic background
        3. Previous marriage, separation, current pregnancy, etc.

II. *Child Development*

    A. (Stage 1) Immediate postbirth stage; birth and postbirth events, early feeding and care, reactivity of infant
    B. (Stage 2) Symbiotic "togetherness" of infant and mother
        1. Fulfillment of needs related to hunger, sleep, emotional closeness; reactions to frustration, excessive demands, coercive efforts to restore omnipotent unity with parent
    C. (Stage 3) Separation of self from mother, reality testing, expanding mastery of environment

1. Developmental data; restraints imposed; achievement in relation to parental expectations
2. Behavior reactions to social discipline
3. Self-assertion, motor activity, play, imagination, hearing, speech
4. Social adaptation: strengths and disturbances in adaptation to siblings, adults, other children and wider environment
5. Illnesses, operations, accidents

D. (Stage 4) Differentiation of parents by sex: significant developments or changes under stage (3), sexual identification, incipient psychopathy

E. (Stage 5) Strengthening of self, expansion of personal identity in extrafamilial contacts and activities: significant developments and changes in previous stages

F. (Stage 6) Sexual maturation and the struggles of adolescent adaptation: physical, emotional, social, sexual and intellectual

G. Clinical diagnosis: Current behavior reactions, structuring of conflict, anxiety; psychiatric and psychosocial, and psychologic tests

III. *Maternal Role and Mother–Child Interaction*

A. Prenatal: conception, emotional attitudes and expectations, strivings, physical condition

B. Postnatal: attitude to baby as reality, strivings and values re child, integration of maternal personality into maternal role, quality of interaction with child at each stage of development, rearing attitudes and behavior concepts

C. Description of mother: appearance, attitudes and behavior

D. Background: personal, family, adaptation at different stages of maturation

E. Determinants of parental behavior: constitutional, childhood conditioning, character, symptoms, traumatic experiences, family interaction, cultural influence

F. Clinical diagnosis: symptoms of psychopathy, character patterns, psychiatric, psychosocial, and psychologic tests

IV. *Paternal Role and Father–Child Interaction* (ditto items under *Maternal Role*)

V. *Marital Interaction*

A. Courtship: origin of relationship, motivations, expectations, goals, conflicts, etc., image and plans for future family life, offspring and child rearing

B. Early marriage: emotional, social, economic and sexual compatibility; emotional communication, sharing of pleasure, responsibility, interests, adaptation to marital role, adaptation to community as individuals and as marital couple; harmony or conflict of goals, values and expectations

C. Current marital relationship (ditto items under B): achievement in relation to goals

D. Analysis of marital interaction:
 1. Integration of personality of each partner into marital role, interdependence and reciprocity of marital roles, effects of ancillary roles
 2. Specific neurotic patterns of interaction: neurotic content of relationship, conflict and complementary trends, intensity and consequences of neurotic components of relationship
 3. Specific patterns of compensation
 4. Specific areas of relatively health functioning and satisfaction

VI. *Interaction of Marital Partners as Parents:* integration of personality into parental role, need for child's love, maturity and realism in parental role function, shifts in attitude and behavior

VII. *Family as a Group*

A. Physical environment, socioeconomic, cultural and religious status and adaptation of family

B. Internal organization, reflected in action, attitudes, statements: strivings, expectations, harmony or conflict; emotional, social, economic compatibility of all family members, patterns of closeness, unity, communication, pleasure, authority, cooperation, sharing, competition, etc.

C. External adaptation to community: strivings, values, expectations; interaction with friends, extended family, social, political, occupational groups, etc.; stability in relation to community, adjustment

We have found it convenient to summarize this data in parallel columns moving left to right as follows:

Column I	Development of Child
Column II	Maternal Role and Mother–Child Interaction
Column III	Paternal Role and Father–Child Interaction

Column IV   Marital Interaction, Parental Interaction and Child's Response
Column V   Family as Group and Child's Response

The integration of individual personality into the marital and parental roles, and the significant background of each parent is placed in the appropriate columns.

With this arrangement there is an orderly chronologic sequence from the top of the column down the page; and chronologic relationships in interactional patterns are preserved, moving across the page from column to column. The total family pattern may therefore be visualized in chart form both longitudinally and in cross section.

On the basis of this data, it is possible to work toward an evaluation of the psychosocial structure and mental health of the family, and thus correlate the child's disturbance with that of his family. Toward this end, we have evolved a set of categories by which to define family relationships, reciprocal and conflicting family roles, and the child's reactions at each stage of family development.

Starting with the marital relationship as the center of family life, we attempt to evaluate the expectations, strivings, ideals and value orientation of the marital partners; current and past patterns of marital interaction, compatibility and conflict at the sexual, parental, and nonsexual levels; and the extent to which the relationship compensates anxiety and counteracts psychopathy in each partner or reinforces it. Specific units of pathologic interaction are viewed in relation to compensatory trends, and also in the frame of the total pattern of marital interaction. We analyze the integration of the personalities of each partner into their respective marital roles, the stability of the relationship, the satisfaction of each partner, and the function of this relationship in the total life of the family.

We move then to an evaluation of the total organization of the family group, its internal functioning and its external adaptation. We estimate unity, emotional security, conflict and adaptability of the group. We measure the integration of the family members into their varied family roles, the degree of satisfaction and fitness of these roles.

We judge external adaptation in terms of the function of such adaptation for the group and its individual members.

The data on parental personalities make it possible to evaluate success and failure of adaptation in the maternal and paternal roles. The character structure and history of each parent sheds light on the determinants of child-rearing attitudes.

In all this, we measure actual achievement in mental health against expectations, strivings, ideals and value orientation, and also against a theoretic model of mentally healthy family life in our society.

Finally, the child's condition, with special emphasis on conflict and anxiety, is analyzed as a response to his family experience at each stage of his development. In these evaluations, it is necessary to weigh healthy against unhealthy areas of functioning—the patterns of family interaction which are disabled by anxiety against those which are relatively unimpaired and reciprocally satisfying. In this way, both positive and negative influences on the mental health of the child can be defined. The specifically deviant behavior of the child can thus be related to multiple environmental influences: the child's family group, his parents as marital partners, as a pair of parents and also as individuals.

It is along these lines, hopefully, that the problem of correlating child and family psychopathy may possibly be worked out. Although the problems involved are now fairly clear, their complexity provides still a great stumbling block to satisfactory solution. However, it seems clear to us that adequate child diagnosis can be achieved only by focusing on the child, not merely as an individual but also within the context of the psychosocial pattern of his family group.

Evaluation of Mental Health of Child and Family

Child patient: age, sex
Composition of family: age, sex of members
Socioeconomic status
Religion

Marital Relationship

1. Relationship from courtship to present
   A. Influence of early patterns of reciprocal motivations, ideals and image
      of future marriage on development of the marital relationship

B. Areas of satisfaction and dissatisfaction; harmony and conflict; healthy and unhealthy functioning

C. Estimate of past achievement in relation to expectations, and strivings; estimate of stability, maturity and realism

2. Success of present marital relationship

A. Capacity for love and growth

B. Mutual adaptability and adaptability to external change

C. Areas of benign and destructive conflict; areas of satisfaction and compatibility

D. Use of relationship and marital roles to compensate anxiety and counteract psychopathy

E. Use of compensatory external relationships to mitigate failures in marital relationship and individual needs

F. Quality of integration of personality of each partner into marital roles, degree of successful adaptation in this role; fitness of reciprocal marital roles

3. Achievement

A. Relation to strivings, expectations and values for relationship and each partner

B. Maturity and realism

C. Stability

D. Disintegrative and regressive trends

E. Success of adaptation of partners in terms of ideal of mentally healthy marital relationship

Internal Organization of Family

1. Performance as a group

A. Influence of motivations, ideals, values, image of future family life and offspring on development of parental relationship and family

B. Areas of conflict and dissatisfaction; areas of compatibility and satisfaction

C. Unity and closeness in:
   (1) Quality and degree of communication and empathy
   (2) Pleasure in group
   (3) Security of members

D. Success and quality of integration and fitness of family members in family roles

E. Adaptability as group over time

F. Capacity for growth

G. Quality of compensatory satisfactions

2. Achievement

A. Fulfillment of strivings and values

B. Stability, maturity, realism of group

C. Regressive and disintegrative trends

   D. Success of adaptation of group in terms of ideal of mentally healthy
   family group

External Adaptation of Family

1. Degree and quality of interaction with community as family, marital
   couple, parents and as individuals
   A. Compatibility and conflict of intra- and extrafamilial roles
   B. Conformity and deviation in relation to community patterns
   C. Capacity for growth in adaptation
2. Achievement
   A. Fulfillment of strivings and expectations
   B. Maturity and realism
   C. Stability
   D. Regressive and disintegrative trends
   E. Success of adaptation to community requirements in terms of ideal
   of family mental health

Parental Roles and Child-Rearing Practices (for each parent)

1. Quality of integration of personality into parental role
   A. Effect of motivations and plans for children on parental behavior
   B. Effect of behavior and attitudes to child
   C. Resultant attitudes and behavior toward other parent
2. Achievement
   A. In relation to strivings, and child-rearing ideals of parents as couple
   and individuals
   B. Success in parental roles evaluated against ideal of mentally healthy
   patterns of child-rearing in our society

Child Pathology

1. Reaction type: structuring of conflict and anxiety
2. Causation of disorder (dynamic content) at each stage of development
   A. Child-mother
   B. Child-father
   C. Child-sibling
   D. Child-family as group

Discussion of Chapters 10–11

By LAURETTA BENDER, M.D.*

THESE TWO PAPERS consider the impact of early family relationships upon the normal and pathologic development of children.
Dr. Child and Dr. Bacon compare the child-training program of our
own culture with that of three other societies in regard to high achievement in early cleanliness and rapid somatic, motor, verbal and habit
maturation and for highly competitive school accomplishments, which
is later reflected in job and professional situations, politics and community activities.

One of the other cultural groups, the Jicarilla Apaches, a North
American Indian tribe studied by Morris Opler, was reported to be
like our own in reflecting a high achievement motivation into the
early training of children. The other two societies showed dissimilar
patterns, with low achievement strivings in the training program for
their children. These were the Wogeo, studied by Hogbin, and the
Mountain Arapean people of New Guinea reported by Margaret
Mead.

Dr. Child and Dr. Bacon present the argument that the excessive
achievement motivation in our own culture produces emotional problems because of the adult sense of frustration and worry over awareness of the universal striving for achievement and high competence;
the possibility of failure due to lack of success, since everybody can't
win or be best or first; the avoidance of failure by withdrawal; and the
conflict over success because of our democratic doctrine of equality,
humanity, etc., which may lead to a sense of guilt.

It is generally believed that high achievement motivation prepares
children for adult life in our culture. The authors raise the question
as to its effects on mental health.

Certainly, any child psychiatrist who sees a large spread of problem
children, sees many who are victims of this high motivation for competition and success. The large mass of children with dull intelligence
and many with special learning problems, such as reading disabilities,

* Senior Psychiatrist, Bellevue Psychiatric Hospital, New York City.

197

respond to frustration either with truancy and all the second line of delinquent behavior; by giving up, withdrawal and regression; or by anxiety and the whole host of neurotic patterns.

Which one of the above patterns is chosen is undoubtedly determined in part, at least, by other so-called constitutional factors. The authors suggest that constitutional factors (by which they may mean to include organic diseases and disorders and their aftereffects) tend to limit the capacities of many individuals to meet the demands of achievement motivation and high standards of competence in our culture.

In the 1930's Paul Schilder and I studied hostile aggression in the children we saw at Bellevue Hospital, and found that one of the major sources of aggressivity was derived from the frustrations arising from constitutional and organic interferences with functioning in children who did not get sufficient supportive love and care from parent figures. The functionings most often interfered with were those which the child most needed to meet what these authors call high motivation achievement, and which represented to the child a failure to be acceptable to adults and to compete with peers in the cultural setting in which they lived. Under our own observation it was possible to see the aggressivity disappear in an environment which modified achievement goals and the competitive pattern, so that each child could achieve, could do or be something as good or better than the other children in the group, and find acceptance with some·adults.

However, our follow-up on these children 15 years later, when they were young adults, showed the consequence of their return to a competitive community. Those whose limitations were too great, and whose socio-emotional or family support inadequate, withdrew from the competition (as Dr. Bacon and Dr. Child implied), regressed emotionally and intellectually, and settled into protective institutions during adolescence. Even if they returned to the community later, it was because they were able to find a dependent situation which protected them from competition or the need to achieve. Some of the more driven, impulsive and disturbed showed episodic aggressivity in conflict with the culture and the law, which finally put them into confining institutions and mental hospitals. Some were given adequate support to meet their needs through adolescence—which often required a combination of foster family and remedial tutoring for learning retardations—and were able to achieve and develop into normal adulthood.

Of equal significance were the studies of Paul Schilder on aggressive adult male criminals, including murderers on the Bellevue prison ward. He found that the significant dynamics was due to the ideology in our culture which equates masculinity with aggressivity and activity, and one could add here our authors' concept of achievement motivation; while femininity is equated with passivity and submissiveness. Paul Schilder found that all of the male aggressive criminals had suffered keenly in their childhood from being "pushed into a passive role," sometimes by their incapacity, constitutionally or organically determined; and sometimes, because of any variety of other traumatic experiences, they were unable to achieve, to compete, to be acceptable in the group. When in adulthood they were pushed into such a situation again they often reacted with violence in order to assert their manhood, to prove their masculinity and defend themselves.

Dr. Child and Dr. Bacon have also mentioned several subcultural problems in our own culture which give rise to special situations in certain groups. They referred, for example, to Negro adolescents who strive to identify with the middle class and who try to satisfy the ambitions of a group; but whose achievement goals, stimulated by our communication broadcasts, too often exceed their level of competence or the opportunities for one of the underprivileged classes to satisfy their desires. Thus we also find a higher rate of delinquency and mental maladjustment in the Negro youth, and more recently also in the Puerto Rican youth for similar reasons.

The authors also speak of the Jewish group and their respect for scholarship which often makes them the most competitive in our culture. This competitiveness is immediately reflected into the upbringing of their children, with a demand for high competence in intellectual pursuits beginning at the tenderest ages. This pattern is reflected in many ways in child psychiatrist practice. The Jewish parents, because of their respect for scholarship and professional competence, bring the children very early for psychiatric advice when the child does not show the competence that they desire. The frustration anxiety of the parent is quickly reflected into the young child. The psychiatrist often has the difficult task of recognizing a child who is constitutionally really incompetent to meet the demands put upon it, and who reacts by withdrawal, anxiety and neurotic mechanisms; one who is only temporarily lagging in maturation (especially in boys) and can not at the age of 5–7 meet the demands of a Yeshiva education and all other demands for achieving; and one who is a truly mentally sick or schizophrenic child presenting a pseudodefective or pseudoneurotic state because of the additional demands and anxiety of the family response. It was especially significant in the early years of our recognition of schizophrenia and autism in early childhood that nearly all of the cases reported were of Jewish parents. This led to some controversial discussions until it became evident that it was the concerned, informed Jewish parents, with high respect for the medical profession, who brought their children to us first. As soon as diagnostic criteria were established, those of us who had a wide range of child patients from different cultural backgrounds were able to observe as many schizophrenic children in every cultural and racial group. However, we also learned that each cultural group had some superficially different patterns which I have related to the different ideologic attitudes in family life which often conflict with those of the dominant culture and often are hard to carry through when the new minority group is also the underprivileged socially, economically, and in respect to housing, school and work opportunities. There are also different ideologies in regard to attitude towards authority; as the Jewish group respect scholarship and any authority so connected, the Puerto Rican group expect authoritative agencies to take care of them and their children. One of these concepts leads to increased maturity, the other to continuing immaturity and dependency relationships.

Thus, every child psychiatrist with a wide range of clinical experience learns a great deal about different subcultural groups—a practical knowledge which could well be better documented. This is the significance of the contribution of these authors.

Dr. Ackerman's paper takes an entirely different approach, and yet whenever we deal with the problems of child psychopathology in one way or another we come back to the same issues. Psychopathology of childhood has little else to deal with than variations in the pattern of development, and the child's interpersonal relationships with whatever family group he is surrounded. This, however, does give us our age-old dichotomy of constitution versus environment. The developmental pattern, although it is a living, growing and goal-directed pattern, merely unfolds the potentialities with which the child is endowed. The family group that surrounds the child can vary as much as environments vary, and yet the child's relationship experiences are determined so much by the developmental pattern as to be to a remarkable extent predictable to those who know the progressive stages in the pattern, excepting as they are modified by quantitative differences in the family group: for example, if there are no family or parental adults to which the child belongs, or unless there are so many that no one is recognized as the significant adult for that child.

Indeed the comparisons made by Dr. Child and Dr. Bacon between our own culture, with its great diversity and numerous subcultures, and the three other cultural groups studied by three different anthropologists is based on this assumption: that the developmental pattern of all children everywhere is so basically similar that it can be considered a constant; and variations in attitudes of the adults in the culture toward child-rearing practices will produce detectable overtones in personality, which can be related to environmental factors alone.

Dr. Ackerman's approach to the problem is nevertheless highly significant. He argues that when a child presents a problem of disturbance in mental health, he ought not be considered in isolation nor in relationship to his mother only, which has become the preferred procedure in many clinical setups; but he should be evaluated in terms of his whole family structure and, what I consider most significant in Dr. Ackerman's contribution, that the view should be a longitudinal one reaching both into the past and the future of the child and his family.

Dr. Ackerman has spelled out for us in careful detail all the factors that should be considered in such an approach, and he has rightly accounted for the many advantages to be derived from it. To illustrate the application of such a method (and to design his own research work in this area) he has collected 50 families who have a child at the Child Development Center of New York. This, of course, he knows gives him a very specific and limited subcultural group. By and large they are lower middle class, young Jewish families; a mother and a father and at least one preschool-age child who is more or less emotionally disturbed. Those of us who have experiences with such matters know that these parents will be very cooperative. As Dr. Child and Dr. Bacon pointed out, they have high respect for scholarship, for the medical profession and for any research that bears on the welfare of their children.

It is indeed well to have this type of a model of family life for such an investigation as Dr. Ackerman has been carrying out. But from the position where I am standing—at the threshold of a large metropolitan clearing center for all types of problem children from every type of cultural background and family life, including some of the children Dr. Ackerman knows at the Child Development Center—I am repeatedly impressed with how much all children are alike, and how overwhelming is the tendency for the inborn developmental pattern to assert itself in all human young, how tremendous is the need to be normal and to respond by a pattern to the environment and enter into relationships, and how readily those of us who are clinically minded may find methods of determining different special needs, aberrant patterns in development, variations in the progress of maturation, and adequate remedial methods to help these children. Race, mixtures of races, language, family pattern, complete abandonment by parents—all these are finally less significant than what the child himself can demonstrate and what the physician, educator and parental figures have to offer the child in terms of his specific problem. In the new adjustment (if it is a new one) or in returning to the old one, it is important that the child have adequate adult figures with whom he can identify, and that these adults have a suitable position in the culture to which the family group will belong. It will undoubtedly be easier for such a child if his previous relationships were sufficiently normal to have given him from the beginning a pattern which can be continued.

I was very much impressed by an article in the June 1954 issue of *The Scientific Monthly* by Dr. Leonard Carmichael, Secretary of the Smithsonian Institute and Editor of the volume on child psychopathology which has just appeared. This article is entitled "Science and Social Conservatism." He gives data to show that the anthropologists, psychologists and physiologists can not find any evidence of change in man, his aptitudes and capacities, his developmental patterns, or patterns of response to environmental stimuli and stress. There has accumulated 15 decades of cultural history, so that the educational problem of acquiring and digesting all human knowledge is expanding, and there is ever-increasing scientific data and mechanical devices. He emphasizes that man is an ancient mammal whose brain has not changed in many centuries, and that this conservative organ is our means of being the social creatures that we are, influenced it is true, by all the cultural impacts from the group in which we live, from earliest infancy through childhood, adolescence to adulthood, and that these things leave their imprint upon "those bases of the individual personality which is inborn," to make each adult human the individual he is.

12

Samuel W. Hamilton Award

OPPOSITIONAL SYNDROMES AND OPPOSITIONAL BEHAVIOR

By DAVID M. LEVY M.D.*

I

THE SUBJECT OF OPPOSITIONAL SYNDROMES will no doubt be linked in the minds of psychiatrists with the phenomenon of negativism, a form of behavior demonstrated so thoroughly and profusely in catatonia, and described so frequently in the major treatises of psychiatry. No doubt also the subject of oppositional syndromes will be linked in the minds of developmental psychologists and child psychiatrists with the period of resistance, or the stubborn period, as some investigators have phrased it—that trying period for parents beginning in the second year of the life of the child, so replete with the expressions "no! no!" and "I do it myself."

The negativism of the infant and the negativism of the schizophrenic, however normal the former and abnormal the latter, have indeed something in common. Manifestations of negativism in catatonia—of speech, of feeding, of elimination and also of defiance—are to be found in the negativism of infancy and early childhood. Is there a relationship of the two, of the supposedly normal and abnormal, of negativism as seen in the mental hospital and as seen in the home, that bears more than a superficial resemblance?†

* Clinical Professor of Psychiatry, Columbia University, New York City.

† (Kraepelin: Dementia Praecox (R. M. Barclay, transl.). Edinburgh, E. & S. Livingstone, 1919, p. 47). Kraepelin considered negativism a form of parabulia, a disorder of volition or of purposeful actions, a form of suppression of volitional movement by a contrary impulse. It plays "an extraordinarily large role in the clinical picture of dementia praecox. To begin with it leads to the instinctive suppression of all reaction to external influences, further to stubborn opposition to interference of all sorts, and in the end to the per-

An answer to this question requires a study of the manifestation of negativism in the early years of life and an attempt to find its meaning in terms of adaptive behavior. Since oppositional syndromes represent selective forms of negativism, clusters of symptoms related to special functions or activities, the same necessity applies to the consideration of that topic and also to generalized forms of oppositional behavior.

In the time at my disposal I think it will be most useful to dwell on the developmental and functional aspects of the general subject of negativism, at the risk of neglecting a clinical description of its special forms.

In general, it may be said that the term negativistic, or oppositional, or stubborn, or any one of its large number of synonyms is applied most commonly to behavior readily explained as refusal to conform to the ordinary requirements of authority and conventional behavior. The refusal to conform involves also the notion of willful contrariness. The individual who acts in this way is thought to derive some kind of satisfaction in pitting his will against others, in opposing the laws of society, in flaunting his disrespect of the amenities. Oppositional behavior, it can well be imagined, is particularly disturbing to parents and educators. Of its various disturbing effects, it is probably the attack on one's sense of prestige, on one's feeling of position of validity and importance, that arouses the strongest reaction. Since it arouses such strong reaction it is understandable therefore that oppositional behavior is so often regarded as personally motivated, as purposefully defiant, even when no evidence of motivation can be discerned.

A dramatic manifestation can be observed during breast or bottle feeding in the first few days after birth, in the case of the sleeping infant who appears to rebel against awakening and against the insertion of the nipple in his mouth. In this situation the two-day-old infant may be observed pursing his lips, clamping his jaws, and

formance of actions which are exactly opposed to those which are suggested by the circumstances or required by the environment."

Intellectual negativism (Bleuler); evasion (Kraepelin) in schizophrenia: e.g., "How many fingers am I holding up?" (four). Patient says, "Three."

See also page 64, Speech negativism, mutism, resistive, evasive answers.

shaking his head vigorously, thereby frustrating all efforts to feed him. Mothers typically regard such behavior as highly motivated. In my records of observations on forty-six breast-feeding mothers, made in a number of hospitals, such expressions as "You bad girl," "You're making me mad," "Don't be stubborn," "Come on, for God's sake," are quite common. The same mothers, however, responded quite differently when they suffered pain due to the infant's sucking. The painful sensations did not evoke critical rejoinders and scolding. Then, mothers hardly ever blamed the baby at all. Presumably that was something the baby couldn't help. Besides, it occurred during vigorous sucking, an achievement which pleased the mother. The baby's failure to suck after all the efforts made to get him to do so was a different story. Mothers felt frustrated, sometimes also humiliated, as the expression, "He won't take my milk," reveals. In this situation it was difficult for mothers not to ascribe a motivation to the infant. Indeed, our common way of describing such persistent behavior on the part of the infant, by saying "The baby has a mind of his own," makes this kind of projection extremely tempting.

Ascribing the term oppositional to the baby who resists awakening merely by remaining asleep seems quite subjective, since the resistance may mean nothing more than depth of sleep. Ascribing the term oppositional to such active resistance as clamping the jaws, pursing lips, etc., seems more logical, since the behavior is clearly designed to prevent sucking and appears to be initiated by the infant. As a descriptive term for such behavior the word oppositional or resistant appears more valid, though, as used, it carries the false inference that the infant is acting on the basis of capacities that require the kind of cognition and motivation for which there is no evidence at all in the early months of life.

The newborn infant's capacity to resist a feeding in an active way appears amazing to us, more so than its mouthing and searching movements, with which we are more familiar and regard as natural components of a sucking instinct. In the absence of hunger the lack of response to the stimulus of the nipple would not be at all surprising, nor of the appellation "passive resistance" to this state. The active resistance, however, would imply an inherited neuromuscular pattern of defense, a defense against activation of a function before an appropriate readiness to respond. Along this line of reasoning, the broader question arises of protective devices for all goal-directed behavior in its various phases, at the point of initiation and on through completion of the act.

My next example of behavior, to which the term stubborn is applied, occurs frequently at five to seven months of age. Mothers of young babies at Child Health Stations were asked, Is the baby shy? Can anyone pick him up? Will he go to strangers? When the mother said "yes," the reply was tested by the two physicians and a nurse who were present. When the mother said "no," her reply was tested in the same way. In most cases it was found that babies could be picked up and held in the arms of others until five to seven months of age, at which time they would give evidence of withdrawing, look at the mother, cry, or even push away and struggle to get back into her arms.

These examples may be included in our subject since such behavior, although regarded generally as "shyness," is at times regarded as stubbornness; as stubborn and rather sudden refusal to respond to the receiving gesture of grown-ups to whom the baby was previously so friendly. This period of "shyness" gradually diminishes, and friendliness is often restored within several months. One explanation for its onset is a change in the infant's perception of the mother; from perception of parts to the perception of the whole. Previous to the change, a series of conditioned responses, all strongly re-enforced, to various aspects of the mother were developing: responses to the sight of her face, the sound of her cooing, the feel of her during the feeding and embracing, etc. Out of these experiences of the infant the whole mother finally emerges and becomes clearly differentiated from the generalized world of others. Whatever the explanation, the fact remains that there is frequently a pushing away of others and a stronger claim on the mother's presence during this period.

In a number of instances the recoil from strangers and the closeness to the mother attains a persistency that makes it allied to the general problem of negativism. The infant stubbornly withdraws from contact with others and clings tenaciously to the mother. The example is appropriate for the study of negativism that is bound up with dependency. As dependency on the mother increases, from whatever cause, there is in some cases an increasing struggle against separation from her, and also a strengthening through repetition, of persistency in withdrawal from other social contacts.

So far I have considered three kinds of resistances; a passive resistance to being awakened, an active resistance to being fed, and a mixture of passive and active resistance to being separated from social contact. The first two, if resistance to being awakened can be included, have more of the quality of physiologic negativism, to use the term employed by DeJong in his experimental catatonia. The third is more strictly a social form, and also presumably a derivative of dependency problems. In all three examples there is a common characteristic; namely, a defense against disturbance of a state of being, or, viewed in a social context, a defense against the person who attempts to alter this state.

My next example, the "battle of the spoon," occurs a few months later than the first period of shyness. Commonly at ten or eleven months of age the baby grabs the spoon from the mother's hand and tries to feed itself. However responsive to this display of independence, the spattering of food all over the room poses a problem. Mothers usually solve it by various compromises; letting the baby hold a spoon while they use another, allowing the baby to spoon-feed itself once for several spoon-feedings of their own, etc. Some mothers, as you might expect, remain adamant. They will stand for no nonsense. A feeding is a feeding and not a game, especially one so disastrous to good housekeeping. Then it may happen that unknowingly and unwillingly they are making an experimental contribution to our subject.

One mother described the difficulty as a hunger strike. At ten months of age her baby suddenly refused to be spoon-fed. The mother's insistence on preventing the baby from doing it himself resulted in his refusal to take the spoon from her hand or his own. The strike was settled amicably after ten days through the intervention of a pediatrician. He advised the mother to put bits of food in front of the baby and let him pick them up with his fingers, which the baby did.

Some babies, in their struggle against interference with their own manipulation of the spoon, even spit out or remove with their fingers food the mother managed to slip into their mouths.

This example of resistance differs from the three previously cited.

It represents a struggle for something new rather than a struggle for something old. The initiative of the infant is now involved rather than his inertia. It is an early manifestation of the development of independent behavior which builds up to climax in the second year of life. Before that state is reached there are other noteworthy examples of pushing away the helping hand and going one's own way. That is literally true in the case of a number of infants who will allow no one to help them while learning to walk. They must do it themselves, no matter how many times they fall.

Others forms of resistance that may be seen in the first year of life are concerned with repetitious movements (perseveration). Their importance in the development of muscular control particularly has been studied pre- and postnatally. Self-learning by repetition applies also to psychologic processes. Many of these activities appear to the adult as annoying repetition-compulsions, as the behavior of children who don't know when to stop. Some head-on collisions of infant and grown-up may result. A mother at a health station, in response to a question about her baby's stubbornness, told us about the first clash of wills that occurred when her baby was 12 months old. The baby was then able to walk and get out of her crib and also understand the mother's forbidding gestures. Because of a fever, the doctor advised the mother to keep her baby in bed. She tried to do so but the baby persisted in climbing out. At first the mother said she took it all playfully, each time putting the baby back. As the baby's activity persisted the mother became more serious. She began to scold and applied more pressure in holding the baby down. The mother was getting tired, but the baby seemed to have boundless energy. The mother became as persistent as the baby. "Then, before I knew it", she said "my hand was red from slapping her behind." She paused and added, "That will never happen again. I'll never fall into that trap again."*

The "clash of wills" example serves our purpose for a number of reasons. It illustrates any number of others in which the adult manages to get himself trapped in an untenable position in which he feels compelled to break the child's spirit. It illustrates the remarkable

* For a history of the attitudes of social philosophers and educators towards the child's obstinacy see the introductory chapter of *Der Trotz, sein Wesen und seine Behandlung* by H. Winkler: Munich, Reinhardt, 1929.

strength and also—a point to be considered later—the peculiar automaticity of oppositional mechanisms, which under certain conditions are self-locking, beyond control. The example illustrates how early in life such mechanisms can occur.

We are now ready to consider the period of resistance, or the stubborn period that seems to be fairly concentrated over a six-month span, at ages one and a half to two years. Whatever the measure of noncompliance,—the intelligence test, the physical examination, observations of spontaneous behavior, experiments, the clinical case record or ordinary inquiry—all studies confirm the existence of a period in the early childhood of most children in which negativism is more frequent than in the period preceding or following.

At one of our health stations, resistance during the physical examination, consisting of crying and struggling to a degree that made it difficult if not impossible to go on, was classified as type III resistance. About 12 per cent of those examined manifested this type of resistance. Among 800 infants and children ranging in age from a month to 59 months, there were about a hundred whose resistance was of type III. The group age 18 to 23 months had the highest frequency of such resistance. In fact, most of the 100 cases were contained within it. There was a clear rise in frequency as the age of 18 months was reached, and a decided fall in frequency when the age of two years was passed. The findings were also consistent with the mother's accounts of the child's behavior at home.*

Of older writings on this subject, reference may be made to James Sully's book, "Studies of Childhood," published in 1898. He devoted one of his chapters to "Extracts from a Father's Diary," of which one paragraph reads as follows:

* Levy, D. M. and Tulchin, S. H.: I. The resistance of infants and children during mental tests. J. Exper. Psychol. *6:* 304–322, 1923; II. *8:* 209–224, 1925.

Levy, D. M.: Resistant behavior of children. Am. J. Psychiat. *4:* 503–507, 1925.

——: Observations of attitudes and behavior in child health center; sample studies of maternal feelings, dependency, resistant behavior, and inoculation fears. Am. J. Pub. Health *41:* 182–190, 1951.

——: The Early Development of Independent and Oppositional Behavior. *In* Midcentury Psychiatry (Roy Grinker, ed.). Springfield, Ill., C. C Thomas, 1953, pp. 113–122.

Third year. The moral side of the child's nature appears during this year to have undergone noticeable changes. The most striking fact which comes out in the picture of the boy as painted in the present chapter is the sudden emergence of self-will. He began now to show himself a veritable rebel against parental authority. Thus we read [at age 25 months] that when corrected for slapping Jingo, or other fault, he would remain silent and half laugh in a cold contemptuous way, which must have been shocking to his worthy parents. A month later we hear of an alarming increase in self-will. He would now strike each of these august persons, and follow up sacrilege with a profane laugh.

The "sudden emergence of self-will," so well described in Sully's literary style, can be found in a number of our cases selected from those referred for treatment as well as those seen routinely at child health stations. The following is derived from presumably normal samples at a child health station in response to a question about a three-year-old girl, "When did she start saying 'no! no!, I won't,' or things like that?" The mother replied, "She didn't say I won't. She showed it by first looking at you, so *blank*, as if she doesn't hear you, and she wouldn't do what you asked her to. . . She used to go out with anybody, even strangers. . . She has changed to people. Other people now call her shy. My friends are surprised about it. She changed to them, like she doesn't know them. After awhile she'll talk to them. She has to be thawed out. If it's a stranger she just won't talk to them at all. She was never shy before two months ago." The mother went on to describe the change from compliance to disobedience toward both parents and the mute-like negativism, which she thought had its onset about a year before the more recent shyness toward strangers.

Careful determination of onset, at least within an approximate period of time, is especially important because of the general tendency on the part of informants to relate the onset to an event, such as the birth of the new baby, the nursery school experience, a period of separation from the mother, an illness or fright. The same tendency is very likely true of most of us. We are always in search of connections between events, and feel more comfortable when we can relate the beginnings of negativism to a tangible disturbing experience to which the negativism is a reaction, rather than to a maturational process. In our studies though, it appears very reasonable to assume that negativistic behavior was ushered in by a specific event; more often the events followed such behavior and were thought to be re-enforcing factors. As re-enforcing factors, however, the "events" are quite significant and help to explain the intensity and duration of a negativism which might otherwise have diminished considerably.

Among two-year-olds referred for treatment because of oppositional behavior, a large variety of manifestations are seen. My cases included mutism, food refusal, bowel and bladder refusals (one patient, age 27 months, said to me, "I should move my bowels, but I won't."), oppositeness and inner negativism (asked to sit down, a 26-month-old boy stood up, asked to stand up, he sat down), also instances of opposing one's own wishes, as in the case of a two-year-old who said "I want to but I won't;" instances of pretending not to understand; and most frequently, as expressed by parents, "persistency in having his own way," "There's no way to make him obey," "You can't talk him out of anything."

Cases were seen in which the child was negativistic to others but not to the mother; in which negativism was the predominant problem and temper tantrums quite secondary, and vice versa. They included one case (unusual) of bowel refusal in an otherwise compliant child. They included cases in which negativism had already been evident in the first year of life, and a few cases in which the onset was sudden and recent. They included cases in which negativism was preceded by shyness, and cases also (and that is a fairly common problem at two years and later) in which there was increased dependency on the mother—an overt representation of conflicting dependent and independent maneuvers.

Negativistic behavior that appears to have its onset with an illness or an operation deserves special mention. In one published case, negativistic behavior became prominent after a minor operation which, through bad handling on the part of the physician, was turned into a frightening episode. The child was then 22 months old. A period of "no," to everything lasted 18 days. During that time her exploring behavior and her interest in people stopped. The improvement in regard to all negativistic manifestations was quite marked within a month of the disturbing experience. Hostility to the mother, however, and increased dependency on her were still present six months later.*

* (Levy, D. M.: On Evaluating the "Specific Event" as a Source of Anxiety. *In* Anxiety (Hoch and Zubin, eds.). New York, Grune & Stratton, 1950, pp.

Oppositional behavior in response to illness, pain, fright and excessive stimuli is commonly observed. In the form of passive resistance, it appears to be a protective device, like physiologic inappetence and general abatement of interest and activity during febrile states. The two-year-old who withdrew from all contact with people and with things after a painful and frightening experience is such an example. Excessive stimuli in the case of children refer particularly to excessive demands by adults for their affection, response and display of brightness; also, requirements of cleanliness, neatness, emotional control and intellectual standards beyond their ability. The problem is thus analogous to the excessive load placed on the back of pack animals. This occasions—in essence the same type of resistance—stubbornness, if not active defiance.

We are now ready to bring all our examples together and consider their common features. A number of them appear to have the common function of resistance to external influence. This influence would determine when an act is to begin, as in the example of sucking stimulation, and when it is to end, as in the example of awakening the baby and of stopping repeated movements. Without this resistant character the organism's response would be determined entirely by external stimuli. The organism would then have no way of responding to inner stimuli, or, in other words, to inner needs. The capacity to resist external influence thus enables the organism to use and develop inner controls.*

The examples of oppositional behavior in response to acute emotional and painful situations are more clearly seen as protective in

---

140–149). A protective recoil in any situation fraught with anxiety may give rise to behavior regarded as negativistic, which has been observed also in animals. The chimpanzee brought up by the Kelloggs refused to take new playthings they gave her in the early days of the experiment. She would take them herself, however, if the playthings were left on the floor and "she, so to speak, found them herself." The behavior as described may be simply the result of withdrawal from social contact because of anxiety (Kellogg and Kellogg: New York, McGraw-Hill, 1933, p. 182).

* In the pursuit of a goal, which in children often involves a struggle against interruption of play, the "obstacle" is often an inner stimulus. Thus, children interested in play may wait till the last moment before going to the toilet. An extreme example is that of a seven-year-old boy who can never be so deterred if he is in the midst of things: he defecates or urinates on the spot and continues with his activity.

function, since the individual is thereby enabled to recoil, to barricade himself against noxious influence and win time for recovery.

A number of the examples are readily seen as primarily biologic activities, and what has been said about them might apply equally well if the external influence were of a purely mechanical nature. When the activities are primarily social and concerned with a wide range of behavior, then the principle of autonomy of the act applies equally well, though on a larger scale.

Now we can see the oppositional behavior in the second year of life as a general movement towards the autonomy of the whole person, as the first flowering of self-determination, of which the budding had long been in evidence. The persistency or stubbornness, the assertiveness or refusals that characterize all our examples, have something in common. They are all self-propelling, and resist all obstacles that bar the way.

II

Animal studies of the separation of mother and young are quite pertinent to our own. To make survival possible, the separation has to be well timed so that the dependency of the young is not terminated too soon. Before this phase arrives there is evidence of behavior that resembles closely the period of resistance. Brückner, a German psychologist, has written extensively on this subject particularly as it pertains to domestic hens. In an article entitled, "Investigations of Animal Psychology," with special reference to "The Dissolution of Family Life," he noted two principal modes of behavior at the time of the break-up of the relationship between the hen and her chicks, the principle of emancipation and the principle of expulsion.* In the first two or three days there is no evidence of either. The hen is constantly on guard and sets up an alarm cry if the chicks walk a few inches away from her perimeter. The relationship is tightly woven and anxious. After three days it begins to loosen. There is more freedom of activity, but for a week or so the hen keeps the chicks in sight and raises the alarm cry if they stray too far away. The maternal bond of chains is transformed, to use Brückner's ex-

* Brückner, G. H.: Untersuchungen zur Tierpsychologie, insbesondere zur Auflösung der Familie. Ztschr. f. Psychol. *128:* 1–110, 1933 (also Schielderupp-Ebbe: Ztschr. f. Psychol., no. 88, 1922 and no. 92, 1923).

pression, to a "bond of rubber bands." There is more flexibility but
the bond tightens at a certain point and the chicks are pulled back.
Thereafter the range of movement grows wider. The chicks stray
beyond the hen's vision. They still form a group, however, at times
still follow the hen, respond to her clucking when she holds up a
special delicacy and also to her alarm cry. During this third stage,
which lasts about four to six weeks, the chicks display the kind of
independent behavior that reflects Brückner's principle of emancipation, behavior that in humans would be referred to as disobedient,
wilful, out-of-hand and oppositional. Indeed the principle of emancipation which operates in emancipating the hen from her maternity,
as it does the chicks from their dependency, is not necessarily a smooth
affair. The hen may cluck desperately without any result. She may
spend time searching for her chicks. They in turn may wander all
over the place and make no appearance until sundown. At least
during their period of growing independence they are bound to come
home to roost. This stage is terminated by the hen's own efforts at
expelling the brood. She pecks them away consistently for two or
three days, even longer. In spite of the fact that the young have
been foraging for themselves they keep returning to the hen, though
the hen is adamant in expelling them. During this ordeal they appear
quite disturbed; according to Brückner, they are in a state of panic.
Finally, they take leave of the hen but for some time thereafter the
young remain together.

According to Brückner the hen procrastinates before she starts
pecking away the brood. Her first pecks may be hesitant and unsure.
She may also be discriminating before the pecking goes on in earnest,
attacking the larger chicks more strongly than the smaller ones.

Whether the pattern as just described holds true in all its details,
and there are numerous variations, the essential principles of emancipation and exclusion are revealed in numerous accounts of the separation of mother and young among birds and mammals. In almost all
of them the final exclusion is timed to meet two exigencies: the capacity of the young to manage for themselves and the imminent arrival
of the next brood or litter. The first filial generation must be cleared
away before the second arrives.

In the human species the analogous problem is seen in a series of
partial emancipations and expulsions until the final loosening, if not

complete freedom, occurs. The question of the relative frequency of the resistant period and of the time of its occurrence was given special cogency through studies of animal behavior. Why does resistant behavior attain its first peak between the age of eighteen months and two years? Is there also in humans a time relationship of emancipation from dependency and the birth of the next offspring? Busemann, in an article published in 1930 on the causes of the first stubborn age and other periods of tension, supported the affirmative answer to this question.* In a series of cases of uninterrupted pregnancies he found that the most frequent interval between a first and second childbirth was two years. He noted that the sucking stage has been passed by then, the child can eat and drink alone, there is readiness for speech and social activity with other children. The infant type of dependency is over.

In this connection the spontaneous remarks of mothers during their second or later pregnancy is of interest. When a mother knows that her next baby will be no more than a year older than the preceding one she wonders, she says, how she will manage; "it's like having two at the same time," "It doesn't seem fair," etc. When asked how she would feel if the difference were two years instead of one, she replies, "Oh, that's different, it's much easier." She takes it for granted that the difference is quite obvious.

The period of resistance might better be called the first period of independence or even, as some writers have named it, the first

* Busemann, A.: Über das so genannte Trotzalter des Kindes. Ztsch. f. pädagog. Psychol. *29:* 42–49, 1928.

———: Uber die Ursachen des "ersten Trotzalters" und der Erregungsphasen überhaupt. Ztschr. f. padagog. Psychol. *30:* 276–281, 1929.

See also Benjamin, E.: Grundlagen und Entwicklungsgeschichte der kindlichen Neurose. Leipzig, Georg Thieme, 1930, chap. III, "Die Trotzperiode als psychopathologisches Phänomen."

Benjamin regards negativism as due to the change of relationship from mother-infant to family and community. See also his paper, Period of resistance in early childhood: Its significance for the development of the problem child. Am. J. Dis. Child *63:* 1019–1079, 1942.

The term "first stubborn age" was employed by Charlotte Bühler in *Das Seelenleben der Jugendliehen* (ed. 4), Jena, 1927.

puberty,* and there are notable resemblances between it and the puberty of adolescence. Evidently the "no-no's" have been more impressive than the words "I do it myself." That there may be an essential relationship between the two, i.e., between negativism and independence, could be determined by comparing children who have never had a period of resistance, with the others. Children of the same family who, according to the mother differ markedly in respect to the "no-no" period, would present a favorable group for this kind of comparison. Our own data are still scanty on this point. One study comparing two groups of seven-year-old children divided according to the presence or absence of "the stubborn period" has been published by Hetzer.† A significant difference in regard to independent behavior was found. Compared with the others, the children who had not gone through "the stubborn period," according to observations made in the classroom, were much more dependent on the teacher's help than the others.

The finding of a resistant period as a developmental stage in animals, as in men, is based on a study of resemblance of behavior and of function. The differences are revealed in the manifold varieties and subtleties of resistant behavior in the human—differences related to family structure, to intelligence, and to the larger varieties of personality constellations.

As soon as the early resistant forms become modified, numerous patterns appear in relation to any particular form of activity. Thus, the refusal to talk at all may be modified to scanty speech, jumbled speech, slowness or procrastination, and a host of other negativistic speech mechanisms. Refusal to eat may be modified to eating very little, to restricting the choice of food, to dawdling, fussiness, etc. All such patterns may have their origins in sources other than negativism, but eventually may be utilized for that purpose.

Since the mother is the infant's most frequent frustrating agent—a necessary part of her function in protecting and rearing—she is usually the earliest and easiest target for the infant's display of rebellion.

* The term "puberty" was first applied to the infantile period of resistance by Häberlin (Wege und Irrwege der Erziehung (ed. 3). Basel, Kober, 1931, p. 136.)

† Hetzer, H.: Entwicklungsbedingte Erziehungsschwierigkeiten. Ztschr. pädagog. Psychol. *30:* 77–85, 1929.

Since her relationship, unlike that of the animals, continues for so many years, the rebellious attitude towards her, aided by a variety of conditions familiar to us, can be expressed in an amazing series of vituperative forms. In the study of mother-daughter antagonisms, it is not difficult to trace, in the selection of every particular negativistic performance, something designed particularly to outrage the mother, and with notable success. In humans the problem of negativism is complicated by the problems of adapting to a large variety of relationships over long periods of time. A difference which affects animals as well as men has to do with the individual's available aggression. If we regard the infant's temper tantrum as an outburst of aggression we can say that such displays of aggression are generally increased during the period of resistance. There are, however, marked differences in the relative frequency of tantrums and negativism. Some children reveal little evidence of tantrums, and express their noncompliance almost exclusively in the form of negativism.

In this connection the fact should be noted also that in some children, tantrums in most instances take the form of "silent rage." The rebellious feelings of people under the control of a strong authority, as of submissive people generally, are much more likely to take the safer form of some variety of negativism than that of open aggression. The aggression is concealed in the negativism. It may be used for the same purpose, but is less likely to become the method of choice of the aggressive child or adult. Incapacity of any kind in childhood—clumsiness, for example—also favors the negativistic type of defense, if the child is subject to much criticism on that account.

Animals supposedly show breed differences as well as individual differences in regard to stubbornness. I am not aware of any special investigation of the genetic aspects of this problem among humans. I am impressed by the number of families of our most negativistic children who are noted for the number of obstinate characters they contain, which our informants are happy to talk about, and point to with pride.

III

The early manifestations of negativism have been represented as protective and self-propelling functions that enable the child to overcome infantile dependency. When first observed they do not appear to be hostile reactions. They appear to be simply a struggle that is part of the process of growth towards self-realization. In time, hostile feelings towards the obstacle appear, whether the obstacle is an object or a human being, and in the case of a human being particularly, negativism may appear largely as hostile behavior.

Inner negativism, a term used in reference to catatonia to denote the reversal of one's own thoughts or wishes, occurs not only in children, as I have described, but also in nonpsychotic adults. In questioning mothers concerning their own stubbornness I have heard some interesting examples. One mother said that when shopping for a dress which she really wants and can afford, the only way she can get herself to buy it is to discuss it with her husband who invariably says no. That enables her to make the purchase.

A number of people utilize opposition as a spur to their own efforts, as an energizer, without which their initiative is inadequate.

Inner negativism, though not in the sense of oppositeness, is used also as a protective device against compliance when a corrective is needed against a strong tendency to yield to the wishes of others or to play a submissive role. The fear of giving up negativistic behavior is sometimes expressed in a similar way by children. In response to the question, "What would happen if you'd give in to your mother just once?" the reply was to the effect that if you give in she will take advantage, make you do everything and never let you do anything for yourself. Actually, in the case of a child who replied in this way, the modification of his negativism during therapy was followed by a close and quite subservient relationship to his mother. The use of negativism as a protective barrier against submissive tendencies should be given consideration.

The danger of surrendering the protective device, when it is felt to be like a cementing substance of the personality without which it would collapse, can be well understood. This becomes particularly evident during the treatment of those congealed children who have guarded themselves for years from expressing any affection for their mothers. Seen in the playroom, when two or three years old, they are initially difficult to approach. Any suggestion or offer to help will terminate their play. They cannot be touched. Their bodies are inviolate. Their play is featured by repetition and destruction. They seem to lack normal fantasy and conversation. My own way of breaking down social barriers has been through the use of fingerpaint. After a period of mutual tolerance has been established, the child is usually happy using a fingerpaint as a messy play. When the child and I both move our hands on the wet surface that is covered with paint, the child will allow my hand to come in contact with his. When such contact is allowed, it helps facilitate a relationship.

Negativistic phenomena of varying degrees are relatively common. They may represent useful outlets of defiance in otherwise well-behaved people who preserve such minor negativistic residues from their childhood as refusal ever to wear an overcoat, or always arriving late at a party. Floyd Allport* has investigated the frequency of specific kinds of nonconformity among samples of the population in various phases of life and finds a similar curve of distribution in most of them. All his groups contain a small percentage who are prone to pass a red light, to violate a factory regulation, to omit a church ritual that is adhered to by the majority, etc.

In our clinical work with adults we are more likely to see the more severe forms of negativism. Among children, the areas of behavior in which negativism is manifested may be more circumscribed. To this area the term "oppositional syndrome" may be applied. Among those whose oppositional behavior is well generalized, the oppositional tactics may be particularly prominent with reference to a special form of activity. The term oppositional syndrome is a convenient label to cover such special forms also. The use of the term "syndrome" may help also to guard us against the tendency to make a diagnosis prematurely.

Some years ago a twelve-year-old boy was referred because he was making just passing marks in school in spite of a superior intelligence. In that regard he was unusually consistent, from the first grade to the seventh. In time, he told me that it took lots of planning to manage never to fail and yet never make more than a passing mark. On occasion his parents hired a tutor to help him with his work. The patient soon learned how to dissipate the tutor's efforts by getting him to talk about certain subjects that claimed his interest.

His difficulty in accepting his studies began presumably as a revolt against his mother for sending him to a nursery school. At that time

* Allport, F. H.: The J-curve hypothesis of conforming behavior. J. Social Psychol. 5: 141–183, 1934.

he put up a feeble protest, though he felt it deeply as an act of abandonment. His revenge took the special form of negativism I have described—a revenge of withholding from his mother, whose own scholastic achievement had been high, the gift of good marks in school. The boy was otherwise a dutiful son. His negativism for school work was never quite overcome. It became a system from which he could never extricate himself. He was graduated from college and a professional school, though only with passing marks. Today he is married and holds an important executive position.

At the time of referral there was evidence of rather compulsive neatness, ritualistic behavior and generally an overly organized personality. He had gone through a long period of resistance in infancy. His mother had the highest standards of ethical behavior and housekeeping. Her relationship to the boy was affectionate. The findings in this case are rather characteristic of many, and reveal also the common relationship of early negativism and compulsive behavior. His Rorschach test also revealed certain characteristic findings—a tendency to turn several plates upside down as soon as they were placed in his hands, generally a high frequency of reversals, one or two plates to which he could not respond at all, and a longer than usual form per cent.

The modification of the original and powerful "no, no" in his case could be traced along various routes, including certain perseverative tendencies, procrastination, negativistic forgetting and dawdling. One of the routes ended in a special syndrome in which the negativism was channelled into a specialized opposition to schoolwork.

I have by now collected a series of such cases and have followed the course of several who have been treated by others. In these cases it would appear that mechanism becomes more powerful than motivation. That may be why such cases are so recalcitrant to psychoanalysis. The patient's full insight into the meaning of his oppositional method is only the beginning of the modifying process, after which we rely primarily on the method of re-education.

In a number of oppositional school syndromes the children were shifted from one nursery school to another, after making an adjustment to the former. In this kind of situation, where the child's protests are in vain and its own problem of meeting new situations fraught with danger, his retaliation is understandable. When out-and-out refusals are not in the cards, negativistic half-refusals become the compromise. In one case a child developed a partial paralysis of the legs which was diagnosed as hysteria. Her selection of the legs was probably due to the fact that much attention had been given her feet since early infancy because of flatness. Numerous neurologic examinations were negative. I mention this case because of the possibility that a negativistic process may be selective enough to be confused with a conversion symptom. The child said during therapy, "I made my legs not to walk and I thought that when I wanted to I could make them walk again." One of the values of delimiting special forms of negativism into syndromes lies in the finding of characteristic patterns in each of them. Seen only as a general expression of negativistic behavior we may lose the significance of certain combinations of symptoms and of the special therapeutic problems involved.

Oppositional syndromes are seen in a number of cases of anorexia nervosa. The large preponderance of females, the frequent finding of mother-daughter antagonisms, and the negativistic behavior are well known. The final outcome of some of these cases into full-fledged catatonia may be explained partly as a quantitative variation, an extreme manifestation of the syndrome, with the complications that arise from the consequent withdrawal of all social contact. Otherwise we would have to say that whatever becomes schizophrenia always was schizophrenia, a position that would rule out the notion of quantitative variations in the intensity and duration of negativistic behavior.

Oppositional syndromes are seen also in certain cases of obesity, speech problems, intellectual inhibitions other than the oppositional school syndromes; in fact, in a large number of functional difficulties which need exploring.

IV

What has been called negativism, resistance and oppositional behavior we see as behavior that has its origin in a basic protective function for biologic as well as social processes. In the clinical pictures which represent an abuse or excess of this function we have lost sight of their original positive values, because our attention has been diverted by the disturbing and urgent manifestations of re-bellious and hostile behavior. Our attention has also been diverted from the study of the adaptive features of the mechanism, and of the mechanism as such, by our absorbing interest in its motivational and diagnostic aspects.

If we consider as a functional unit of behavior any on-going process that appears to have an initial point and an end point, we have a large variety of units to consider, from the simplest to the most complex. In all of them we may delineate that part of the process which is concerned primarily with the problems of initiating and maintaining goal direction and of removing hindrances to its purpose. In the case of the simplest functional unit—the reflex—this would involve neurophysiologic studies beyond our scope; the persistence of a reflex after interruption by various stimuli would be one example of many related to our problem. The unit of behavior represented by a biologic process involving the satisfaction of a "basic drive" would represent an act of greater complexity. The social act of which the obstacle to goal achievement is another human being, or influences derived from social relationships, represents a still higher degree of complexity. Whether the unitary act considered is short-range or long, an immediate satisfaction or the fulfillment of a life-long ambition, the same aspects of the on-going behavior in terms of goal persistency and reaction to interference can be discerned.

As resistance against modification of an on-going process by external or internal stimuli, we may see the problem as that of the autonomy of the act, as it pertains to neural, biologic or social behavior. Without such autonomy, the act could be so easily inhibited, deflected or terminated that it could hardly function. This principle of autonomy of the act in social behavior has been revealed in the mother-infant relationship as a process of emancipation from the earliest stage of dependency on the parent, a process which the parent has aided. Within the process of emancipation, which is complicated by the numerous factors that bear on any variety of human behavior, a maturational factor has been delineated as its most important feature.

Resistant behavior or negativism serves to favor the individual's separateness and independence. It serves also as a protective function in situations of emotional stress. The recoil in such situation may involve inner as well as outer negativism, cessation of exploratory behavior, social withdrawal and hostility.

As a reaction *vs* interference with self-determined behavior, negativism runs counter to malleability or plasticity. In the same sense it runs counter to suggestibility. Since excessive malleability or suggestibility may be felt by the individual as threatening to his autonomy, as a fear of complete domination by others, he may cultivate negativism as his main protective device. That may be one of the reasons for the clinical finding of negativism and marked suggestibility in the same individual.

In general, it may be said that when negativism is used as a characteristic mode of defense for whatever reason, it favors the development of contrariness, rigidity of personality and social isolation.

In the examination of apparently normal though negativistic children, it may even appear in the form of muscular rigidity of the limb as a reaction against flexion of the knee during examination of the knee reflex. Inasmuch as it involves persistency in attaining a goal regardless of all obstacles, it favors purposive or goal-directed thinking as opposed to undirected, spontaneous thinking. Both kinds characterize normal individuals, even when there is a preponderance of the one kind of thinking as compared with the other. The point at which the preponderance may be regarded as abnormal is determined by clinical criteria.

In the rearing of children, the mother, of necessity, must modify or frustrate many of the child's struggles for self-assertion and self-determination. At such times she becomes the target of the child's hostility. Under certain conditions (especially when the mother is strict and unloving) hostility may take the form of persistent oppositional behavior and give rise to spiteful reprisals and the development of personality traits that run counter to those of the mother's. A number of oppositional syndromes are determined by the special kinds of reprisals that are selected.

The limitation of negativistic behavior in regard to duration, intensity, areas of function and the number of people concerned, requires, for its explanation, study of the individual case. Numerous syndromes of oppositional behavior may represent an adaptational stage that need never advance any further. The assumption that all of them, and particularly those with obsessional symptoms, represent wild or abortive or developing forms of catatonia, is unproved. The danger of the spread of the oppositional mechanism, viewed psycho-pathologically, can be understood most readily when it involves all social contacts. Every person is then regarded as hostile and danger-ous—at least thwarting—and social isolation follows. In childhood, when the withdrawal tendency is still modifiable, we have the most favorable opportunity to overcome it. The study of the spread of negativism might include also the study of its special lines of direc-tion when one is more pronounced than the others: for example, the special line of persistency, of reliance on one's self alone, of the no-saying phase, etc.

Negativism has been contrasted with aggression and referred to as a more primitive and also safer expression of antagonism. In the form of open defiance it is difficult and probably unnecessary to differentiate it from aggression. As in the case of aggression, numerous modifications of the extreme act are seen. The assault is modified to teasing; the refusal is modified to procrastinating. Any form of negativism can be used as an instrument of, and a substitute for, aggression. It may be said that this is the method of choice of the submissive individual, or of the individual in any situation in which aggressive behavior is regarded as too dangerous. The mixtures or patterns of both forms of behavior depend on the situation and on the available aggression in the personality.

Finally, we must consider briefly the relation of anxiety and nega-tivism. When the infant struggles against the physician during the physical examination he may be expressing in that manner his anxiety about an inoculation rather than oppositional behavior. That differ-entiation must often be made by parents, physicians and teachers. The question is sometimes put in the form, "Is he anxious or just stubborn?" When we are in doubt, we assume for safety's sake that the answer is anxiety.

In the case of anxiety, the individual may use oppositional tactics as a protection against any situation that may incite it. That is one of the reasons for the conviction on the part of some investigators that the source of negativism is anxiety.

Anxiety, as we see it in relation to negativism, arises most frequently from the feeling of fear and guilt of hostility against the frustrating agent. Since negativism, when expressed in a social relationship, is so often charged with hostility, it is a fertile source of anxiety derived from the fear of loss of the love and support of the social object, the fear of retribution, and the fears emanating from the feelings of the guilt of hostile and shameful behavior.

In closing, I realize that I have yielded to the temptation, in spite of my resolve, of covering too much ground. If, in spite of that fact, I have succeeded in stimulating your interest in the original adaptive function of oppositional behavior, and in its study as a mechanism in its own right, my own on-going and purposive behavior will be completed.

13

NOTES ON THE FOLLOW-UP STUDIES OF AUTISTIC CHILDREN

By LEO KANNER, M.D.* *and* LEON EISENBERG, M.D.†

THE SYNDROME OF EARLY INFANTILE AUTISM was first reported in 1943 under the heading, "autistic disturbances of affective contact." The eleven patients, who had been observed in the course of the preceding five years, showed characteristic peculiarities intrinsically similar to each other, yet different from any of the known psychopathologic patterns of infant and child behavior. The uniqueness of the symptom combination suggested as the first task an orienting study of the specific features and an attempt to view them not merely in enumerative juxtaposition but with an eye on their meaningful interconnection. The two principal *diagnostic criteria*, presenting themselves as extreme self-isolation and the obsessive insistence on sameness, could be recognized as the source from which the other clinical manifestations derived. One may, therefore, not unmindful of Bleuler's systematic grouping of schizophrenic phenomena, refer to the two consistent, pathognomonic matrices as "primary" and assign to the derivatives a position of "secondary" value. This is of major importance for purposes of the differentiation from other conditions in which a few corresponding behavior items may raise the question of nosologic allocation. In our experience, caution has been indicated, especially in some instances of congenital sensory aphasia, the incipient stages of Heller's disease, and—with increasing frequency—severe inherent intellectual deficiency with behavioral oddities bearing superficial

* Associate Professor of Psychiatry and Pediatrics, Johns Hopkins University Medical School; Psychiatrist in Charge, Children's Psychiatric Service, Harriet Lane Home for Children, Johns Hopkins Hospital, Baltimore, Maryland.

† Assistant Professor of Psychiatry and Pediatrics, Johns Hopkins University Medical School; Psychiatrist, Children's Psychiatric Service, Harriet Lane Home for Children, Johns Hopkins Hospital, Baltimore, Maryland.

resemblance to some of the "secondary" symptoms observed in the majority of our autistic patients.

A group of disturbed children was thus singled out whose distinctive design, not encountered in any other disease, called for some form of terminologic identification. The choice of the designation, "early infantile autism," was suggested by the unmistakable evidence of the typical symptoms in the first two years of life and the self-centered, at least in the beginning often impenetrable, aloneness. Since the initial publication, many more cases have come to our attention; at the time of this writing our material comprises 105 children. Additional observations were made and reported by Despert, Mahler, Rank, Weil, Murphy and others in this country, Cappon in Canada, Creak in England, Stern and Schachter in France and van Krevelen in Holland.

We are justified in regarding the job of description and diagnostic formulation as reasonably accomplished. The details of the symptomatology—the detachment from people, the peculiarities of linguistic and motor performance, the type of relationship to objects, the conceptual fragmentation, the obsessive trends as shown through repetitiousness and ritualism—are well known and need not be reiterated. But once the matter of phenomenology had been settled, a number of significant issues arose which required further elucidation.

Paramount among them was the question of *etiology*. In this respect, no valid help came from the exploration of somatic factors; physical and laboratory examinations failed to furnish leading clues that might point to specific acquired or constitutional organic anomalies. A consideration of genetics, if confined to the incidence of psychoses and socially or vocationally handicapping neuroses, produced a figure of less than 5 per cent for progenitors and other kin, including collaterals. Our attention was directed to the undisputable fact that the patients came from intelligent, sophisticated stock: not less than 94 per cent of the parents, both fathers and mothers, were high school graduates and 74 per cent of the fathers and 49 per cent of the mothers had completed college. The majority of the parents, though competent in their chosen vocations, were cold, detached, humorless perfectionists, more at home in the world of abstractions than among people, dealing with their fellow men on the basis of what one might call a mechanization of human relationships; they themselves had escaped the psychotic proportions of their offsprings' aloneness and sterile obsessiveness. One is therefore led to think of a familial trend toward detached, obsessive, mechanical living. At the same time, it cannot be forgotten that the emotional refrigeration which the children experienced from such parents could not but be a highly pathogenic determinant of their early personality development, superimposed powerfully on whatever predispotition may have come through inheritance.

The *dynamic aspects* of the interplay between the patients and their parents have been made the focus of thoughtful investigation on the part of several authors. Three points of view have been put forth in the literature. One regards the parental behavior as a reaction to peculiarities which have existed *a priori*: the parent's personality has no etiologic significance and matters only in so far as it governs the nature of the response to the sick child's needs and demands. At the opposite pole, there is an insistence on considering the parents, and more especially the mother, as the basic source of pathogenicity; the assumption is that a healthier maternal attitude would have precluded the psychotic development of the child. A third group of investigators feels that the patient, endowed with an innate disability to relate himself to people, is further influenced adversely by the personality deviations of the parents and their resulting manner of handling him; this in no way discounts the possibility of a reciprocal relationship which, in turn, causes the parent to shrink from the child or to "overprotect" him in a more or less stilted fashion.

Similar divergencies exist also with regard to *nosology*. Van Krevelen argues that early infantile autism represents an "oligophrenia with affective defect." It is true that the solid barrier between mental deficiency and psychotic illness has been removed, or at least allowed to crumble, thanks to the efforts of Clemens Benda and others. It is also true that Weygandt, as far back as 1915, has described varieties of psychotic behavior in children thought to be idiotic or imbecile. Nevertheless, the observed fundamental differences between autistic and oligophrenic children cannot be simply dismissed as differently structured variants of essential feeblemindedness. Proceeding, therefore, on the conviction that early infantile autism is a true psychosis, the next issue was one of seeing whether it could be linked up with the category of childhood schizophrenia. Stern and Schachter suggest that, at least for the time being, it be kept apart as a syndrome *sui generis.* It certainly does present a picture of sufficient specificity to be sifted out and recognized as being unlike other psychotic behavior constellations, but there surely can be no objection to its inclusion in a broadly conceived framework of "schizophrenia." Differences in onset, content and course of schizophrenia in children have been discussed for some time. Ssucharewa and Grebelskaya-Albatz in Russia and Despert in this country have distinguished cases with acute onset and cases with insidious onset. After the publication of the first eleven cases of autism from our clinic, Despert and Mahler were among the first to study autistic children concurrently with our own work. It was Mahler who, on the basis of phenomenology and the nature of mother–child relationship, eventually worked out the helpful division between autistic and symbiotic infantile psychoses, presented in her excellent papers of 1949 and 1952.

Enough time has elapsed since the initial observation of many of our patients to enable us to follow their destinies over a period of years. It was felt that a follow-up study might throw some light on prognostic evaluations and, if subsequent events could be correlated with the absence or presence and mode of treatment, might give some indications of the most promising therapeutic approach to the problem. Letters were written to the parents or to the hospitals or residential schools in which the children were living. The age range at the time of this inquiry extended from 8 to 24 years (average of 14 years), the interval between the first acquaintance and the present from 4 to 19 years (average of 8½ years). The total number thus reached was 42. Wherever possible, a return visit was arranged and the patients examined again.

Before launching on a discussion of our data, we should like to mention a report by Darr and Worden about the condition of a woman 28 years after she had been seen (at four years of age) at the Henry Phipps Psychiatric Clinic by Drs. Meyer and Richards with what undoubtedly was an infantile autistic disorder. Even though no formal diagnosis was made, the child's behavior and the parents' personalities corresponded in every detail to the typical findings in early infantile autism. Dr. Richards wrote: "From the examination it seems probable that defectiveness and mental retardation are not responsible (or at least not wholly so) for the child's peculiar behavior. The mental picture seems to be more frankly that of a psychopathological condition characterized by preoccupation and impulsiveness." Dr. Meyer suggested "a natural, direct and affectionate handling without any pushing or undue demands." The mother carried this out by hiring people to take care of the child, who was placed in a home for special training; then spent three years in the care of a man interested in the treatment of the mentally ill; lived at home and was privately tutored for one year; from ten to seventeen she lived with a psychiatrist who looked after a number of problem children; then for about six years back home with her mother and—the father having died and the mother remarried—her stepfather. Following this, she was sent to live with a series of four companions during the next four years. She took piano and voice lessons, learned to speak Spanish fluently, and was able to take care of her personal needs. But at the same time, she lacked any intuitive social sense, had temper tantrums when thwarted, seemed most comfortable when she lived by precise routine, and showed marked hypochondriac tendencies which caused her to go into seclusion when contact with people became too upsetting. At the age of 27 years, she was sent to a school for disturbed children, but soon the authorities insisted that she be removed because of severe temper outbursts. She was transferred to another school, where she remained for two years. On a home visit for the Christmas holidays, there was an acutely psychotic exacerbation of her symptoms. Deep coma insulin and electroshock resulted in a brief period of remission. A second series, instituted because of a recurrence of her outbursts and occasional assaultive episodes, brought no improvement. After nine months of group and individual intensive psychotherapy, it was reported that she had established no particular relationship with either patients or personnel in the private sanitarium where she was being treated. There was an apparent lack of relatedness to other persons, real or imaginary, in the content of her psychosis. The authors state specifically that "none of her productions has indicated delusional content."

We have dwelt on the study by Darr and Worden at some length because it represents the first opportunity to follow an autistic child into adulthood. It is offered by the authors correctly as "one example" of how such a person has adjusted over a period of years. A more generalized prognostic statement was made by Mahler as a result of her rich experience. She wrote: "Establishment of contact and substitution therapy over a long period of time may sometimes give spurts of impressive and gratifying results. But they are usually followed by an insuperable plateau of arrested progress, which usually taxes the patience and frustrates the renewed hopes of the parents. Impatient reactions and pressures are then exercised and progress forced. But, if the autistic type is forced too rapidly into social contact, ... he is often thrown into a catatonic state and then into a fulminant psychotic process ... If such catastrophic reactions cannot be avoided, it seems that such autistic infants are better off if allowed to remain in their autistic shell, even though in 'a daze of restricted orientation' they may drift into a very limited degree of reality adjustment only. Diagnosis of their 'original condition,' of course, then usually escapes recognition; they are thrown into the category of the feebleminded."

Every point of this statement was borne out by our follow-up studies: the spurts of gratifying results, the insuperable plateau, and the more or less permanent capsulation, occurring in different patients under different circumstances. Our findings suggest strongly that there are, from the beginning, differences in the intensity of autistic aloneness and fragmentation. We have as yet been unable to match them even approximately with somatic, genetic or dynamic factors which might possibly be held responsible. But they do exist and it would be a mistake to assume, as has been done sometimes, that autistic children are exactly alike in the manner in which, let us say, mongolian children are expected by some to be exactly alike. In this respect, a clear distinction between "primary" and "secondary" features proves of great value. Presence of the primary signs of aloneness and insistence on sameness is a sure diagnostic guide and holds the group together, regardless of the number and nature of the secondary manifestations.

When the children were first seen at our clinic, and on subsequent visits, we were impressed by differences in speech development. Some of the patients had completely renounced the use of speech; they either were mute throughout, or began to avail themselves sparingly of the linguistic tool only after five or more years of age, or—having said a few words—abandoned articulate language altogether. The utterance of whole sentences by some of these patients in emergency situations gave substance to the impression that a working vocabulary and at least a modicum of grammatic competence had been stored up but, except for those rare occasions, were kept locked up in storage.

There were 19 of these children in our follow-up series. The other group comprised 23 patients who had begun to speak either at the usual age or after a slight delay. The mechanics of articulation presented no problem; phonation was either normal or manneristically altered to sing-song or a sort of Donald Duck quality. The children had learned at an early age to repeat an inordinate number of nursery rhymes, prayers, lists of animals, the roster of presidents, the alphabet forward and backward. Aside from the recital of sentences contained in the ready-made poems or other remembered pieces, it took a long time before they put words together for the purpose of oral communication with others. Even then, phrases heard were taken over in their totality, often with the same inflection, and reproduced in the form of what one might call delayed echolalia. This brought about the phenomenon of pronominal reversals, which continued into or beyond the sixth year of life, until eventually a give-and-take kind of conversation could be established with varying degrees of spontaneously communicating content.

Our follow-up survey indicates that the distinction between the mute and the speaking patients may have some useful prognostic implications. Of the 19 children who did not talk at around four years of age, 18 are still firmly enveloped in their autistic shell and would, as Mahler pointed out, impress a casual observer as essentially feebleminded. One brief case abstract may serve as an illustration:

John T. was first seen at three years and two months because of suspected mental deficiency. Undescended testicles were the only physical anomaly. Electroencephalogram was normal. He had been delivered at two weeks before term by elective caesarean section and weighed slightly above six pounds at birth. Vomiting after meals during the first three months ceased abruptly and did not recur. He was believed to be deaf because he did not respond to the presence of people. He sat up at eight months and did not try to walk until two years, when he "suddenly" began to walk without difficulty. He refused to accept fluids in any but a glass container; once he went for three days without fluid because it was offered in a tin cup. He became upset when there was any change in his accustomed routine.

His parents separated shortly after his birth. The father, a psychiatrist, was described as an intelligent, restless, introspective man, mostly living within himself, at times alcoholic. The mother, a pediatrician, said of herself: "I have little insight into people's problems."

At the time of the first visit, John displayed good motor coordination and determined purposefulness in pursuit of his own goals. He was able to build skilfully a high tower of blocks. He responded to other persons only when they interfered with his privacy; then he shoved them away and screamed. There was no speech whatever. At five years, he showed great dexterity with the Seguin formboard and kept removing and replacing the pieces all through the examination.

John, now 16 years old, has been living for the past ten years on a farm with simple and accepting country people. He gets along well under the extremely primitive demands of his protective environment. There is no speech and little response to verbal address. He takes walks in the area and always finds his way back to the foster home. On examination, he continues to show the typical signs of inner preoccupation, obsessiveness, perseveration, and lack of affective contact.

This extreme functional limitation is the general picture obtained in the follow-up of 18 of the 19 mute children, except that quite a few of them are more restless and disturbed than John. It is necessary to emphasize that, in this group, the present condition has come about regardless of the manner in which the patients had been handled. In fact, two of them had received intensive psychotherapy in good treatment centers; in both instances, slight apparent progress had given rise to guarded temporary optimism. Only one of the 19 originally mute children has emerged sufficiently to attend public school.

George O. was first seen at four years with the complaint that he "behaved very queerly." His mother reported that he did not chew his food, would not feed himself, and did not respond to toilet training. His behavior was markedly obsessive. Frustration resulted in temper tantrums. Interest in people was totally absent. He said only a few single words on very rare occasions. Health history and motor development were satisfactory.

The father, a busy surgeon, was a perfectionist and a detached individual who spent his vacations all by himself and boasted that he never wasted his time talking to his patients and their relatives. When asked specifically, he was not quite sure whether he would recognize any one of his three children if he met them on the street; he did not resent the question and its obvious implication. The mother, a college graduate, looked bedraggled at the time of the first visit. She felt futile about herself, was overwhelmed by her family responsibilities, and gave the impression of drabness and ineffectualness.

George showed no response at the clinic except when he was interfered with in any way. He did well with the Seguin formboard and was neat and precise in his activities. When pricked with a pin, he related only to the hand which held the pin, and there was no carry-over of feeling to the person who pricked him. When the mother (upon request) attempted to embrace him, he squirmed away from her.

Therapeutic emphasis was placed on the mother, who came to realize her own latent abilities. The carefully-timed question when she had stopped being "Dorothy" (her first name) brought forth a burst of tears and a spurt of self-appraisal. She became more animated, dressed more attractively, developed an erect posture, and took George over as a challenge. The newly-established symbiotic relationship between her and the child proceeded without disturbance on the part of either. Her ministrations to George were a novel, enriching experience for her. After a year, George began to use language for limited communication. George, now approaching his twelfth birthday, is about to be promoted to the sixth grade in a school connected with a teachers' college. He does fairly well in his studies. His drawings show remarkable artistic ability. Conversation, though limited mostly to a question-and-answer pattern, is fairly adequate. He still has marked obsessive features; he has recently gone through a period when he refused to shake hands with anybody. He has attached himself to a couple of quiet, studious classmates whom he calls his "friends." His latest IQ was 91.

Of the 18 nonspeaking children (not counting George O.), seven are now in institutions for mental defectives, seven are kept at home in a state close to biologic helplessness, two are on farms, and two are in psychiatric state hospitals.

The 23 patients who had used speech in any form and for any purpose from an early age offer a somewhat less disheartening picture. Ten, or less than half, are doing very poorly; of these, five are chronic state hospital patients, three are in schools for retarded children, one is on a farm, and one is at home. Most of them, even at the low ebb to which they have receded, still show remnants which distinguish them from the demented or pseudodemented level of the mute autistic children. This is perhaps illustrated best by the psychologist's report on Barbara M., who is now 20 years old and a resident of a state hospital. It says: "This patients presents a complex and contradictory picture throughout all aspects of her personality. Intellectually, she is a paradox. Her successes and failures range from the very difficult to the very easy material. Verbal capacities are not consistent with a congenital mental deficiency. There is no real power to see herself as a separate entity, to test reality adequately, and to establish some sort of distance between the test material and herself. Her forte comes in abstract, very difficult 'intellectual' material where she can use rather erudite, pedantic words and concepts with ease. Her concept of the world is that of a threatening, overwhelming place, giving her no security. Her affect is for the most part blunted, yet she is capable of, and at the mercy of, explosive, violent feelings of aggressiveness."

Barbara and the other nine patients of this subgroup are much less likely to be mistaken as inherently feebleminded than the 18 mute autistic children of our follow-up series. They have given up much of their earlier ritualism, and the typical features of autism shown in their childhood are much less in evidence. At no stage of their development did they display any delusional content, and there is no certain indication of the existence of any hallucinatory experiences.

Not less than 13 of the 23 speaking children have at this time reached a plateau which allows them to function at home and in the community. One, Robert F., first seen at the age of 8 years in consultation and now 23 years old, has reached a higher pinnacle than the rest. Even at the time of the initial examination, though exhibiting unquestionably the characteristic signs of autism, he had begun to show signs of emergence. He served two years in the Navy as a meteorologist, is married, has a healthy son, and is now studying musical composition. Some of his works have been performed by chamber orchestras.

The other twelve are capable of attending school. They relate well to books and blackboard but have few, if any, real friends, and have retained some of the earlier obsessive-compulsive qualities.

Jay S., now almost 15 years old, presented in the lower grades considerable difficulties to his teachers, who were exceptionally understanding and accepting. He wandered about the classroom, masturbated openly, and staged temper tantrums. He learned to conform, did phenomenally well in mathematics, was sent to an accelerated school, and is now finishing the eleventh grade with top marks. He is a peculiar child, rather obese, who spends his spare time collecting maps and postage stamps and has little more to do with people than is absolutely necessary for the maintenance of a superficial relationship. He achieved a Binet IQ of not less than 150.

All of these twelve children can be said to be markedly schizoid in their make-up and behavior. It is not easy to be particularly optimistic about their adjustment to adult life. For the time being, they maintain a tenuous contact with reality.

We should like to discuss one of these patients in greater detail.

Susan T., an attractive, intelligent looking child, was first seen at six years of age. Her mother stated that she had noted "peculiar traits" from the first year of her life, when she displayed an insistence on adherence to routine. She never looked at people nor did she ever address herself to her parents. As an infant, she banged her head and rolled in her crib. She did not play with other children and was content to be alone. Although she spoke distinctly, she did not use language for communication. There were echolalia and pronominal reversals. After one hearing, she could repeat a song or a nursery rhyme. She had a remarkable memory for unimportant details, such as the number of tiles on the bathroom floor.

As soon as she entered the office, she began to ask questions about the objects in the room. She was able to give her name, age, and birthdate. She became very angry and struck the physician when a block was taken from her; as soon as it was returned, all traces of anger disappeared. Noticing a crack in the ceiling, she remarked: "Why did this ceiling crack itself? Poor wall and ceiling, cracked all up." She did well on the performance tests, though her Binet responses were erratic. Physical and laboratory examinations showed no abnormalties; there was sensitivity to hyperventilation in the electroencephalogram though the child never presented any clinical dysrhythmic phenomena.

At 16 years, Susan is attending a private boarding school, where she is making satisfactory academic progress. The school noted that she does better in items requiring memory than in those which require reasoning. Susan said of herself: "I am not really a student. I am a plugger. Up to last year, the fundamentals of learning have been easy because of my memory, but this year it's interpretations, and this is difficult for me. I wanted to go to Wellesley but I may be hitching my wagon to a star. Maybe it will be too much pressure." She then sized up her social adjustment: "The girls in school are very nice and I have a good time with them but I don't have any real friends. I am so very sensitive. I feel I am not as mature as I should be and I don't have the interest in boys that I should have." On the Wechsler-Bellevue test, Susan had a verbal IQ of 119, performance of 98, and full scale IQ of 110.

The twelve children of this group have shown marked rises in psychometric rating because of their increased responsiveness.

Robert K., seen in a psychiatric outpatient clinic at five years, was diagnosed as a congenital defective, and his parents were urged to send him to a small private place for seriously retarded children. The parents did not "cooperate." After he completed the sixth grade at 13 years, his peculiar behavior caused the school to refer him to our clinic in 1948. He achieved a Binet IQ of 129. But this sample of his "conversation" throws light on his preoccupations: "We had lots of thunderstorms in 1940. Where do you live? (He was told.) Was it windy out there on Friday night? In our section it was still while the rest of Baltimore had plenty of wind. That is very freakish. How can that happen? Do you know Mount Washington? Why don't they get many thunderstorms in

Mount Washington?" Robert was hospitalized at the Henry Phipps Psychiatric
Clinic for four weeks. He eventually graduated from high school and is in the
National Guard Reserve. He is unable to hold a job for any length of time.

It must be pointed out, for whatever this is worth, that only two
of these twelve children have had any help which might be regarded
as psychiatric treatment, while several of the others had received intensive psychotherapy. This is perhaps also the place to speak of
Robert L., who at four years presented a picture very much like those
shown by our twelve children with the relatively better adjustment.
This child was electroshocked (not by us) at five years. Immediate
deterioration set in. He is now, at eleven, in a state hospital, completely
out of contact and shows emotional blunting interrupted by periods
of excitement.

In summary, the life histories of 42 autistic children at an average
age of 14 years indicate that we deal with a distinct syndrome which
may well be considered as falling within the broad category of the
schizophrenias. As adolescents, they have retained the primary characteristics of the condition and have lost some of the earlier secondary
symptoms, such as echolalia and pronominal reversals. At no time
did they give evidence of delusions or definitely ascertainable hallucinations. The follow-up survey has led us to the conclusion that the
presence or absence of language function in preschool age may serve
as a criterion of the severity of the autistic process. All but one of the
19 nonspeaking children have remained in a state of complete isolation and, on superficial observation, can hardly be distinguished from
markedly feebleminded persons. None of the varieties of psychiatric
treatment employed had any noticeable effect. Of the 23 speaking
children, not less than 13 have achieved sufficient emergence to function in more or less schizoid fashion at home and in school, while ten
are now clearly psychotic. These findings force us to believe that, over
and above any contributions from external intervention, the child's
own psychologic structure, resulting from inherent factors and the
dynamics of parent–child relationship, must be regarded as the main
determinant of subsequent development. The decisive impact of the
early constellation on future destiny is in itself another demonstration
of the specificity of early infantile autism. The favorable experience
with George O. in connection with his mother's response to treatment
introduces a melioristic note. It is true that even in most of the chil-

dren who have reached a higher plateau, the emergence must be considered as partial, and further follow-up studies of these and other patients will be needed. Hence, this paper is presented as a preliminary report.

BIBLIOGRAPHY

BENDA, C. E.: Developmental Disorders of Mentation and Cerebral Palsies. New York, Grune & Stratton, 1952, pp. 500–503.
CAPPON, D.: Clinical manifestations of autism and schizophrenia in childhood. Canad. M. A. J. *69:* 1, 44–49, 1953.
CREAK, M.: Psychoses in Childhood. Proc. Roy. Soc. Med. *45:* 797–800, 1953.
DARR, G. C. AND WORDEN, F. G.: Case report twenty-eight years after an infantile autistic disorder. Am. J. Orthopsychiat. *21:* 559–570, 1951.
DESPERT, J. L.: Some considerations relating to the genesis of autistic behavior in children. Am. J. Orthopsychiat. *21:* 335–350, 1951.
KANNER, L.: Autistic disturbances of affective contact. Nerv. Child *2:* 217–250, 1943.
——: Early infantile autism. J. Pediat. *25:* 211-217, 1944.
——: Irrelevant and metaphorical language in early infantile autism. Am. J. Psychiat. *103:* 242–246, 1946.
——: Problems of nosology and psychodynamics of early infantile autism. Am. J. Orthopsychiat. *19:* 416–452, 1949.
——: The conception of wholes and parts in early infantile autism. Am. J. Psychiat. *108:* 23–26, 1951.
——: To what extent is early infantile autism determined by constitutional inadequacies? A. Research Nerv. & Ment. Dis. *33:* 378–385, 1954.
VAN KREVELEN, D. A.: Een Geval van "early infantile autism." Nederl. Tijdschr. v. Geneesk. *96:* 202–205, 1952.
——: Early infantile autism. Ztschr. f. Kinderpsychiat. *19:* 91–97, 1952.
MAHLER, M. S.: On child psychosis and schizophrenia. Psychoanalyt. Stud. Child *7:* 286–305, 1952.
——, ROSS, J. AND DEFRIES, Z.: Clinical studies in benign and malignant cases of childhood psychosis. Am. J. Orthopsychiat. *19:* 295–305, 1949.
RANK, B.: Adaptation of the psychoanalytic technique for the treatment of young children with atypical development. Am. J. Orthopsychiat. *19:* 130–139, 1949.
STERN, E.: A propos d'un cas d'autisme chez un jeune enfant. Arch. Franç. Pédiat. *9:* 1952.
—— AND SCHACHTER, M.: Zum Problem des frühkindlichen Autismus. Praxis d. Kinderpsychol. u. Kinderpsychiat. *2:* 113–119, 1953.
WEIL, A. P.: Clinical data and dynamic considerations in certain cases of childhood schizophrenia. Am. J. Orthopsychiat. *23:* 518–529, 1953.
WEYGANDT, W.: Idiotie und Imbezillität. Leipzig, Deuticke, 1915, pp. 211–215.

14

DIFFERENTIAL DIAGNOSIS BETWEEN OBSESSIVE-COMPULSIVE NEUROSIS AND SCHIZOPHRENIA IN CHILDREN

By J. LOUISE DESPERT, M.D.*

INTRODUCTION

THE TITLE more precisely should limit the subject to differential diagnosis between *severe* obsessive-compulsive neuroses and certain forms of childhood schizophrenia with insidious onset and gradual development.

My interest in the subject stems from a frequently encountered diagnostic confusion, clinically and psychometrically—severe obsessive-compulsive neurosis diagnosed as schizophrenia and vice versa, the latter less frequently. Also, noteworthy is the fact of residual neurotic symptoms in the course of therapeutic resolution of schizophrenic illness (the rigidity, the compulsiveness, the lack of plasticity which often remain after the psychotic symptoms have receded.)

REVIEW OF LITERATURE

Obsessive-compulsive neuroses in children are not so rare as noted in the literature[1-2]; even when the syndrome is later recognized, it is seldom formulated at the onset of treatment as the presenting complaint.[3]

The above, when brought in the light of the recent tendency to overdiagnose schizophrenia in children, probably reflects this diagnostic confusion. In the literature, several authors bring out the fact that in adult cases of obsessive-compulsive neurosis the symptoms can be traced back to childhood,[4-6] Kanner fixing the level of onset at approximately 14 years and Greenacre "before puberty." Severe obsessive-compulsive neurosis, however, can be traced to an earlier age level, and one of the six cases to be presented briefly in this paper was

*Department of Psychiatry of the New York Hospital (Payne Whitney Psychiatric Clinic) and Cornell University Medical College, New York City.

first seen at seven and a quarter years and had a history of severe symptoms of more than one year duration. Mahler[7] in a recent article refers to a case of severe obsessive-compulsive neurosis in a boy of seven.

CLINICAL DATA

In a series of 401 consecutive cases from the author's files, there were 68 children (52 boys, 16 girls) with a diagnosis of obsessive-compulsive neurosis of varying degrees of severity. This does not refer to the common rituals of early childhood, and the neurosis was considered severe when the interference with intellectual and social functioning was marked, owing to the intensity of the anxiety.

A point of special interest is that in this group there were six pairs of children (i.e., two siblings in the same family): three pairs of six boys in three families, one pair of two girls in one family, two pairs of boy-girl in two families.

PRESENTATION OF CASES

Six cases are to be presented: four obsessive-compulsive (three boys, one girl) and two schizophrenic (one boy, one girl).

Girl N. J. came to treatment in 1947 at the age of 7¼ years, has been treated for three years and is followed at long intervals. At the time of writing, close to 14 years old. Diagnosis: *severe obsessive-compulsive neurosis*. She is the younger of two girls. Her sister, 3 years older, was referred for treatment in 1948, with the same diagnosis; her symptoms, however, being milder, as well as relating to different objects.

Complaint as formulated by the mother at the time of N. J.'s referral was "she's incessantly speaking of her 'minds'—it's like a phonograph record. She rushes from her play saying, 'I've got more minds' and becomes frantic if you don't agree they are silly." These minds were later identified as numerous and complex obsessive thoughts associated with compulsive acts. The symptoms were of more than one year's duration and had been preceded by night terrors which began at approximately 5½ years. The obsessive-compulsive symptoms began at about *6 years of age*.

She had been treated at a clinic for about 6 months. A report from the clinic where she was given a Rorschach indicates that N. J. was "a bright child . . . very sensitive . . . subject to great fears and anxieties . . . all spontaneous emotional expression repressed . . . disturbance in the areas of both masculine and feminine identifications . . . . The over-all picture was that of an obsessive-compulsive adjustment, which was not entirely successful in that the controls which N. J. attempted to set up would sometimes be broken through and she would experience excessive fears and anxieties." IQ 122 obtained at a later date.

Both parents come from Victorian, inhibited homes. Father, now in his late forties, an only child of his father's second marriage, with one half-brother and one half-sister respectively 15 and 18 years older than himself, "thought a sissy" all through his school years. He has through his life suffered from asthma and a severe anxiety state for which a variety of physical treatments, as well as prolonged psychoanalysis have been applied. Although suffering from many inhibitions, sexual to begin with, he had made it a practice to walk about the house in the nude, in an attempt to apply modern psychology to the bringing up of the children. The mother also followed this practice.

The mother in her early forties, in a slip of the tongue, referring to her siblings, said: "I *had* two brothers," although they are still living. She is a verbal, anxious, unstable woman with a variety of somatic complaints. Following the birth of the patient, N. J., she had severe abdominal pains, a condition which was not clearly identified but was treated with several abdominal operations. She said of this first year of the patient's life, "I didn't care if I lived or not," and left the care of the baby to a maid. She paid no attention to her until the 2nd or 3rd year, and significantly had blocked all knowledge of the child's early development, constantly bringing up information about the older girl instead.

Birth had been difficult in the case of both girls, and each time a caesarian had been considered. Of significance, and recalled by the mother, were early phobias (noise, fire) beginning with the end of the 2nd year. When 23 months old, her parents and older sister went away for about two weeks, and she was left in the care of a stranger. When the family returned, she screamed; and for months after, she screamed at night before going to sleep. As an infant, she had a transitory compulsion to rub a blanket on the mouth, and she was 5 when a persistent ritual began: every piece of clothing, and bed clothes had to be put at exactly the same place, head or foot of the bed, before she could fall asleep. At 5½ she had a tonsilectomy with no recognized ill effects. At 6 years, the "toad stool" incident took place: she had inadvertently stepped on the excreta of a toad. She screamed that she was poisoned, and developed a compulsion to rub the toad stool on her toe, then suck her toe. She had to be forcibly prevented from carrying out the act. Following this incident, she gradually developed a multiplicity of compulsive acts, and complained of a variety of obsessive thoughts, which she called "having minds."

When first seen at 7¼ years, the child was in good contact, freely communicative. Her affect was appropriate, intense anxiety as she told of her minds. "The mind tells me that if I touch the table (or other objects) the mind is going to kill me . . . the minds bother me mostly at night . . . they tell me to pinch my finger in the door . . . to kill myself . . . to break my arm . . . poke scissors into my eyes . . . I won't drink water because my mind tells me it would be poisoned . . . " etc. "I go to my mother and beg her to tell me it's silly, tell me! tell me! I pretend I'm a bare Indian with a band in the middle!"

etc. She tells of "playing with my doodle" (frequent masturbation). Draws very well, draws "a horse's doodle," tells of her fear of a horse's penis, that it will kill her (later associated with incest fantasies about father's penis). Tells of *obsessive thoughts* too numerous to be given in toto: the house will be on fire . . . her parents will die . . . her genitalia will be poisoned, etc. Tells of many *compulsions:* she is compelled to look under and behind things, to touch keys, to touch door knobs, pencils, thermometers. She recognizes the "minds" as thoughts she cannot get rid of, not voices. She is aware of the abnormal character of the thoughts.

Rarely does an obsessive-compulsive syndrome so clearly present itself at the onset of treatment.

With the next case, although the obsessions and compulsions were as clearly defined in the therapeutic situation, they were not recognized in the child's environment, and were not brought up as complaints.

Boy J. S. was brought to treatment in 1952, and is soon to be discharged. Diagnosis: *Severe obsessive-compulsive neurosis.* He was 11¼ years old at the time of referral, the older of 2 boys. He came to treatment as a result of investigation of the family when his younger brother was being treated. This younger brother, IQ 131, 5½ at time of referral, had himself been brought to psychiatric attention at the request of his teacher. A Rorschach pointed to "a possible underlying schizophrenia," but clinically the diagnosis was formulated as an obsessive-compulsive neurosis, with symptoms milder than those found in the older patient, about to be described.

The mother, when formulating the complaint in the case of J. S. the older brother, simply said that he had peculiar habits, such as taking a wet rag to bed; also, "he's talked a lot about being a woman when he grows up"; however, the only time when to her "he appears effeminate is when he coos to animals." She was mildly troubled by the fact that he was not a leader, and did not do as well in school, academically, as she felt he should.

A series of psychometric tests established that the boy had an IQ of 143, and that "the over-all picture is that of a very able but extremely anxious, unhappy child who feels that the world is turning its back on him. His sense of rejection stems from his own inability to resolve his problems with authority figures and to deal constructively with his aggressive impulses. His efforts consist primarily of withdrawal, self-absorption, and the development of compulsive mechanisms. Paranoid trends are strongly indicated."

The family background of this child is grossly pathologic, which may in part explain how the mother, a trained psychologist, could have been so completely unaware of disturbance in both children.

The father, an only child, is in his late thirties, a brilliant scholar and a corporation lawyer. He was always considered "puny," has made a poor adjustment to people, comes home to close himself in his room with music records;

not only withdraws from social contact but does not tolerate social contact for the children, at least when he is at home. He is a sadist, and has been very punitive toward the patient. He has for several years given his support to a British organization, "The National Society for the Retention of Corporal Punishment." He is impotent, except in a set-up of sadistic practices accompanied by obscene expressions. The mother agreed, early in the marriage, to "go through a routine ending in flagellation twice a month—lately only once a month," only because she wanted to have children. Emissions without erections have occurred infrequently.

The mother, the oldest of four, also in her late thirties, was very precocious and went through her education at least 2 years ahead of her generation, to which she attributes her emotional immaturity. She is very obese, and was unloved and rejected as a child, and as an adolescent was always "the wall flower." She has attempted to protect the children, in particular the older boy, against the father's sadism by bargaining with him on the frequency of flagellations she would accept. She was referred for psychoanalysis, and has now been several months in treatment. It was not possible to reach the father, who is probably an ambulatory psychotic.

When seen, J. S. was a thin, alert-looking youngster, under great tension, rigid facial expression, barely opening his mouth, although he was eager to communicate. He spoke with appropriate affect, with considerable anxiety, and described a multiplicity of *compulsive acts* and *obsessive thoughts* of great complexity. He said he "must do everything in fours" (which made it difficult to hold his attention at school). This was a very involved scheme: "the thing I want to look at the last, I look at first, then last, second before last" etc. This was described as his "base." The base must always be four-cornered; for instance, upon entering a room, if he looked at a point on a wall, he must immediately look for the other three points. If no convenient point is available or visible, he must fall back on some part of his body, fingers, toes, eyes, etc., and visualize a base. If, in going from one corner of the base to the next, in a compulsory sequence, he overlooks one, he must start all over again. It is easy to understand how the simplest activity became fraught with insurmountable difficulties, and in particular how concentrating on any task became impossible. His previous summer's experience at camp was "ruined" by the fact that the partitions were made up of knotted pine, and the maze of knots prevented him from establishing safe "bases." Walls, with their minute surface imperfections, were preferred because "I know the walls are always going to be there. I feel safe to look at them." Furthermore, and perhaps more troublesome, is his obsessive thought regarding a long, flexible pipe-like structure issuing from his chest, in the region of the upper sternum. He knows this is only a thought, that there can be no pipe coming out of his chest. However, he must behave as if the pipe were there, and move in such a way that no one, or no object, crosses the mid-line in front of him. He adds that the reason the pipe is "rubber-like" is to allow some leeway, and demonstrates the complex maneuvers he uses to avoid the pipe being "tangled-up . . . the line has to bend . . . so I try to walk around (the other person) catch up around him, then I am straight again." This was vividly demonstrated when I deliberately crossed his path one day when he was coming in.

In the course of therapy, the "base four" was found to represent his total family in the following order: mother, father, brother, himself, and the long pipe-like line to be associated with a protective penis. Throughout, he reiterated his awareness that the experiences he described were thoughts he couldn't get rid of, which were very disturbing to him, but he knew them to be only thoughts.

While the lack of awareness of the mother with regard to such severe symptoms is remarkable, it is not unusual, and children with obsessive-compulsive symptoms are not often brought to treatment for this specific complaint.

Boy A. S. came to treatment in 1948 at the age of 9⅙ years, was treated for 2½ years and has made a fairly good adjustment, his progress being followed through his mother's therapist. Diagnosis: *severe obsessive-compulsive neurosis*, although two psychologic tests done at one-year interval by two independent psychologists formulated a diagnosis of *schizophrenia*.

The first psychologist commented: "The distortions in personality structure revealed through these Rorschach findings are such that there would seem little doubt that he is suffering from schizophrenia . . . outstanding are the deviating fashion in which he perceives and organizes the environment, the aggression he projects into almost every situation he encounters, and the compulsion which pushes him to deal with every situation—for him everything seems monstrous, distorted and threatening." The findings on the revised Stanford Binet, Form L, gave him an IQ of 130, and also suggested "a seriously deviated personality." The first test was made several months before referral, the second several months after; the IQ with the same scale was then 140, and the Rorschach showed "a severely disturbed child with many neurotic features, and some indications of a schizophrenic process."

This child, the second of two boys, could be considered an only child were it not for the fact that the death of his brother at two years, of nephrosis, eight years before the patient was born, had grave repercussions on his mother's attitude toward him.

Complaint, as formulated by the mother at the time of referral, was that "his imagination makes up talks. At school he is said to be a genius, yet his accomplishments fall short of his intelligence. He laughs, giggles. He masturbates extensively, stays in the bathroom a long time, says he does magical things there. He has many compulsions, must square things. Has obsessive thoughts regarding his parents' death."

The father, in his mid-forties, is the fourth of six children (last of the four older brothers who are artists, and the least successful of them). He is a passive, ineffectual individual, a poor provider—a schizoid person who "went through several crises, one religious." He is tense and moody.

The mother, in her late thirties, is an only child. She has a severe cleanliness compulsion and, for instance, would sterilize the nursing bottles many times in succession, in the belief that at some point she might have contaminated her hands. As a result of her "germ" phobia, she kept the child from human contacts for several years. She suffered a depression lasting five or six weeks after the birth of the child. She is overanxious and, for instance, said: "It's an abnormal thing with me that I must know every minute where he is."

Psychomotor development was precocious, the child was breast-fed for four months, and growth was normal. He had many fears, especially fear of death. At 1½ years, following the death of maternal grandmother, he refused to visit his grandfather.

When seen, the patient was overactive, excitable. He spoke under great pressure, with some incoherence. This was, however, due in large extent to the rush of ideas, and clarification could be obtained. There was a wealth of fantasies regarding his phobias, some of which were expressed in bizarre manner; for instance, he related his nightmares about bugs: "I found some kind of seeds, buried them, a plant grew and some big giant bugs came out at the ends." Coincident with and following these nightmares, his bug phobia and his obsession regarding bugs were such that "I was almost a bug myself." There were similar fantasies about a crocodile in his cellar. Once he had actually pushed his parents on the street, then fantasied them "lying still, dead on the street." However vivid were these fantasies, he knew them to be fantasies; while he was troubled by them, he felt that he got lost in these fantasies because of his intense anxiety. He was much troubled by his constant indecision, his inability to make a choice, owing to obsessive thoughts he had about himself, his parents and his friends. "How can I make a decision? I'm never sure . . . I have two friends. I'm quite mixed up about them." Many compulsive acts and prayers were carried out in a partly conscious attempt to relieve his guilt: guilt regarding masturbation, guilt regarding death wishes toward the parents (when his parents quarreled, he had obsessive thoughts about death and suicide of either one, or both).

Of the total series, this case is probably the closest to a psychotic illness. However, it could be argued that the compulsions, as defenses, were effectual; that the patient had some insight into his need to carry them out; that he was still actively testing reality. A clinical diagnosis of schizophrenia, therefore, did not seem warranted at the time, and later observations in the course of therapeutic progress proved this formulation to be correct. What the outcome would have been in the absence of therapy can be speculated upon. Defenses might have broken down, and the break from reality might have taken place.

The next case, while presenting milder symptoms, had a history of learning block which was serious.

Boy J. D. came to treatment in 1947, was treated for two years, and his progress has been followed through contact with the analyst of the father, who was referred to treatment in the course of the child's therapy. Diagnosis: *obsessive-compulsive neurosis.*

He was 9 years old at time of referral, an only child. The mother listed the following complaints: "his inability to make friends, his poor opinion of himself, his short attention span, his rituals in his room at night—he has many compulsions, touching things." He had recently been tested at school, and with an IQ of 125 was doing poor work, especially in arithmetic. The latter complaint, however, was not given spontaneously.

The father, in his mid-thirties, the sixth of nine children, was an effeminate passive man, working in his father-in-law's business and resenting it. On several occasions he broke away, started on his own, then shortly after returned to his in-law's firm. He was dominated by his wife, showed a great deal of hostility toward the patient, whom he considered a rival. He was referred to analysis.

The mother, in her early thirties, was the second of two children with a sickly older brother who had throughout claimed the attention of the parents. An aggressive, masculine woman who made all decisions, a state of affairs she described as "we agree on a course of action."

Of significance in the child's early development are the two following points: when he began sucking his thumb at 4 or 5 months, guards were used, but after several methods of coercion had failed and the baby sucked through guards and bandages, they were given up; the second point refers to early elimination training and history of smearing "all over his crib, for months." Rituals began at 5½ or 6 years, and were numerous and persistent. Nightmares were noted coincidentally.

When seen, the child showed marked anxiety, and in communicating about his early experiences gave evidence of a long history of anxiety, obsessive thoughts and compulsive acts. He recalled that "when little" (later traced to period 2 to 3 years) he "saw a man on top of the maid on the sofa," and insisted he was told by the man that he was "making doody." Following this experience, he kept thinking about toilets and "ladies toosheys." Probably during the same period, not later than 4 years old as later checked, he saw his mother standing naked in the bathroom. She asked him to get a towel for her. "That's when I began to make things even." He made a number of drawings of his mother as he had seen her, a creature with long pendulous breasts and an enormous penis-like pubic region. He begged me never to say "ladies toosheys," or equivalent expressions but to refer to "the part that's below the stomach." At sight of his mother in the recalled episode, he had an erection, and he later had the same experience repeatedly, associated with obsessive thoughts regarding female buttocks. These experiences caused him great anxiety, which he could relieve by the "even-up" compulsion. This "even-up" (bringing any experience to an even number, later associated with the two buttocks and the two breasts) was the cause of his school difficulties. Any arithmetic problem became involved as a result. There was also great preoccupation with sex, and one obsessive thought referred to asking his parents to demonstrate sexual intercourse, in an attempt to dissociate sexual intercourse from defecation.

The function of the compulsion as an atonement to relieve guilt is here clearly formulated in the "even-up" compulsion.

The last two cases are clear-cut cases of *child schizophrenia.*

Boy H. K. came to treatment in 1952, and is still in treatment. He was referred at 8 years 11 months, after nearly 3 years of treatment elsewhere. He is the younger of two boys.

The parents reported that the patient had been expelled from public school and was now doing poorly at a private school, where he was no longer to be kept. "Absorbed in play with miniature toys, destroys them. Talks to himself in whispers. Sees lobsters and bears under his bed. Behaves peculiarly. Deathly afraid of being ill."

A psychometric test done at the beginning of treatment gave him an IQ of 113. Report on Rorschach findings stated: "The over-all picture is that of an extremely agitated, disorganized frightened boy, who is attempting without much success to relieve his fears and agitation by indulging in constant activity . . . His perceptions of all circumstances are so deviant that it is impossible for this boy to organize his experiences in line with commonly accepted reality. Rather, he has created a world of his own where destructive, frightening, horrible things are going on all the time." Diagnosis: *child schizophrenia.*

The father, in his late thirties, is a professional man, a punitive father who saw the child's sick behavior only as bad behavior, which deserved corporal punishment.

The mother, a few years younger, is, on the other hand, warm and sensitive, and since she has recognized the child's illness, has tended to be overindulgent toward him, and to infantilize him.

The child had a precocious development—there was no pressure in training. At 2 years he had croup, was at the hospital for several weeks in an oxygen tent, and had been told, but later reported as his own recalled experience, that "if it had not been for the doctor, I would have died." A few months after his return from the hospital, he was left with a comparative stranger while the rest of the family went away for one week. When the parents returned, they found him "wasted, depressed." The nurse had spanked him because of his refusal to eat, and because he had begun rocking. He became withdrawn following this traumatic experience.

When seen, he was a peculiar, oldish-looking child, with an odd lurching walk, a thin anxious face, constant blinking and a sniffing tic. He spoke in a monotone, mostly to himself, while engaging in scenes of violence with the toy people, calling them on occasions by appropriate names: father, mother, sister, brother, etc. Owing to the fact that he spoke in whispers, and also to the rush of speech, it was rarely possible to follow his play other than by witnessing it. He did not tolerate interruption, and went on with whatever theme he was acting out. Predominantly, this was about death, killing and being killed. At intervals, statements as follows could be made out: "Anyway, I'm still living . . . I'll never be dead. I keep myself young with pills . . . I wish I was more dead than alive. I'd be livid with anger. I'm not afraid because one might die because of heart attacks." Oral incorporation fantasies were accompanied with chewing and sucking of all objects. A check on the blood picture showed anemia due to lead absorption. There were fantasies of parents' death, as in one of the rare statements he addressed directly to the physician, at the beginning of treatment: "You know that father who came with me is only my step-father, my real father is dead—every father of mine is dead." Most of his utterances were incoherent, and it was at first impossible to reach him. Aside from relatively few direct references to his family and to himself, as involved in destructive acting out, the death theme was displaced in time and space and he acted out his emotional conflict in terms of Confederate soldiers and Civil War personalities. Bizarre symbolism was expressed, as when he told of question marks hanging from trees and ready to eat him.

This case clearly illustrates the pathognomonic signs of schizophrenic illness which are in the nature of loss of affective contact with reality.[8] The anxiety generated—during the pregenital phase—in the two early traumatic experiences has been overwhelming to the ego, which is weak, amorphous, and which fails to fulfill its primary function: reality testing, reality defining.

The last case presents many similarities with the case of boy H. K.

Girl M. D. was referred in 1954 at the age of 9¼ years and has been in treatment for the past two months. Diagnosis: *child schizophrenia*. She is the oldest of three children, the other two being boys.

She was treated during two earlier periods: the first, at a clinic during the summer, lasted three months, beginning at 5½ when the complaint was that "the child garbled her speech." TAT and Rorschach given then showed "aggressive hostility, cruelty," and there was a question whether the child was "schizophrenic." The second period began at 6¾ years, also at a clinic, and lasted about three years. A report from the latter clinic shows that "an IQ of 88 was not considered an accurate estimation of her intelligence because of withdrawal, negativism, infantile behavior." A diagnosis of schizophrenia was formulated. The whole family was brought into treatment.

At the time of referral, the complaint as formulated by the parents was "she is definitely odd, not socialized, can't get along with children—needs intensive treatment."

The father, in his late thirties, the second of two boys—who said of his brother still living, "I had a brother"—is a professional man who doesn't mingle easily, feels lonesome and was for two years actually isolated from his family because of pulmonary tuberculosis, now arrested. In addition, he was in the Armed Forces from the time of the child's birth to 17 months, during which period the mother lived with her parents, and the child became close to her grandfather, calling him Daddy.

The mother, also in her late thirties, is the older of two girls, who is still very close to her family; a vigorous and domineering woman who described herself in the following terms: "I am a driving woman. I have compulsive cleanliness, moodiness, and I am a little paranoid." She was for several years an occupational therapist in a state institution for mental diseases, and made the diagnosis of schizophrenia on her child—correctly—before the first period of treatment.

With regard to development, birth was normal and so was the infant's early emotional response. Thumb-sucking has persisted to date, and elimination training seems to have been free of tension. She was reared in the home of maternal grandparents while mother worked. She called her grandfather "Daddy" and at 17 months was told for the first time that her Daddy was coming home. The grandfather was "extremely jealous" of the father, in spite of which both parents insist that the child "took right away to her father because of his uniform buttons." However, it is noted that the child who had started to talk early, stopped at 18 months. Furthermore, in the course of treatment, the child has frequently referred to her confusion over these two fathers, and many fantasies involve grandfather as alternately dead and alive. At 3½, after her first brother was born, she actively lived the fantasy of two imaginary companions, one good little boy, and one bad, each one with his own name. At about 6 years she fused the two under the bad boy's name. When the brother was one year old, she asked for an ax to "chop his head." She was 7 when her maternal grandfather died. (In therapeutic sessions, she has given the time as 3½, i.e., when her brother was born.) The grandfather had died suddenly, following a chest operation for carcinoma of the lungs, and the child expressed then, and still does crucifixion fantasies involving her grandfather as "Daddy," herself and, less frequently, other members of her family, and people outside of her family. She would not go to school without a large doll which occupied a desk next to hers, and with whom she engaged in long, whispered conversations.

When seen, she was "definitely odd," unrelated, overactive, wandering about the play room with no apparent purpose, with an anxious expression, talking incoherently in a loud staccato voice with inappropriate affect. Extreme hostility was shown in the many fantasies of violent death which involved father, mother, babies, whom she drowned, buried alive, shot, burned, hung, etc. The figure representing the mother was fairly consistently referred to as "the bad guy's wife." There were acted out, world destruction as well as omnipotence fantasies, and the usual outcome was, several times during one play session, the death and burial of all people, with successive rebirths. "Everything is destroyed except me—I'm too smart—I'm a God." Nevertheless, she acted out her own death at intervals. She draws very well, and made innumerable dynamic drawings, such as the following, briefly described and typical: a girl, herself by name, at the bottom of a body of water, bubbles going up to the surface, to show that she is alive. A ladder rises from the bottom, going on and on, up toward the sun, around which birds are dying, being burned by the sun's rays. The girl climbs the ladder and frees the birds. They are alive again. Once, seeing a drawing by another girl patient, she asked: "Is she living?"

In this case, obsession with death is not a mere obsessive thought, as found in the obsessive-compulsive neurosis; it is an acting out of the death theme, and a total identification with the dead person or the person who causes death. There is no insight into the compulsive act or the obsessive thought as alien to the subject; and while the subject may experience severe anxiety, this anxiety is not related to the compulsiveness of the act or the obsessiveness of the thought.

DISCUSSION

The essential difference between severe obsessive-compulsive neurosis and schizophrenia in children is that the ego function (reality testing) is little or not damaged in the neurosis, whereas in schizophrenia (as is well known), it is badly shattered. However bizarre the obsessive thought or compulsive act, if the patient experiences them as alien to his personality, the break with reality has not taken place.

When girl N. J. seeks parental reassurance that her "minds are silly," she seeks additional and unchallengeable evidence that her obsessive thoughts have no basis in reality. She shows objectivity toward them. She can tell under what circumstances they appear, and when they trouble her most—at night. Through the anxiety panics which these thoughts arouse, her reality testing continues unabated. Similarly, when boy J. S. tells in great detail of his obsessive thoughts about the sternal pipe-line and the base four, of the compulsive acts he must carry out to relieve his anxiety, he emphasizes his awareness of the irrationality of these experiences.

In children, neurotic compulsions rarely coexist with the psychotic process, as observed in adults and adolescents. This coexistence means that the compulsions as defenses have failed, and taken on a different character: they have become symbolic acts detached from the ego and no longer subjected to reality testing.

If one considers the remarkable complexity and intricacy of the obsessions and compulsions, and the intensity of the internal struggle in some of the children studied, one cannot fail to question why ego disorganization does not occur more frequently. Incidentally, the amount of anxiety which arises in the test situation is often a precipitating factor which brings on transitory disorganization. This would explain the frequently noted discrepancy between test situation and clinical findings. The discrepancy is usually one of greater severity of symptoms and poorer prognosis in the test situation.

As illustrated in the brief presentation of the six cases, the anxiety arises from different sources at different stages of psychosexual development. In the obsessive-compulsive neurosis the anxiety is part of the unresolved oedipal conflict, as seen in every one of the four obsessive-compulsive cases, whereas in early schizophrenia the anxiety is a result of devastating emotional deprivation experienced in the pregenital phase.

The onset of obsessive-compulsive neurosis in children is noted to be considerably earlier (5 or 6 year level) than generally reported in the literature.

Also to be noted, as a point in differential diagnosis, is the strong guilt reaction invariably found in the obsessive-compulsive, and the function of the compulsion as a defense against guilt. This is particularly illustrated in the case of the boy J. D. The preoccupation with death as self-punishment is commonly noted. Preoccupation with death in the schizophrenic is of a different character, and has been discussed.

The compulsive character of masturbation must again be interpreted in a different light, whether it applies to the neurotic or the psychotic.

The intellectual function in the schizophrenic, especially with regard to abstract thinking, usually is severely damaged, whereas in the neurotic, even in the presence of severe distortion fantasies, the intellectual function is interfered with only—and not structurally—insofar as fantasy removes the child from his environment and prevents the full utilization of his intellectual potentialities.

REFERENCES

1. Kanner, Leo: Child Psychiatry. Springfield, Ill., C. C Thomas, 1948.
   ——: The conception of wholes and parts in early infantile autism. Am. J. Psychiat. *108:* 23–26, 1951.

2. PEARSON, GERALD: Emotional Diseases of Children. New York, W. W. Norton, 1948.
3. KANNER, LEO: *op. cit.*
4. KANNER, LEO: *op. cit.*
5. GREENACRE, PHYLLIS: A study of the mechanisms of obsessive-compulsive conditions. Am. J. Psychiat. *2:* 527–538, 1923.
6. PIOUS, WILLIAM L.: Obsessive-compulsive symptoms in an incipient schizophrenic. Psychoanalyt. Quart. *9:* 327–351, 1950.
7. MAHLER, MARGARET S.: Remarks on psychoanalysis with psychotic children. Quart. J. Child Behavior *1:* 18–21, 1949.
8. DESPERT, J. LOUISE: Schizophrenia in children. Psychiatric Quart. *12:* 366–371, 1938.
———: The early recognition of childhood schizophrenia. M. Clin. North America, 680–687, May 1947.

15

EXPERIENCE WITH THERAPY OF PSYCHOSOMATIC PROBLEMS IN INFANTS

By REGINALD S. LOURIE, M.D., Med.Sc.D.*

THE THINKING IN ETIOLOGIC TERMS in the field of psychosomatic medicine has consistently implicated infantile experiences as basic factors in establishing points of fixation. Therefore, there has been increasing interest in the actual psychosomatic involvements in infancy, and a body of information has been building up concerned with the genesis of such problems. This has not been matched by an equivalent interest in overcoming these disturbances. Spitz's suggested approaches[15-16] have been the most definitive thus far.

In the past six years the Department of Psychiatry of Children's Hospital has been concerned with fourteen infants ranging from five to eleven months of age in whom psychosomatic symptoms have had such profound effects, in spite of the best medical thinking, that, if uninterrupted, a fatal outcome could be expected. The diagnoses included two cases of cyclic vomiting, eight cases of diarrhea and four ruminators.

In most of these infants, where the psychosomatic process had progressed to a physically dangerous point, we could see a characteristic picture of marasmus. They looked like worried, wizened old men, with sunken eyes and sucking pads prominent in their otherwise sunken cheeks. Their skin was loose, in folds, nonelastic. When they were not crying or sleeping they turned away from their environment, staring at crib sides or ceiling. Some followed the movements of people within range of vision, only to cry or turn away when anyone came near. There was often preoccupation with parts of their own bodies—usually the hands. Fingers or fists were in the mouth, or the hand waved rhythmically in front of the eyes. Some indulged in head-rocking.

* Director, Department of Psychiatry, Children's Hospital of the District of Columbia; Associate Clinical Professor, Department of Pediatrics, The George Washington University School of Medicine, Washington, D. C.

Usually, these children had been thoroughly studied, having almost literally "an instrument in every orifice," with negative or equivocal results. A characteristic case had been hospitalized at least twice before. There had been definite improvement each time, before the more serious manifestations of severe physical depletion were prominent. A point was reached where there was only transitory benefit from special dietary regimes and/or parenteral approaches. As soon as the latter were abandoned, there would be physical regression in the presence of continuation of vomiting, diarrhea or rumination.

Sometimes the pattern of occurrence of symptoms forced the medical staff into an awareness of large emotional components in the illnesses. For example, an infant with a history of ten to thirty watery stools per day stopped its diarrhea within twenty-four hours after hospital admission. Medical, bacteriologic and chemical studies were negative. The child was discharged in good chemical balance, only to be returned again with ten to thirty watery stools within a few days. Again this cleared up within twenty-four hours and again physical and laboratory studies were negative. Sometimes such recurrent episodes were repeated three, four or more times before the severe downhill course began, and referral for psychiatric therapy was initiated. There is still an understandable reluctance to refer an infant less than a year old for psychiatric attention.

Since these were infants for whom the outlook was critical, strong efforts were necessary. The nursing staff came to recognize that special, individual care for these babies was as important and as lifesaving as special nursing for a tracheotomy. The babies were first of all placed near the nursing station so that there was some activity to be seen and heard much of the time. This served one specific purpose—it brought them out of the back cubicles where they usually were placed, possibly because there they would be less anxiety-producing for the helpless staff.

Since these infants had obviously turned away from the world, having withdrawn their object cathexis and reinvested it in the self, any attempt at emotional "replacement" therapy to' accompany the dietary, blood and biochemical replacements were blocked. It quickly became apparent that the important primary goal was to help these children to trust those around them, and reinvest their libido in the substitute mothers available. This was not difficult in some of our patients, but nine of the fourteen were not interested in people, continuing to turn away, to scream when picked up, or to look vacantly or remain inert when held. Four of these began slowly to respond to continuing carrying, fondling and being talked to by specific nurses, nurses' aides or attendants. These personnel, selected as it were by the babies themselves, were assigned to them alone.

Four other babies were quite challenging in that it became clear that any tactile contacts were the signals for further withdrawal, or were obviously anxiety-producing, or even seemed to be painful at times. Experimenting showed that three of them responded to being talked to, one could be interested not in a person, but by bright colored articles of their clothing or some of their jewelry. These auditory and visual stimuli were gradually combined with rhythmic movement patterns, usually in the form of rocking their cribs. As there came to be gradual acknowledgement of the persons involved, obvious pleasure in being with them developed, as was evident with the others. This group suffered themselves to be held as time went on, but never apparently really enjoyed it.

One ten-month-old infant could not be interested in any of these approaches from adults. It was accidentally discovered that when put in a crib with another baby, he was attentive and seemed to enjoy his incidental physical contact with the other child. Thereafter he was placed in a playpen with one or two active older children and began to reach out to them, was fascinated by their motility. Gradually, by holding another child on one knee, a nurse could hold the patient on her other knee, and finally there could be acceptance of and satisfaction from the mother substitute.

The second step was to observe the patients for any pattern in their symptoms. In the majority it was found that an approximation could be made, i.e., it was possible to predict within limits when the rumination, vomiting or diarrhea would take place. Thus, some of the babies brought back food or had loose stools immediately after a feeding. Others waited a half hour. Still others held off sometimes until two to three hours later. Some confined their manifestations to the afternoon or evening.

When such patterns were known, an effort was made to be sure that holding, carrying or other physical contact would overlap with those periods when the symptoms could be expected to occur. In other words, if substitute satisfactions, particularly relationship satisfactions could be available to the infant at the time when the symptom seemed to be needed, it was hoped that the symptom could be foregone for that moment. If this happened consistently enough, possibly the altered physiologic state could be brought back into balance. This alone was effective in a few cases. In a few others it resulted in a shift of the times when the symptoms occurred, so that there had to be a remapping of the times when the staff's efforts would have to be concentrated on the patient.

The most difficult to control with this tactic were those who shifted their ejective maneuvers to times when their special nurse was not available. Hazards to be watched for with this approach were the ease with which these physically-depleted children could be overstimulated and fatigued. Also, if the nurses became emotionally fatigued by the unresponsiveness of a baby or by failure or by relapses, it could easily end in the attendant becoming bored.

The next step was to provide other forms of satisfaction and stimulation, once these children were willing. Standard equipment on the wards began to include high chairs next to the nurse's desk, strollers, playpens and baby carriages. Toys which trial and error showed would interest individual infants were supplied for them. Their own motility patterns were used and encouraged, as most of them emerged or re-emerged into more purposeful and consistent standing and crawling.

Once the first two stages were accomplished there was, in almost all cases, an improvement in the physical symptoms. (The chief exception was case ⚹4 below.) One baby, after losing its special nurse, regressed, and was able to make a more permanent recovery in a foster home. The disappearance of vomiting in the cyclic vomiters was comparatively rapid (36 to 48 hours). In five cases, diarrhea cleared up within four days. The others took from two weeks to a month to clear up. There was a wide variation in the length of time it took for the chief symptoms to subside in the ruminators (see below).

The four ruminators presented such wide variations in etiology and response to therapy that it seems worthwhile to report them briefly. Rumination (or merycism) is a well known clinical syndrome[9] which consists of regurgitation of food without nausea or retching. Often part of the food is reswallowed. The return of the food is usually stimulated by fingers in the mouth (all our ruminators had big mouths and long fingers). It is obviously a pleasurable act, is voluntary and can become habitual. Loss of food may end in malnutrition and, where the more severe cases continue uninterrupted, the outcome is often fatal (up to 50 per cent). In each of our cases the onset of rumination was shortly after the establishment of the hand-to-mouth stage, at about three months. There had been true vomiting intermittently since birth. Each of our cases had had series of allergic tests and diets, antispasmodic and sedative medication, thick, sticky feedings, and restraints. The latter included arm splints, chin straps and bonnets tied under the chin so the thumb could not get into the mouth. The patients, however, developed the ability to work the jaws and back of the tongue so that they could gag themselves and purposefully produce the return of food. Where the jaws were immobilized, some could accomplish this return of food by throwing their heads back and arching their backs.

Case #1

Joan was a five-month-old white female whose parents were young, quite immature and unsure of themselves though well motivated. They were living a precarious existence in furnished rooms. When the patient was three months of age they moved out into the country where the mother was alone a great deal and became somewhat disorganized, tense and fearful of her welfare and the baby's. She was constantly doing something to the baby, who had no rest. In addition, she described days when she carried the baby back and forth from the store, half a mile away, only to have to make two or three more round trips with baby under arm for items she had forgotten. Phobic and compulsive thinking was prominent. Mother devoted herself to the child to the exclusion of the husband.

The child became irritable, and then began the rumination at about three months. She lost weight consistently till she was hospitalized, weighing about seven pounds at four months. She improved somewhat, gained two pounds in two weeks and was sent home on an antiallergic diet. She was readmitted at five months in a state of marasmus, still ruminating.

Medical study was negative except for a mild dilatation or relaxation of the cardiac end of the esophagus. Therapy for this produced no benefit. Neither did special and thickened feedings, antispasmodics, sitting up in a sling on the bed and arm restraints. Permission was obtained on psychiatric ward rounds to participate in the therapeutic approaches.

Joan turned out to be quite apprehensive of and unresponsive to any of the ward personnel except a thin, wiry, tense nurse's aide. With the assistance of this woman the program outlined above was begun. The baby began to respond slowly, taking feedings avidly from this person after having been reluctant about eating when held by anyone else. Within a week her ruminating became infrequent during the day and was evident only at night when the nurse's aide was not on. Her weight went from eight pounds to ten pounds in two weeks. In the third week the mother was brought in to replace the mother substitute gradually, and after each session with the child saw a resident who talked over her reactions and worked out with her the subjective feelings involved in the day's experience. A family agency was brought into the picture and helped the young couple make better living arrangements and to work out the family problems.

At eleven months there had been no rumination or vomiting, and Joan weighed eighteen pounds. No difficulties were reported and she was developing normally.

Case #2

Jimmy was an eleven-month-old white male whose vomiting had been in evidence for his first three months. Rumination began at three months but dropped out within two weeks following hospitalization because of severe weight loss. At eight months it began again, so severely that in a week he had lost 2½ pounds. He retained only water and was rehospitalized. Frequent small, thick feedings plus antispasmodic medication were able to reverse the pattern of weight loss, and he went home again in a week. Three months later he returned to the hospital in an emaciated state, weighing twelve pounds. For two weeks he had increasingly lost interest in his mother, in eating and stopped putting anything in his mouth but his thumb. After ten days of varying combinations of restraints, clyses, thick feedings, transfusions (because of nutritional anemia) and sedation, his hydration was improved but he was withdrawn, unresponsive, whining upon any approach by the ward personnel.

Psychiatric study showed him to be the only child of a college graduate mother who was a very dependent person, unsure of her judgment. She had lived near her own mother in a small western city and had leaned on her mother for many decisions about the care of the baby. Her husband was a much more mature individual who was able to deal with his wife's anxieties, except for those centering around the dependency status of the baby. He had left medical school temporarily for a career which involved considerable traveling, based in Washington where he brought his family when Jimmy was six months old. This meant leaving his wife alone in a city where she had no friends. She felt increasingly helpless and depressed, and built up considerable tension. Jimmy was apparently comfortable in spite of this for about two months. At eight months, shortly after his father went on a trip, the rumination began again.

When the outlined therapeutic regimen was introduced, Jimmy responded quite rapidly and within a week gradually stopped bringing back food, even though, when alone, he would sometimes suck his thumb. He remained in the hospital with this regimen for fifteen more days, with mother who was being given some help, gradually spending more and more time with him until she had much more of his time than the special nurse. Weight gain was 2½ pounds in this period. Six months later he weighed twenty-five pounds and was reported to exhibit no rumination. The family was back in their home town and mother was actively in contact with a casework agency. One year later, reports were that physical and personality development were continuing normally.

Case #3

Jack was a nine-month-old Negro male brought to the dispensary by his foster mother because he had been slowly losing weight for the past two months. This was in spite of his having been placed back on three-hour feedings, and even 2 a.m. feedings during much of this time in an effort to counteract the weight loss. There was a vague history of vomiting. He appeared to be so severely malnourished and stuporous that he was admitted immediately to the hospital. Physical and laboratory studies were negative. In the first week he vomited varying amounts, and closer observation showed that this was accomplished by sucking briefly on two fingers. Arm restraints, a ruminator's cap, plugging the nostrils, thick feedings, sedatives, etc., proved to be of no value. He brought back food in spite of this regimen by working his tongue and the angles of his jaw.

When psychiatric referral was made on the nineteenth hospital day and the above routine applied, Jack proved to be the one of the group that had to be approached without too much handling, and chiefly by auditory contacts. There was a slow cessation of rumination, matched by a slow weight gain. There were still remnants of it two months later but his weight increased from nine pounds to almost thirteen pounds.

The history shows Jack to be the child of a nineteen-year-old unmarried mother who had arranged for his adoption following delivery. Nothing was known of the father. He was born two months before term weighing $2\frac{1}{2}$ pounds and was kept in the hospital nursery for three months and discharged to the foster home weighing five pounds. The foster mother was middle aged and had four older children and another foster child under a year of age. It appeared that Jack was kept off in a small back bedroom, kept always in a bassinet which became too small for him, and the other children were limited in being allowed near him. When the added feedings were ordered for him they were given via propped bottles. He developed few motor skills and began to rock his head rhythmically from side to side. The foster mother put him in this restricting and confining environment because he was an "irritable" baby, so easily upset by the noise made by the other children in the house.

A series of psychologic studies, Gesell and Cattell scales, done because of the problem of his adoptability, showed that, with weighting for prematurity, at seven months he was considered superior, at nine months he had regressed, and at eleven months had made considerable strides in recovery. These gains were evident clinically in his learning to crawl and stand. His head-rocking also became less evident as he derived increasing satisfaction from motility.

Jack went to another foster home where the agency kept close consultative liaison between the hospital and the foster mother. He gave up rumination entirely in six weeks after his new placement. When last heard from, before his adoption at eighteen months, he had no recurrence of rumination. Although he was still responding more acutely and actively to loud noises and sudden temperature changes than most children, this was progressively less marked.

Case #4

John was a seven-month-old Negro male who had been vomiting since birth. His weight gain was slow, and stopped at five months. He remained irritable, relatively sleepless and at times was impossible to pacify. Rumination began at six months of age, and he began to lose weight and was hospitalized. Referral was made to the Department of Psychiatry in the first week of hospitalization, because of previous experience with ruminators. John was found to have days when he was able to be interested in his environment, but there were more times when he was withdrawn, expressionless, cried a great deal and resisted the approaches of the special attendant assigned to him. He was not losing weight, however, and his rumination was intermittent but never out of the picture for more than half a day at a time.

During an intercurrent specific diarrhea, a pediatric resident became suspicious of a diaphragmatic hernia because of upper abdominal distension and a peculiar tympany in the chest. Barium studies confirmed the diagnosis and there was surgical correction of the diaphragmatic defect. This was the beginning of a marked change in the infant's response to his environment and reversal of his presenting symptoms. It became apparent, in retrospect, that his manifestations had been attempts to relieve anxiety due to organic disturbances, probably chiefly pain.

Discussion

We were faced in these cases with severe regressions, possibly better described as a form of recoil from the environment and the people in it. Where object relations had been established in these infants, external and internal conditions were encountered that necessitated a reinvestiment of libido from the object to the self. It was necessary to find ways in which the narcissistic energy could become free again to reverse this process. We were counting on the normal drive for such reinvestment of libido if the situation and the object were safe, particularly nonanxiety-producing. The return to a state of primary narcissism which we encountered in these children was not the same as that found in some cases of severe autism or childhood schizophrenia, although at the height of symptoms it would be difficult to distinguish them from each other. The chief difference appeared to be in the constitutional endowment of these infants. Thus, when an organic deficiency was produced by the psychosomatic defense in addition to the unsatisfying or traumatic environment, the combination apparently produced a decompensation which became anxiety-producing in itself. The combination of internal and external sources of anxiety seemed to so overwhelm the baby that the greatest possible regression to the safest possible state was the solution. In the schizophrenic infant the as yet unknown constitutional elements which make it difficult for the individual to tolerate anxiety are apparently irreversible in most cases. The regressions in most of our cases had no opportunity to become well fixed and were reversible. We do not know whether, if untreated, some of the babies who did not die would remain in this regressed position, but the possibility cannot be overlooked.

In case ⚹3 the background of the child is not too different from those Spitz describes in his cases of anaclitic depression[15] and which Bender describes as "institutional psychopaths."[1] Even though in a home with a mother figure, the neglect of our patient was of a magnitude that permitted no satisfactory love object to be available to him. This is in contrast to the first two cases where overstimulation or too much environmental tension made it unsafe to maintain an investment in the love object. In each case the first step was the same: a gradual turning to its own body for erotic satisfactions. In the early stages of this regressive process the mother was not excluded. This recreation of the narcissistic state seemed to depend on the addition of the psychosomatically-maintained organic process. The normal "eighth month anxiety," long recognized by pediatricians, cannot be excluded as an added factor in cases ⚹2 and 3, but is not a factor in ⚹1 and 4. The question arises whether temporary organic depletion may be a precipitating factor in some of the cases of hospitalism described by Spitz, and of infantile autism described by Kanner.

The regressions we have discussed in these cases are not the true psychophysiologic regressions to fixation points that are reported in older children and adults.[14] Some of the infants possibly could be said to be going back to previously established fixation points in the selection of psychosomatic symptoms. For example, the cyclic vomiters had earlier vomiting, but not of the same cyclic type. Some of the ruminators had dropped this manifestation for months, only to pick it up again. Overstimulation of the anal area (enemas, suppositories, etc.) was found in some of our infants with psychosomatically-determined diarrhea. In other words "reflex sensitivity (could be) established by mother's handling of a particular organ."[7] Freud's observation that, when the organism is faced with excessive excitation, it attempts to get rid of this by subsequent active repetitions of the situation that induced the excessive excitation,[3] would seem to be applicable here. In other cases, however, the selection of the psychosomatic manifestation seemed to be determined by the stage of motor development and ego awareness the individual happened to be in, at the point where it could not deal by other means with the dose of anxiety present.

The rationale behind the second stage of the therapeutic program described in this study (i.e., the attempts to make sure the substitute mother was actively in the picture when the child's psychosomatic expressions were most active) was to interrupt the symptoms. There was a two-fold basis for this. Firstly, it was felt that if the physical state could be enhanced, the organically, internally-induced anxiety would need to be dealt with less and less by the child. Secondly, we were dealing with a psychosomatic symptom that was potentially self-destructive. If it could be interrupted for a long enough period, at the same time that anxiety-producing situations or frustrations were avoided, it was postulated that the immature ego's defensive, especially restorative, attempts in its use of the symptoms would be needed less and less. It has been the repeated experience, at the early age levels of functioning, that if a pattern is interrupted for a long enough period (one to two weeks) under proper conditions, a new pattern could be substituted for it. There seems to be individual, constitutionally determined flexibility in making such adjustments to new standards and pressures.

The chief mechanisms used by the children in this study were denial and projection (ejection). The denial of the reality situations which the patients faced seemed to be accomplished by the retreat to a narcissistic state. The return to hallucinatory experiences to substitute for painful reality is possible, but in the ruminators, at least, a substitute reality seemed to be established. This took the form of re-experiencing the oral gratification of the feeding situation and the safe mother—implied in bringing back the food and reswallowing it. It is to this that we referred in describing restorative attempts on the part of the ego.

This function of the symptom was apparently of such great importance to the organism that it took precedence over the homeostatic mechanisms of the body. Therapeutic approaches, therefore had to be geared toward creating evidence that the new reality situation was not overstimulating or understimulating, was minimally painful and frustrating, and was capable of offering satisfactions untinged with anxiety on the part of the mother figure, particularly at the times of the day when the child was feeling most threatened.

It would almost seem a banality to indicate that considerable work had to be done with the responsible adults in the environment of these infants. This was individualized and in the form of various combinations of educative, medical, psychotherapeutic, casework and nursing approaches. Manipulation of the environment was sometimes necessary. The Children's Hospital Well Baby Clinic with its psychiatrically-oriented pediatricians and nurses was of considerable assistance on a follow-up basis. Family and welfare agencies and the hospital's medical social work staff helped some mothers on a continuing basis. Such measures were usually started, where possible, before the baby left the hospital. In most cases there was maternal anxiety in the presence of the infant's acute manifestations, if it had not been present before, and this as well as guilt had to be relieved before the baby was sent home.

It seemed that we could not establish any correlation between the type of psychosomatic manifestation encountered in the child and the predominant attitudes and personality structure of the mother. Thus, we were not able to confirm the studies of Spitz[13] and Gerard.[7] Our material was limited, however, and not many of the mothers were studied sufficiently to know whether, as in cases ✻ 1 and 2 for example, in spite of different external behavior, they had the same basic emotional make-up.

The constitutional element in these cases cannot be overlooked. As both Gerard[7] and Deutsch[4] have pointed out, organic defects and illness, through causing pain or malfunctioning, produce anxiety. Certainly, in at least one of our cases (✻ 4) this was the major element behind the psychosomatic symptoms. In other words, the hyperstimulation comes in such a case from within the organism itself, forcing it to experience painful stimuli at an intolerable level, with resulting anxiety. Freud's concept of the *Reizschutz* or protective barrier[6] is based on constitutional variations of the ability to tolerate anxiety. The mystery of what goes into these variations has begun to be revealed by recent studies, such as those of Leitch and Escalona[10] and Bergman and Escalona[2] which show that a wide range of constitutional responses is possible. Extrasensitivities and characteristic organ responses are described by these authors.

In our cases we can confirm much of this. These infants have responses which suggest fields for further investigation along these lines. At the head of this list is autonomic nervous system function, which has been shown,[11–12] to be susceptible to at least macroscopic laboratory approaches, providing data to match against such clinical variations as found in disturbances in temperature regulation, vasomotor imbalances and syncope; in addition, such minor organic brain involvements as are found in constitutional hyperactivity, motion intolerance, aphasias and defects in perception. These involvements may place the developing ego at a distinct disadvantage in its efforts to establish an understanding and mastery of its environment. These conditions could well be scrutinized in our efforts to understand better the intolerance to anxiety, and hopefully to prevent these anxieties from overwhelming the organism.

Spitz's suggestions for psychiatric therapy of infants[16] fit in with our findings and experience. To the processes of restitution, substitution and modification we would like to add interruption of the symptom.

This study has excluded many of the manifestations more commonly thought of as psychosomatic in the first years of life. However, those involvements related to allergy for example, such as asthma and eczema, do not usually yield reactions as severe as those reported here, and usually are dealt with by diets and desensitizations. Therefore, it is not until past the second year that emotional factors are usually scrutinized. It would seem important, from the hopeful experiences in early treatment, to encourage psychiatric scrutiny in the first year if possible, and before many studies are forced by the baby itself.

It is hoped that a follow-up of these cases will eventually be possible, particularly to see if any correlation can be made between character structure, symptom choice and these early psychosomatic manifestations.

REFERENCES

1. BENDER, L.: *In* Anxiety. New York, Grune & Stratton, 1950, pp. 119–140

2. BERGMAN, P. AND ESCALONA, S. K.: Unusual Sensitivities in Very Young Children. *In* Psychoanalytic Study of the Child. New York, International Universities Press, 1949, vol. 3–4, pp. 333–352.

3. DAWES, L.: Discussion. *In* The Psychosomatic Concept in Psychoanalysis. New York, International Universities Press, 1953, pp. 64, 67.

4. DEUTSCH, F.: Choices of the organ in organ neurosis. Internat. J. Psycho-Analysis *20:* 252, 1939.

5. FREUD, A. AND BURLINGHAM, D. T.: (a) War and Children. (b) Infants Without Families. New York, Medical War Books, 1943, 1944.

6. FREUD, S.: Three Contributions to the Theory of Sex. New York, Nerv. Ment. Dis. Pub. Co., 1910.

7. GERARD, M. W.: Genesis of Psychosomatic Symptoms in Infancy. *In* The Psychosomatic Concept in Psychoanalysis. New York, International Universities Press, 1953, pp. 82–95.

8. GREENACRE, P.: The Predisposition to Anxiety. *In* Trauma, Growth and Personality. New York, W. W. Norton, 1952, pp. 27–83.

9. KANNER, L.: *In* Brennemann's Practice of Pediatrics (McQuarrie, ed.). Hagerstown, Md., W. F. Prior, 1948, chap. 13.

10. LEITCH, M. AND ESCALONA, S. K.: The Reactions of Infants to Stress. *In* Psychoanalytic Study of the Child. New York, International Universities Press, 1946, vol. 3–4, pp. 121–140.

11. LOURIE, R. S., BARRERA, S. E. AND STRONGIN, E. I.: Autonomic nervous system in children with behavior problems. Am. J. Psychiat. *99:* 419–425, 1942.

12. LOURIE, R. S.: Parotid gland secretion in normal children: A measurement of function of the autonomic nervous system. Am. J. Psychiat. *65:* 455–479, 1943.

13. ———: The role of rhythmic patterns in childhood. Am. J. Psychiat. *105:* 653–660, 1949.

14. MARGOLIN, S. G.: Genetic and Dynamic Psychophysiological Determinants of Pathophysiological Processes. *In* The Psychosomatic Concept in Psychoanalysis. New York, International Universities Press, 1953, pp. 3–35.

15. SPITZ, R. A.: Anaclitic Depression. *In* Psychoanalytic Study of the Child. New York, International Universities Press, 1946, vol. 2, pp. 313–342.

16. ———: Psychiatric therapy of infants. Am. J. Orthopsychiat. *17:* 623–633, 1950.

17. ———: The Psychogenic Diseases in Infancy. *In* Psychoanalytic Study of the Child. New York, International Universities Press, 1951, vol. 6, pp. 255–275.

16

ADOLESCENT FRUSTRATIONS
AND EVASIONS

By LAWSON G. LOWREY, M.D.*

IT IS MY GENERAL IMPRESSION, altered only to a limited degree over the years, that the phase of life we call adolescence is the least understood of "the seven ages of man." This is the case whether we speak of the views of those who work professionally with adolescents, or of those who live with them. It is certainly true for the adolescents' understanding of themselves, and what is happening to them physically, mentally and socially. This, which seems to me a correct judgment, presents some very real issues, whether we think of normal development through this crucial epoch, of the pscyhopathology, or of the deviations in behavior and their social effects.

There is a voluminous literature about the adolescent and the processes which take place during adolescence, but much of it is not really helpful because of variations in terms and definitions, or because of an *either-or* circumscription in approach. Some writings are so vituperative and fanatic that the viewpoints are arrant nonsense. At the risk, then, of seeming to elaborate the obvious—that neglected body of data aginst which we should at all times project our observations and interpretations—let me start by defining as precisely as possible my conception of the age period of adolescence. You may not agree with my definitions, and perhaps it is not desirable that you should (certainly there is no necessity to do so) but at least the limitations of my presentation will be clear. Some of us seem to have got into a twilight dream world of one-to-one correlations of cause and effect, elaborated in fanciful polysyllabic phrases. Many of these analyses are as remote from reality (even unconscious reality) as are the daydreams of the adolescent. It seems necessary briefly to outline first

* Associate Psychiatrist, Vanderbilt Clinic; Assistant Clinical Professor of Psychiatry, Columbia University, College of Physicians and Surgeons, New York City.

some of the simple and obvious points about the period of adolescence: its physiology, psychology and psychopathology. The present synthesis is based upon my contacts with normal and abnormal adolescents, their families, schools, activities, ideas and emotions. It may seem oversimplified, but my experience has been that unless we constantly bear in mind this outline (for that is all it is) of the major facts, we often go astray in understanding and treating the adolescent and his problems.

MAJOR CHARACTERISTICS OF ADOLESCENCE

The Span of Adolescence

Many of the difficulties encountered in the interpretation of published reports occur because of what seem to be widely varying concepts of the age period involved in the adolescent process. In much of the older literature, the chief stress appears to be on puberty, and this often seems practically to be equated with adolescence. In one formal definition, adolescence is: "the period of life between puberty and maturity;" literally, the period of "growing up." In another, it is: "the process of growing up from childhood to manhood or womanhood." It must be clear that the periods of childhood, adolescence and adulthood are not sharply delimited, except by arbitrary definition.

The physical changes which mark puberty, culminating in sexual maturity evidenced by menstruation in girls and ejaculation in boys, occur over a period of two or more years. But this series of changes is preceded by alterations in the growth curve and in some other aspects of functioning, also lasting about two years, and commonly labelled the prepubertal phase. The onset of the adolescent process, therefore, seems to me to be when the physical growth curve turns sharply upward, at about nine to ten years in girls, and eleven to twelve years in boys. The ages for this and for the beginning of the definite pubescent changes are subject to a normal range of variation, rather wider than that ordinarily stated.

When adolescence ends is a much more difficult question to answer. Legally, that is to say, socially, it is presumed to end at age 21. Physically, it ends when there is no more new tissue formation. To determine this, about the only precise information at hand has been obtained from x-ray studies of the closure of epiphyseal lines, which occurs at approximately ages 21 to 25. If we use the concept of the cessation of growth in capacity as the criterion for intellectual development, then according to psychometric tests the adolescent period would end at 14 to 16 to 18 years of age. It is perhaps unnecessary to say that this has nothing to do with the utilization of the intellectual capacity; or, for that matter, with the validity of the structure of the tests employed.

In the most important area, that of the emotions and instinctive drives, the state of personality development which we call maturity comes much later, probably around 30. Or this aspect of maturity may seem never to occur.

Each of these stages of adolescence—the prepubertal, the pubertal and the postpubertal—has rather well defined characteristics in normal development—physically, mentally and socially—though there is no sharp line of demarcation. Rather, for the most part the developmental processes pass unevenly from one stage to the next, with regressions of greater or lesser importance complicating the maturational picture.

Latterly, emphasis has been on the "teen-age" period, since we are in the grip of a widespread publicity campaign about the delinquencies and crimes of the teen-agers. For at least the tenth time during the last forty years, the period with which I am most familiar, the teen-ager is being blamed for just about everything, even as was true 6000 years ago. But teen-agers belong in two groups: the pubescent (or even prepubescent) and the postpubescent. Actually, it is a little difficult to see how a 25-year-old parolee leader of a "gang" of 19-year-old boys can be classed as a teen-ager, unless perhaps mentally.

From the standpoint of psychopathology, especially as revealed in socially inadequate behavior and in various sorts of mental difficulties, each of the three phases also presents fairly clearcut differences, which will be taken up in more detail later. Suffice it to say here that, because of time and space limitations, the later discussion of psychopathology will be chiefly confined to the postpubertal ages, when the most marked difficulties occur, to exemplify the frustrations and evasions.

Physiologic Changes

This point is mentioned merely to emphasize the fact that the physical and chemical upheavals in this period have profound effects upon both mental and social functioning, as well as physical capacities, and play an important part in any psychopathology which may occur.

Psychologic Adjustments

Under the best of circumstances, there is a stormy period, varying in duration, of psychologic adjustment and readjustment. Adolescent mentation in general is characterized by a high degree of ambivalence involving many issues and people; egocentricity; the reactivation of narcissism; varying degrees of anxiety expressed in diverse ways; clearcut distinctions between right and wrong, good and bad, with positive opinions expressed as fixed and immutable "facts" (obvious defense reactions); marked indecisiveness and ambivalence on many points, contrasting sharply with the fixed convictions on others; rebellious drive for independence and escape from adult standards and authority, which enters into the great need for the protective coloration of the group of peers; fantasy formation and numerous other overcompensatory mechanisms evolved in the effort to solve the new or intensified conflicts which also characterize this epoch.

Behavior disorders, neuroses, and psychoses, especially schizophrenic types of reaction, become important. Despite the generally unstable personality, at least by comparison with some other stages of life, it is worthwhile calling attention to the fact that the 1950 U.S. Census shows that 14 per cent, or approximately 21,700,000 of the population, were in the 10–19 age group; some 15,000,000 being in the 14-20 (inclusive) group. On the basis of available figures, the number of individuals in these age groups who presented serious difficulties seems small, by comparison with the publicity given them. About .023 per cent (or some 5000) were admitted to state hospitals (in 1949), approximately three-fourths in the 15–19 group. This latter group accounted for around 4 per cent of the first admissions, and about 3 per cent of the psychotic first admissions. Approximately one-third of the admissions in the "under 15" group (in round numbers, 1000) were psychotic; while 70 per cent of the 15–19 group were so classified. Schizophrenic reactions account for half of the psychotic "under 15", and two-thirds of those in the 15–19 group. "Primary behavior disorders" as a diagnosis drops sharply, while "psychopathic personality" increases ten-fold, when the two age groups are compared.*

Accurate figures for antisocial behavior are much more difficult to obtain. It appears that of some 2,037,000 arrests recorded by the F.B.I. in 1952, at least 40 per cent, or about 800,000, were "persons under 21." Age 19 seems to be the critical age in this connection. Whether this report covers all the Juvenile Court cases is not clear, nor is the lower age limit, but it is certainly indicated that not over 6 to 8 per cent of the age group under consideration is involved. Figures for special schools, private practice and clinics are not available, but it seems reasonable to believe that not over 10 per cent of the "teen-agers" are psychotic, neurotic or exhibit delinquent behavior. That another 10 or 15 per cent may show signs indicating lack of smooth mental and social adaptation would not destroy this thesis: that the vast majority of adolescents weather the storm quite successfully, by what means we have not yet even begun to try to discover. How much the conflicts of the adolescent period contribute to later mental upsets is a matter of conjecture; there nevertheless is evidence

*What is called schizophrenia is, without doubt, the most serious disorder (or disease) of the young, from the standpoint of psychopathology, as it also is socially and epidemiologically. We may lay aside all theoretic and practical questions of etiology, pathology, diagnosis and psychodynamics for present purposes. But it is important to remember that 27.7 per cent of first admissions "with psychosis" to state hospitals in 1949 were diagnosed "schizophrenia" (22,212 of 79,980 psychotics). Of these, almost 10,200 (46 per cent) were male and slightly over 12,000 (54 per cent) were female. The median age was 32.6 years, by contrast with a median age of 50.3 for all psychotics. The ages on admission present some points of interest for this discussion, especially in view of the recent intensive researches on childhood schizophrenia, on types of schizophrenic psychologic patterns revealed by the Rorschach and other projective tests, on chemical production and alleviation of schizophrenic symptoms, and so on. The decade 25–34 accounted for 34.7 per cent of schizophrenic admissions, with 23.8 per cent under 25, giving a total of 58.5 per cent under the age of 35; with 41.2 per cent under 30. Since schizophrenia is, on the average, slow in its development, the psychopathology as well as other pathology involved thus seems to have a clear relation to the upheavals of the adolescent period in a high percentage of cases which reach the hospitals. Here again figures regarding those who do not reach the hospitals are unavailable, and speculation regarding them is profitless.

that the processes of adolescence help to resolve more conflicts than they intensify.

Unconscious Drives and Reality

In recent literature, much has been made of the struggle between the id impulses (or drives), the super-ego and, particularly, the ego, especially the "weak" ego. The "Oedipus complex" seems to be the only libidinal component which is seriously emphasized. The "re-awakening" of this complex in the early pubertal period is supposed to set off a chain reaction of approach and withdrawal of libido between parent and child of the opposite sex. Anyone who has observed carefully should realize that in usual circumstances it is not the child but the parent who has the major difficulties in resolving this situation. There is an exception here—when parent and child of the same sex find a strong relationship which means a great deal to both. This will be on the conscious level, yet the unconscious components will be related to the Oedipus complex.

My own judgment is that the ego is not usually so weak—it is merely confused. The upsurge of id impulses toward supremacy in all fields—such as social relations, personal adequacy, sexual adjustment, domination of the parents and other adults, revived narcissism, and a form of exhibitionism quite different from the infantile, immediate gratification, plus many others, all of which are inadequately met by the super-ego—leads inevitably to ego confusion and definite conflict between drives. On theoretic grounds, these points could be argued *ad infinitum* without much result, but it can safely be said that id, ego and super-ego present many types of conflict during this period of physiologic and psychologic upset. It is possible that interpretation of what goes on may depend upon our own ids, egos and super-egos, but this I am inclined to doubt. Only those who can remember clearly what happened to them during this period, and have since brought out associations to help them interpret their own failures and successes, will understand what is meant here.

Let me make this point. The adolescent has no idea of the dynamics of the situation. He is his own, but very much doubted, self. He doesn't know where he is or where he is going. Ego, id, super-ego, wouldn't even be words to him; which, on occasion, is all they are to the rest of us, when our own frustrated egos get in the way of considering what is happening to *this* adolescent, and our id impulses over-ride the super-ego; or the super-ego sadistically squelches all.

Reality is not always unpleasant, though the literature would indicate that it is or must be. This seems to mean only that those who write in this fashion would like to live in a world of hedonistic dreams. Fortunately, *most* adolescents have the capacity to reconcile their grandiose visions of themselves with the demands of social living, and even living with themselves. All of us are faced with the constant necessity of meeting the commonplace demands of everyday life in the world which surrounds us. Both conscious realizations and unconscious drives help us to do just this.

The basic conflicts seem to be between the hedonistic, narcissistic impulses and several group-oriented drives; and of these contrary compulsions, the needs for self-preservation, for group conformance, and for object-love appear to be the most important.

ADOLESCENT FRUSTRATIONS AND REACTIONS

Very few frustration reactions arise *de novo* in adolescence, despite some contrary opinions which seem to be rather widely held. The internal changes and the external pressures which tend to characterize the period are, from at least one point of view, only intensifications of biosocial processes which have been going on in varying combinations and intensities from the time of conception. Biologically, the changes represent the culmination of the maturational processes which will eventually result in the adult plateau. In terms of social pressures, this is the period of transition from a dependent-independent, protected, ordered, child status, to one of a reversed independent-large group-dependent, individually responsible, adult status. (May I point out that this last is true in any type of political economy, not just in a democracy or a republic? This is related to the evolutionary spiral of transition from small [family] to larger [school and neighborhood] and on to still larger and more numerous groups composed of individuals of varied backgrounds and strengths.)

Most of the adolescent's reactions are not only preconditioned but are predictable, if one has sufficient information about the sequential physical, mental and social factors involved in personality development. By this it is *not* meant that specific items of behavior or of symptomatology may be pinpointed, but that the categories of response will be reasonably certain.* What *is* meant here is that the person in the adolescent phase is the product of all that has gone before, and that adaptations will be evolved in terms of already existent patterns. Should this point of view be challenged, let me ask this question. Have any of you ever seen an adolescent neurotic, psychotic or delinquent, whose "past history" *did not reveal* trends in behavior (social adaptation) and elements in personality organization which clearly foreshadowed the probability (at least) of marked difficulties at this period? There are also many cases in which the abnormal trends are resolved in this period, while the psychologically healthy make their adjustments with what seems to be comparative ease.

How the adolescent reacts to the evolving changes will depend to a considerable extent upon the previously formed patterns of response to inner drives and conflicts, and inner and outer stimulations and frustrations.

Because of space limitations, it seems preferable to present the data in the form of a summary statement which is not elaborated. The areas of conflict to be considered may be grouped into: (1) the psychosexual (libidinal); (2) the concepts of self (ego); (3) group pressures and conformance (social). Super-ego factors must be correlated in relationship to all of these. It is the behavior, expressive of successful or unsuccessful adaptation, internal and external, which must be the focus of attention. The groupings given above are for convenience in constructing a useful outline, rather than being rigid and exclusive categories. Our major concern is with the processes which tend to facilitate or to interfere with the integration of the total personality.

Psychosexual

It is not only physical sexual maturation, with its accompanying poorly understood and poorly oriented drives for the release of sexual

---

*It seems incredible that anyone should claim to be able to spot potential murderers by their thumbs while riding in a street car, or prophesy individual types of antisocial behavior, often violent, from some other minutiae of physique or behavior. Yet, precisely this has been claimed by psychiatrically and psychologically trained people occupying responsible positions. This is a matter of personal experience, not hearsay.

tensions, which is important in this period. Certainly as essential, and perhaps more so, is that emotional aspect of personal and interpersonal awareness which is commonly called love (which I shall not attempt to define), and its opposite, hostility. The bipolarity is especially marked at this time, and is usually rather uncritically subsumed in the term ambivalence. "Love" is ordinarily regarded as a creative force, attached to various aspects of functioning and having many connotations beyond the sexual. But love—at least so designated— is often destructive, because of its possessive, egocentric, cannibalistic orientation. Contrariwise, hostility, which is usually destructive, may be constructive when it actually protects a vulnerable personality.

One of the major problems for the adolescent is the identification of love objects and a corollary focusing of hostility. The first step is that of psychologic self-identification as male or female—a very difficult matter for many. There is a sharp recrudescence of narcissism, which can only be resolved by the refocusing of object love and identification of the love object. To avoid disaster, the narcissism must be projected not to parents, but to peers. Also to "safe" adults, not members of the ascendant family group, but to the "hero" and "heroine," or the universal "uncle" and "aunt"—in fact, any safe, nonthreatening, adults or adult images.

The peer-group identification is important in all fields, but especially in the realization of the self as masculine or feminine. That this results in several manifestations of rivalry and even hostility between the sexes is insignificant by comparison with the pathology which may arise if the identification does not occur. Fears of sexual differences and their possible meanings may complicate the competitions within the own-sex group, determine hostility toward the opposite group, and even interfere with self-identification.

If conflicts are marked regarding, for example, the establishment of his identity as a male, the boy may withdraw libido into the self, which becomes the sexual as well as love object. Anal and oral erotic elements become prominent, and elaborate sets of fears and other symptoms, varied by excessive activity related to these fixations, develop. Masturbation is the usual direct sexual outlet, though many types of anal and oral expression occur, not just symbolically in symptom formation but in practice (including self-performed fellatio). This is the general psychopathologic nidus of schizophrenia.*

There are, however, far more numerous situations where the difficulties in establishing sexual identification are not so marked; where the partial fixations are less compelling; where compensations and sublimations are more possible and more effective, so that there is not only no psychotic break with reality, but the neurotic solution of the general problem may not even be recognized. The list of possible compensations is far too long to attempt to enumerate. The particular type will depend upon such factors as intelligence level, special abilities and disabilities, motor abilities and skills, social pressures and opportunities. One group of outlets should be mentioned—that of compensatory activity in abstract fields. For the adolescent whose male-female identification is clouded with difficulty, the further the field of intellectual activity is removed from personal-social contacts, the better. On the surface, these activities often seem to be quite personal—even at times homosexual—because of the "great arguments" about philosophy or art or music or communism or what-not. The truth is, however, that these are only evasive reactions to basic conflicts which have multiple roots, one of which, and perhaps the most

*The several syndromes which we call schizophrenia are not specifically characterized by any definitely pathognomonic signs or symptoms, while the clinical pictures are diverse and variable in almost every aspect within the so-called types. Along with others, I have observed cases with "typical schizophrenia" where there were proved organic and toxic factors in causation. While localization is uncertain, such evidence as there is often points to mid-brain and hind-brain arrival platforms, where interference may distort connections so that associational patterns become disturbed and symptoms such as hallucinations, delusions (not systematized as in the typical paranoid), and varied emotional deviations result. Such schizophrenic patterns, often temporary and spontaneously recoverable, have been observed in many specific and proven pathologic processes. For example, head trauma (with cranial fracture), pulmonary and meningeal tuberculosis, meningovascular syphilis, alcoholism, occasionally in brain tumors, pituitary and thyroid disorders. It is not enough to say that these anatomically or otherwise proven pathologic processes "released a schizophrenia." What they do indicate (the definitive work remains to be done or completed) is that the schizophrenias as we define the groups today are not solely the result of a psychopathologic process. This idea must, as of now, remain a matter of clinical conjecture.

important, is in this area of male-female self identification. (Obviously there should be no difficulty in this area if the Oedipus complex reaches a healthy solution.)

Efforts to intellectualize what are really rather severe emotional conflicts often result in marked disturbances and failures of integrated, goal-centered functioning. The conflicts are not only in the psychosexual field, but in other areas where competitions threaten libido and ego—in fact, they affect the whole personality structure. The mechanisms which operate, and the results, lead to a wide variety of "diagnoses," such as inadequate personality, dillettante, fanatic, paranoiac or paranoid, pseudologia fantastica, psychopath, schizophrenia. It is certainly true that all of these conditions occur, and these characterizations are correct for particular individuals. But in the great majority of cases as they occur in private practice, it is rather a "pseudoparanoid" picture which is seen. These adolescents reveal, very quickly, the paucity of their actual understanding of the philosophy, psychology, anthropology, sociology or literature of which they claim to be such profound scholars. Or in which, as in music, art, the drama, poetry, etc., they claim they have invented new forms, and are skeptical and rejecting of all or most of whatever has previously been done in the field of choice. They are "misunderstood," "far in advance of their time," yet the immaturity, the inadequacy of approach and the pseudological character of thinking are all too obvious. Within this intricately woven cocoon of fact and fantasy, the pupa is inhibited in its efforts to emerge as a mature adult by fears, hostilities, anxieties and the incomplete picture of the self, which keep the individual in a state of confusion and turmoil.

The basic emotional difficulties are distressing to the patient, yet are verbalized only hesitantly and in irregular spurts. Fear of adult "moral judgments," and of seeming to be traitors to peers, is obvious early in contacts, as is hostility toward adults and adult forms of expression. Regarding sexual identification and what is expected of the individual by his own and the opposite group, anxiety tends to predominate, leading to impulsive and inconsistent variations in action and reaction. Any real or imagined difference from group expectations as visualized by the adolescent, areas in which there has been explicit or implicit rejection from the family group, inconsistencies which have caused confusion in the sense or feeling of personal adequacy—these and many other factors profoundly influence the compensatory strivings.

One striking point is that the intellectualization of defenses into a defiant front of superiority does not carry over into areas of general conduct. These youngsters tend to dress as sloppily and try to act as tough as their compeers who have not adopted such defenses. It is as though their general behavior showed that they have some sort of awareness that theirs is a pseudo-adjustment, or pseudo-intellectualization.

Whatever the type of compensatory effort to resolve conflicts, there is likely to be much to little direct acting out of the sexual impulse. Where this is experimental, it can be and often is of considerable value to the individual. It helps in self-identification, in the separation of peers into male and female psychologic and social groups, and in the final establishment of heterosexuality. This would correlate with reduction of hostility toward the father; altering the fear of the female, so that sexual designs may become permissible; lowering the need for being in the protection of the male group, while at the same time changing the values of competitions with the own sex.

There are several sets of difficulties which may arise as the result of sexual experimentation, which need only be mentioned. The homosexual pattern may be intensified, especially the factor of feminine identification. Oral and anal and other partial trends may become fixated. Hostility toward the parents may be strongly released, often shown through the active homosexual role or as excessive drive to conquer females, frequently with sadistic reactions (which appear to me to be most often based on fear of females related many times to partial impotence). The pleasure of sexual activity *per se* may be so great that it alone can compensate for many types of frustration, not only in the pyschosexual field.

It is during this period of maturational change that variations in the strength of the sexual drive become patent. As with all other measurable aspects of the human personality, sexual activity has a normal range of variation which cannot as yet be correlated with definite facts about endocrines. Excessive sexual activity, however defined, varies with two sets of factors—the physical and the psychologic, and their intercorrelations. During adolescence, even with males who are promiscuous (and often sadistic) in their numerous "conquests," masturbation is apt to be the most excessive activity. This will certainly be true of the inhibited male who has little or no heterosexual experience.

Hostile acts toward either sex, up to and including murder, are often substitutes for sexual assaults, although sexual assault may be secondary to other hostile acts. The roots which determine the objects of this generalized hostility are deeply buried and quite complex, and no really satisfactory explanations or mechanisms of universal application have so far appeared, except for individual cases. The Oedipus, or inverted Oedipus, complex may explain certain situations, but certainly not all, any more than sadism as a generalized concept could. There is too much diffuse fear, hostility and anxiety, plus some of the definitely distorted object fantasies (and realities), along with impotence factors in sexual and other fields.

It is in this general area of anxious, fearful hostility—associated with the sexual urge and fear of reprisals, complicated by inadequate repression and compensation, with distorted images leading to sexual pleasure fixations at odd and inferior levels—that we must look for the explanation of the *real* perversions, i.e., object-fixation on other than reciprocating humans. I would exclude as perversions the partial fixations or inclusions involved in the foreplay to actual intercourse between two people—the fetishisms, submissions, minor sadisms, etc, even masturbation—if the fantasies involve a person or persons. There is a marked difference between this sort of activity and that involved when sexual gratification is *only* obtainable by sadism, masochism, fetishism, masturbation, necophilia, etc., without actual sexual contact with a live, responsive person. The psychopathologic connotations are, on the whole, quite different.

It appears, then, that the complicated emotional reactions regarding sexual activity depend on a balancing of narcissism, projected narcissism, male-female identification, parental and sibling attitudes, and identification or separateness with or from the mate. Included must be the possible factor of resentment at providing sexual satisfaction for another, which brings in ego and super-ego attitudes.

What has been said regarding the male applies also to the female, with appropriate modifications. For example, feminine rivalry as to the "conquest" of the male is not based on strength (and penis size), but on subtlety, feminine curves, appearance, dress, and the like.

Feminine hostility toward the male and female may be demonstrated by frigidity, often associated with promiscuity; by seducing and holding a particular male (often against opposition); or by the rejection of a male for a female sexual object, who may also be the object of hostility. The unconscious motive of castrating the male shows in much activity, such as flirting, "leading on," with subsequent rebuff, and so forth. Or the rejection of the feminine role may be shown in an extreme degree of a "career" drive, tending to exclude interpersonal relationships (especially the relationships with males) except on an abstract level. Fetishism, sadism and masochism certainly appear, perhaps in the form of direct expressions, when there is no special difference from the masculine type, except perhaps in the choice of objects. The indirect expressions are likely to be more subtle, perhaps more verbal, and almost certainly more anxiety-laden than in the case of males. Primarily, it would seem, this is the result of social pressures from infancy on as to what girls should accept as their roles, without regard to what they really are or can be as people.

The literature is replete with "penis envy" as a factor in feminine inversion and perversion, in determining the "masculine protest," etc.,—I'm inclined to say, *ad nauseam*. Some facts have been overlooked here, except by a few observers. For small girls, and for many adolescents, penis *envy* is anatomic rather than functional. Much more important is penis *fear*—what kind of a weapon is this? This is revealed (rather reluctantly, it must be said) during analysis by those who have developed and retain the *conscious* idea that their penis (weapon) is concealed within their genital tract and is a safeguard against penile attack. That it is also a protection against pregnancy and fulfillment as a woman seems obvious. The connotations when this is repressed into the unconscious also seem clear.

It is true that the idea of the buried penis is common in younger girls; but this is again apparently anatomic. The idea is usually repressed. If not successfully, there may be a marked recrudescence of emotions during the adolescent period, which may interfere seriously with feminine identification and with sexual activity; apparently also with conception, though in other cases conception may be facilitated (to prove femininity, it would seem). This would mean the reversal of some of the usual thinking—the girl has not been castrated by the father, but he has given her strength of a "concealed weapon" which the mother has not been able to remove. There is ample evidence that the mother is a greater castration threat for both girls and boys than is the father. Perhaps most important here is the idea of the ultra self-sufficiency of the female.

When the drive to be masculine is unusually strong and persistent, we may find the situation of the adolescent girl adopting masculine types of delinquencies, even to the extent of becoming the leader of a mob of boys. The hostility patterns are, however, the same; the acting out differs merely in the details.

Whatever the mechanisms, the indication of conflicts and imperfectly resolved drives can always be found before this period, though they are intensified at this time. The sexual components only present new outlets, often frightening and even overwhelming.

Ego

The adolescent problem here is the identification of the self, in all of its ramifications—sexual (already analyzed), in relation to position in the group, in the family, in school, in all sorts of competitions, in the general social order. The most complicated problems are in relation to the intensification of the conflicts over difference, of whatever order, and with regard to any type of competition. The further the departure from the peer-group average range of variation, the greater the threat, and the greater the compensatory efforts. By the time adolescence is reached, the many areas of variance will have been emphasized over and over again. The differences cover the entire gamut of possiblities—intelligence, disposition, fears, enthusiasms, size, appearance, color, skills, disabilities, observable handicaps, social and economic position, race, success or failure in peer-important competitions, and so on through a long list. The isolating effect of group criticism or fun-poking can be tremendous. It so easily leads either to a crushed withdrawal into the self, or attempted compensations in motor or intellectual fields. These ego threats contribute markedly to the "pseudoparanoid" reactions previously mentioned. Not only the peer-group, but parents, teachers and other criticizing adults—with their needs—contribute greatly to the confusion of the adolescent. In fact, all the impinging forces of the period, internal and external, confuse the issues of self-status, peer-status and adult identification. It is the last which represents the ultimate ego goal.

Among the self-realization problems of importance are those of the educational and vocational present and future. Independence and responsibility are necessary and important, but their realization is interfered with by the restlessness and the uncertain self-confidence which complicate the sense of timing and timeliness. "It must happen now" is an ego-imperative. Effort and time to achieve, as concepts, are often severely threatening. Hence many adolescents fall back on material possessions—theirs or their parents'—as evidence of their own adequacy. Having little to do for self-maintenance, and lacking knowledge and skills, such things as houses, cars, maids, "glitter" possessions, "social position" and the like, become compensations for their own feelings of weakness. Too much of this sort of inadequate facing of reality leads to a permanently juvenile adult.

Also, lacking the sense of personal adequacy, the need for a feeling of power leads into rough-necking, drinking (which may be following the adult pattern), flights of speed in high-powered cars, dangerous to themselves and to others (though the 25–45 year old emotionally adolescent are here more dangerous), into "gangs" and gang activities, even into crusading for logical or illogical causes.

Hedonistic and altruistic as the ego is at this time, the major problem is the "not-quite status." Not quite child or adult or person, or competent for self-realization. The issue of modesty, so-called, also enters—the fears of revealing oneself, of embracing masculinity or femininity, of sex as such, of competition in all fields of experience, of adults, of dominance (leadership) and submission (following), of the need to assume responsibility for the self, of independence, of group pressures. Compensatory reactions may make a great deal of trouble for the adolescent, and for the adults who do not understand what is going on.

Group Pressures and Performance

The conflicts related to internal evolutions are intensified by social stimuli and repressions, which also operate to interfere with the resolution of the conflicts. These social pressures are increased or modified by the threatening challenge to adults from the changing, inconsistently evolving adolescent. The pressures are contradictory: on the one hand "you're grown up now"; on the other, "you're too young" for this or that. Dozens of examples could be given, but two or three will suffice. Boys of 16 and 17 may be accepted by the armed services, but in some states may not drive cars; in all but one or two they may not vote or marry without their parents' consent until they are 21; at 18 they are subject to the draft, with no one's consent—not even their own.

In school, they are subject to the compulsory educational laws, even though they may have insufficient aptitude for an academic career. It is a fair estimate that no school system in the country provides adequately for the needs of the approximately 20 per cent who do not profit from an academic curriculum beyond (at most) the eighth grade, but who could realize considerable potential through motor-manual and trade training. Discontent with school, increased restlessness, greater feelings of inadequacy, truancy, intensified hostility unleashed on the community—these are in the train of consequences. Work which is satisfying, profitable and has a future is almost impossible to be had, especially in the larger industrialized communities. These restrictions still further repress finding necessary outlets in physical activity, and less healthy ways and means are eagerly embraced by the adolescent.

In the home, the contradictory and confusing pressures are well known, and particularly overwhelming. On the one hand, "do as I say;" on the other, "do as you please"—often about the same issue at different times. Parents attempt to dictate education, vocation and social activities, all too often in terms of their own frustrated ambitions or fears. Or, this is an expression of the intensified rejection the parent had for the child, such that the youngster cannot be permitted to do what he is best fitted for. The adolescent must be grown-up, but must still be "my baby"; the threat to the parent's ego of "slipping" because of the age factor must be minimized somehow. It is no wonder so many adolescents say "My parents wouldn't understand." Fact is, they don't.

Considering all the inconsistencies shown by parents and society in general, together with the rather fantastic behavior (morally and ethically) of adults, and the high valuations they give to those of relatively unimportant accomplishments, it seems remarkable that so many adolescents do develop adequate super-egos. For the evolution of a thoroughly internalized, organically integrated, adult type of super-ego—with all that this means in the way of accepting personal and social responsibility; of being independent, yet an accepted and valued member of the group; the maintenance of self-sufficiency, and the like—is one of the the important goals of the entire maturing process.

Finally, what are the adolescent defenses against all these internal and external pressures? Only some of those which are troublesome and unhealthy are listed.

1. Increased ambivalence, in all attitudes.

2. Increased hostility to all adults, and to all parental figures. This can be socially very serious.

3. Increased hostility to school, teachers, "law and order"—any sort of regulation or disciplinary training.

4. Flight into adventure, of all sorts, which leads easily into gang fights, and many types of delinquency, such as stealing cars, etc.

5. Increased fantasy formation, where fantasy may take the place of attempts to work out ambitions or ideas realistically.

6. Increase in hostile fantasies, often to the point where the driving force of the hostility makes it necessary to act out some particularly senseless act of brutality.

7. Greater and greater seeking of the protective coloration of the peer group. (It has already been pointed out that this is a necessary procedure.) But it happens that "follow the leader" can be fraught with great danger, if the "leader" is a particularly hostile, vengeful personality.

8. Intensification of previous insatiability and egocentricity, with decrease to actual elimination of any sympathy for others. (This is neither schizoid nor psychotic.)

To summarize: ambivalence toward the self and the world; hostility to adults and "authority;" flights into activity and fantasy, both grandiose and hostile; retreat into the own group; and intensification of egocentricity with pseudocompensations—these are the elements comprising adolescent psychopathology.

Discussion of Chapters 13–16

By MARGARET S. MAHLER, M.D.*

D R. KANNER'S pioneering, ingenious and now classical work established one clearcut clinical picture, one nosologic entity among the schizophrenic-like conditions in childhood. Though many others have also made contributions to this still hotly contested area of psychopathology of childhood, it was Dr. Kanner's definition of the syndrome of "early infantile autism" which finally forced psychiatrists to recognize and accept the existence of psychoses in children.

In 1947 I suggested that there seemed to be an emotional block to recognizing frank psychotic pictures in children.† Cases belonging unequivocally in the group of schizophrenic-like conditions in children were arbitrarily forced into one or the other better established psychopathologic categories, such as severe phobias, obsessive compulsion neuroses, impulse-ridden character formation, oligophrenia, and so on. But as usually happens in science, the diagnostic pendulum, only seven years later, is swinging to the opposite extreme. It seems that today many workers dispose of the diagnostic dilemma by throwing, only too readily, any unusual clinical picture into the catch-all category of child schizophrenia. As Dr. Despert has pointed out, there is now a tendency to over-diagnose child schizophrenia. Her paper dealt with *one* such differential diagnostic problem.

It is well known that not only obsessive-compulsive neuroses, but all other multisymptomatic neurotic conditions, lend themselves to the erroneous diagnosis of child schizophrenia. We find that conditions in which impulsions or anxiety-ridden, agitated behavior dominate the picture, are most often among those misdiagnosed. Conditions in which unbound, free-floating, diffuse anxiety prevails, and the ego defenses are erratic and fluid, are characteristic of the unconsolidated personality structure of the child. The finding of scientifi-

---

* Clinical Associate Professor of Psychiatry, Albert Einstein College of Medicine; Associate in Psychiatry, College of Physicians and Surgeons, Columbia University, New York City.

† Various Clinical Pictures in Child Schizophrenia, given at The Schilder Society, 1947 (unpublished).

cally sound differential diagnostic criteria is of paramount importance in present-day child psychiatry.

One pivotal differential diagnostic criterion seems to be whether or not object relationship is still maintained. If this can be objectively or clinically ascertained, the case in question cannot be called psychotic.

Both Dr. Kanner and co-author's and Dr. Despert's papers help us to understand how some of the diagnostic errors come about. Dr. Kanner described the primary symptomatology of "early infantile autism" as consisting of self-isolation, an "impenetrable aloneness in the first two years of life" together with an *"obsessive* insistence on sameness." Thus, there is an obvious superficial resemblance betwen the clinical pictures of certain cases of infantile autism, especially when seen at a later age, and of severely disturbed obsessive-compulsive younger children.

I thought it would help, for our orientation and correlation of the unusually interesting papers which we heard this afternoon, if we clarified the question of onset of obsessive-compulsive neurosis, because textbooks of child psychiatry do not seem to make it sufficiently clear that the onset of obsessive compulsive neurosis *is* during *the latency period*. Yet, on page 270 of Fenichel's standard book (The Psychoanalytic Theory of Neurosis) it is clearly stated that, though the onset of obsessive compulsive neurosis is not as early as that of hysteria, nevertheless, the onset *is* in latency. For three decades, and specifically since Anna Freud's first book in 1927 (Introduction to the Technique of Child Analysis), it has been a known fact that so-called systematized compulsion neurosis *may be* well established and usually begins in school age. A case in question was described by Anna Freud in the above-named book. This was a six-year-old girl, analyzed by Anna Freud in the middle twenties. The author described her as follows: "For such a tender age this little patient showed an unusually severe and unusually well demarcated compulsion neurosis, coupled with highest intelligence and sharpest logic." This little girl called her bad thoughts "the devil in me."

It was the child analysts who established empirically, and not through reconstruction from adult cases, that in obsessive compulsion childhood neurosis, there is a peculiar precocity of ego as well as super-ego development; also, that this prematurity augured poor personality development for later life, because, when untreated,the originally high intellectual and other ego endowments did not always remain intact. We know from Sigmund Freud, Anna Freud and her co-workers, and from the more recent contribution of Despert, Anne-marie Weil and others, that there are two ominous possibilities indicated by early severe obsessive compulsive neurosis. *The one ominous outcome* is, that the obsessive compulsive defenses may succeed in counteracting a break-through of the repressed. They may succeed in holding off, with increasing effort, the avalanche of deep unconscious material. This, however, occurs at the expense of the energy supply of the ego. It has as its result, as Freud has found, an impoverishment of the personality. These energy-depleted, obsessive children may then superficially resemble clinical pictures of certain cases of infantile autism. The main distinction of the former from psychosis is *that contact with reality*, particularly object relationship, remains fairly intact.

The *second possible outcome* of early severe compulsion neurosis may be that the obsessive defenses prove inadequate, essentially because the child's object relationship had been of the anaclitic parasitic type and therefore *tenuous* all along. Thus, an *acute break of the symbiotic type* may result. In this instance the former compulsive obsessive behavior *may* change into obstinacy, negativism and catatonic-like temper tantrums. These are signs of the explosive inner tension and of the panic of the impending loss of the symbiotic object. This constitutes a secondary restitutive struggle. It aims at recapturing the vanishing external love object by coercive omnipotence. *These children put up an heroic struggle against the slipping away of the object world.* The primary symptom of these cases is abysmal panic—a fear of disintegration, of annihilation.

Dr. Despert gave us graphic clinical examples of the catastrophic distress of such children. However, their struggle is not always prolonged and not always conspicuous. It is often brief or subterranean, and then it escapes clinical observation. Only under rare and optimal conditions can we clinically observe the actual psychotic break and clearly trace the process of restitution. This process consists of the building of a psychotic superstructure upon the primary symptomatology of ego fragmentation. The immediate trigger, which sets off the psychotic break, seems to be the actual loss of the love object by psychotic introjection in the sense of Melanie Klein and Lauretta Bender. Usually, we see these cases at a stage when "the mother in reality" has lost meaning, when the child has sunk into absorption in his psychotic inner reality. These cases do hallucinate. The hallucinatory content can, in some cases, be discerned to be communications with the introjected objects. To gain respite from abysmal panic, these children resort to such restitutive defenses as mutism, rigid stereotyped behavior, obstinate negtivism and catatonic-like temper tantrums. This can obviously be confused with *primary* autistic pictures, though the autistic superstructure in these cases—the self-isolation and obsessive insistence on sameness—are merely secondary mechanisms.

The most interesting point of Dr. Kanner's and Dr. Eisenberg's report was the high prognostic significance of the presence or absence of language in the autistic patients at a certain age. We know from Dr. Kanner's previous work that speech is not used by the autistic child for social communication. We have heard that the emotional isolation of Dr. Kanner's cases, their relative lack of social contact, remained evident throughout the follow-up study. Therefore, we would be inclined to regard the difference between Dr. Kanner's and Dr. Eisenberg's two groups as indicating that speech in the autistic child signifies innate autonomous ego equipment in Heinz Hartmann's sense. In other words, language seems not a measure of the autistic child's capacity for social adaptation, but a measure of his intellectual endowment. It would then seem, in those cases in which the hereditary endowment indicated by language development was good or excellent, that language served as a tool or bridge for orientation in, and adaptation to, outer reality. Thus, it would seem that language gave these individuals a nucleus for structuring and organizing their personality through ability to learn.

The importance of individual endowment was illustrated in Dr. Reginald Lourie's remarkable paper. His contribution marks a substantial beginning to supply sorely needed observational data to questions of psychopthology of the preverbal stage. Dr. Lourie's work demonstrates, in a carefully experimental therapeutic set-up, the vital role of object-relationship for somatopsychic health and disease. Dr. Lourie indicated that the return to a state of primary narcissism, which he and his workers encountered in the infants—with cyclic vomiting, diarrhea or rumination—was not the same as in some cases of severe autism or childhood schizophrenia, although "at the height of the symptoms it would be difficult to distinguish them from each other." Dr. Lourie assumes, "the chief difference appeared to be in the constitutional endowment of these infants"; in the schizophrenic infant, the as yet unknown constitutional element seems to make it difficult for the individual patient to tolerate human contact. The regression in most of the five to eleven-month-old infants with grave psychosomatic symptomatology had no opportunity to become well fixed; it was reversible and became reversed because these babies accepted human contact, unlike the constitutionally autistic infants.

This symposium is especially gratifying because the papers complement each other to such an extent, though their topics are seemingly far apart. Summarizing the highlights of my discussion:

(1) Drs. Kanner and Eisenberg revealed the prognostic significance of the development of language function, which seems to be a measure of autonomous ego endowment.

(2) Dr. Despert's contribution to differential diagnosis implicitly (though not explicitly) emphasized the criterion of object relationship in the differential diagnosis of the psychotic from the nonpsychotic.

(3) Dr. Reginald Lourie's therapeutic experiments, substantiating both the importance of primary object relationship and that of constitutional endowment, in infants between five and eleven months. I would infer that, had there been an autistic infant in his series who, to quote Kanner, lacked the innate capacity for emotional contact "to which the human species is destined," Dr. Lourie's ingenious devices could not have arrested the inevitable outcome of the depleting psychosomatic disease.

I cannot comment in extenso on Dr. Lowry's paper, but I may add that, according to recent experiences, final prognosis of grave childhood psychopathology will have to include thorough knowledge of the outcome of longitudinally studied cases, through and beyond the crucial period of puberty.

The scientific world is looking forward to further data explicitly or implicitly promised by all four of our distinguished contributors.

APPENDIX

E. Stanley Abbot, M. D.*
P.O. Box 119
Wayland, Massachusetts

Theodora M. Abel, Ph.D.
815 Park Avenue
New York, New York

David Abrahamsen, M.D.
1035 5th Avenue
New York 28, New York

Nathan Ackerman, M.D.
42 East 78th Street
New York 21, New York

Alexandra Adler, M.D.
32 East 39th Street
New York 16, New York

Leo Alexander, M.D.
433 Marlboro Street
Boston, Massachusetts

Edward B. Allen, M.D.
121 Westchester Avenue
White Plains, New York

George S. Amsden, M.D.*
Acworth, New Hampshire

Victor V. Anderson, M.D.*
Anderson School
Staatsburg, New York

Leslie R. Angus, M.D.
138 Greenwood Avenue
Jenkintown, Pennsylvania

Irma Bache, M.D.
1 East 368
The Pentagon
Washington, D.C.

Lauretta Bender, M.D.
140 W. 16th Street
New York 11, New York

William Berman, M.D.
204 Martine Avenue
White Plains, New York

Daniel Blain, M.D.
American Psychiatric Association
3126 Woodley Road, N.W.
Washington 8, D.C.

A. Louise Brush, M.D.
55 East 86th Street
New York, New York

Dexter M. Bullard, M.D.
Chestnut Lodge Sanitarium
Rockville, Maryland

Ernest W. Burgess, Ph.D.
University of Chicago
1126 East 59th Street
Chicago 37, Illinois

* Asterisk indicates Associate Member.

Donald Ewen Cameron, M.D.
1025 Pine Avenue, W.
Montreal 2, Canada

Norman Cameron, M.D.
Northford, Connecticut

Carl D. Camp, M.D.*
304 South State Street
Ann Arbor, Michigan

Douglas G. Campbell, M.D.
490 Post Street
San Francisco, California

G. Colket Caner, M.D.
63 Marlboro Street
Boston, Masschusetts

Edward J. Carroll, M.D.
121 University Place
Pittsburgh, Pennsylvania

Brock Chisholm, M.D.†
World Health Organization
Geneva, Switzerland

Robert Clark, M.D.
Western State Psychiatric Institute
3811 O'Hara Street
Pittsburgh 13, Pennsylvania

Hollis E. Clow, M.D.
121 Westchester Avenue
White Plains, New York

Eugene Davidoff, M.D.
1101 Nott Street
Schenectady 8, New York

Oskar Diethelm, M.D.
525 East 68th Street
New York 21, New York

John M. Dorsey, M.D.
1401 Rivard Street
Detroit 7, Michigan

Roy M. Dorcus, Ph.D.
University of California
Los Angeles 24, California

Franklin Smith DuBois, M.D.
Silver Hill Foundation
Valley Road
New Canaan, Connecticut

H. Flanders Dunbar, M.D.
1 East 69th Street
New York, New York

William W. Elgin, M.D.
Sheppard and Enoch Pratt Hospital
Towson 4, Maryland

Milton H. Erickson, M.D.
32 West Cypress
Phoenix, Arizona

Robert H. Felix, M.D.
National Institute of Mental Health
U.S. Public Health Service
Bethesda 14, Maryland

Arthur N. Foxe, M.D.
25 West 54th Street
New York 19, New York

Jerome D. Frank, M.D.
Johns Hopkins Hospital
School of Medicine
Baltimore 5, Maryland

Richard L. Frank, M.D.
745 Fifth Avenue
New York, New York

† **Dagger indicates Honorary Member**

Fritz A. Freyhan, M.D.
Farnhurst, Delaware

Frieda Fromm-Reichmann, M.D.
Chestnut Lodge Sanitarium
Rockville, Maryland

Daniel H. Funkenstein, M.D.
74 Fenwood Road
Boston 14, Massachusetts

William Goldfarb, M.D.
Ittleson Center for Child Research
5050 Iselin Avenue
Riverdale 71, New York

William Horsley Gantt, M.D.
Johns Hopkins Hospital
Baltimore 5, Maryland

Francis J. Gerty, M.D.
University of Illinois
College of Medicine
912 South Wood Street
Chicago, Illinois

Arnold Gesell, M.D., Ph.D.
185 Edwards Street
New Haven, Connecticut

Bernard Glueck, M.D.
7 Parkway Road
Briarcliff, New York

Bernard Glueck, Jr., M.D.
Department of Psychiatry
University Hospitals
Minneapolis, Minnesota

Jacques Gottlieb, M.D.
University of Miami
College of Medicine
Miami, Florida

Ernest M. Gruenberg, M.D.
746 Irving Avenue
Syracuse 10, New York

Roscoe W. Hall, M.D.
St. Elizabeth's Hospital
Washington, D.C.

Volta R. Hall, M.D.
422 Beacon Street
Boston, Massachusetts

A. Irving Hallowell, Ph.D.
Box 14, Bennet Hall
University of Pennsylvania
Philadelphia, Pennsylvania

Donald M. Hamilton, M.D.
121 Westchester Avenue
White Plains, New York

Irving B. Harrison, M.D.
142 Garth Rd.
Scarsdale, New York

Harry H. Harter, M.D.
82-42 Kew Gardens Road
Kew Gardens 15, New York

W. Linwood Heaver, M.D.
61 Irving Place
New York 3, New York

Morris Herman, M.D.
30 East 40th Street
New York, New York

Paul H. Hoch, M.D.
1165 Park Avenue
New York, New York

Leslie B. Hohman, M.D.
Duke Medical School
Durham, North Carolina

Justin Morrill Hope, M.D.
New England Center Hospital
Boston, Massachusetts

William A. Horwitz, M.D.
722 West 168th Street
New York 32, New York

Joseph Hughes, M.D.
111 North Forty-Ninth Street
Philadelphia 39, Pennsylvania

William A. Hunt, Ph.D.
Northwestern University
Evanston, Illinois

George A. Jervis, M.D., Ph.D.
Letchworth Village
Research Department
Thiells, Rockland County, New York

Ernest Jones, M.D.†
The Plat, Elsted,
N. Midhurst,
Sussex, England

Lothar B. Kalinowsky, M.D.
115 East 82nd Street
New York, New York

Franz J. Kallmann, M.D.
722 West 168th Street
New York, New York

Abram Kardiner, M.D.
1100 Park Avenue
New York, New York

Solomon Katzenelbogen, M.D.
The Woodner
16th Street, Spring Road, N.W.
Washington, D.C.

Edward J. Kempf, M.D.
Wading River, New York

Isabelle V. Kendig, Ph.D.
Ashton, Maryland

Richard D. Kepner, M.D.
P.O. Box 3119
Honolulu 2, Hawaii

Lawrence Kolb, M.D.
6645 32nd N.W.
Washington 15, D.C.

David M. Levy, M.D.
15 East 91st Street
New York, New York

Nolan D. C. Lewis, M.D.
Neuropsychiatric Institute
Princeton, New Jersey

William T. Lhamon, M.D.
1 Blalock Circle
Houston, Texas

Vladimir Theodore Liberson, M.D.
62 Roslyn Street
Hartford, Connecticut

Howard S. Liddell, Ph.D.
Department of Psychology
Cornell University
Ithaca, New York

Reginald S. Lourie, M.D.
Children's Hospital
Washington 9, D.C.

Lawson Lowrey, M.D.
25 West 54th Street
New York 19, New York
also
2 Topland Road
Hartsdale, New York

John G. Lynn, M.D.
305 Royal Hawaiian Ave.
Honolulu 15, Hawaii

Charles A. McDonald, M.D.*
106 Waterman Street
Providence 6, Rhode Island

Edwin E. McNiel, M.D.*
3875 Wilshire Boulevard
Los Angeles 5, California

Donald J. MacPherson, M.D.
270 Commonwealth Avenue
Boston 16, Massachusetts

Benjamin Malzberg, Ph.D.
New York State Department of
    Mental Hygiene
Albany, New York

Edward E. Mayer, M.D.*
5601 Forbes Street
Pittsburgh 17, Pennsylvania

William C. Menninger, M.D.
Menninger Foundation
Topeka, Kansas

Joseph S. A. Miller, M.D.
Hillside Hospital
Glen Oaks, Long Island, New York

John A. P. Millet, M.D.
25 East 92nd Street
New York 28, New York

J. Allison Montague, Ph.D.
25 East 10th Street
New York 3, New York

Merrill Moore, M.D.
382 Commonwealth Avenue
Boston 15, Massachusetts

Thomas Verner Moore, M.D., Ph.D.†
Carthusian Foundation in America,
    Inc.
Sky Farm
Whitingham, Vermont

Harry Merrill Murdock, M.D.
Sheppard and Enoch Pratt Hospital
Towson 4, Maryland

Henry A. Murray, Ph.D., M.D.*
48 Mount Auburn Street
Cambridge, Massachusetts

Leo P. O'Donnell, M.D.
Harlem Valley Hospital
Wingdale, New York

Raymond L. Osborne, M.D.
140 East 54th Street
New York 22, New York

Winfred Overholser, M.D.
St. Elizabeth's Hospital
Washington 20, D.C.

Grosvenor B. Pearson, M.D.
5555 Forbes Street
Pittsburgh 19, Pennsylvania

Harris B. Peck, M.D.
135 East 22nd Street
New York, New York

Zygmunt A. Piotrowski, Ph.D.
New Jersey Neuropsychiatric Insti-
    tute
Skillman, New Jersey

Phillip Polatin, M.D.
722 West 168th Street
New York 32, New York

Hyman L. Rachlin, M.D.
33 East 39th Street
New York, New York

Sandor Rado, M.D.
50 East 78th Street
New York, New York

George N. Raines, Captain (MC)
  USN
U. S. Naval Hospital
Portsmouth, Virginia

Evelyn B. Reichenbach, M.D.
St. Elizabeth's Hospital
Washington, D.C.

Thomas A. C. Rennie, M.D.
525 East 68th Street
New York 21, New York

Esther L. Richards, M.D.
601 N. Broadway
Baltimore 5, Maryland

David McK. Rioch, M.D.
Neuropsychiatric Division
Walter Reed Medical Center
Washington 12, D.C.

Margaret Rioch, M.D.
4607 Dorset Avenue
Chevy Chase 15, Maryland

Fred V. Rockwell, M.D.
Grasslands Hospital
Valhalla, New York

Howard P. Rome, M.D.
Mayo Clinic
Rochester, Minnesota

Theodore Rothman, M.D.
444 North Bedford Drive
Beverly Hills, California

William S. Sadler, M.D.*
533 Diversey Parkway
Chicago, Illinois

G. Wilson Schaffer, Ph.D.
Johns Hopkins University
Baltimore, Maryland

David Shakow, Ph.D.*
National Institute of Mental Health
U. S. Public Health Service
Bethesda, Maryland

Alexander Simon, M.D.*
Langley Porter Clinic
San Francisco, California

John L. Smalldon, M.D.
Brattleboro Retreat
Brattleboro, Vermont

George W. Smeltz, M.D.
Chalfonte Hotel
Atlantic City, New Jersey

Lauren H. Smith, M.D.
111 North 49th Street
Philadelphia, Pennsylvania

Harry C. Solomon, M.D.
74 Fenwood Road
Boston, Massachusetts

Rene A. Spitz, M.D.
1150 Fifth Avenue
New York 28, New York

Edward J. Stainbrook, Ph.D., M.D.
University Hospital
150 Marshall Street
Syracuse, New York

Charles W. Stephenson, M.D.
South Hero, Vermont

Gregory Stragnell, M.D.
272 Old Short Hills Road
Short Hills, New Jersey

Joseph G. Sutton, M.D.
Essex County Overbrook Hospital
Cedar Grove, New Jersey

Hans C. Syz, M.D.
The Lifwynn Foundation
Westport, Connecticut

William S. Taylor, Ph.D.
55 Dryads Green
Northampton, Massachusetts

Harry A. Teitelbaum, M.D.
1801 Eutaw Place
Baltimore, Maryland

William B. Terhune, M.D.
Box D
New Canaan, Connecticut

Charles B. Thompson, M.D.
The Lifwynn Foundation
Westport, Connecticut

Clara Thompson, M.D.
12 East 86th Street
New York, New York

Kenneth J. Tillotson, M.D.*
1265 Beacon Street
Brookline, Massachusetts

Vladimir G. Urse, M.D.*
1447 Keystone Avenue
River Forest, Illinois

Roy McL. Van Wart, M.D.*
10431 Bellagio Road
Los Angeles 24, California

Heinrich B. Waelsch, M.D., Sc.D.
722 West 168th Street
New York 32, New York

Raymond W. Waggoner, M.D.
University Hospital
1313 East Ann Street
Ann Arbor, Michigan

James Hardin Wall, M.D.
121 Westchester Avenue
White Plains, New York

George A. Waterman, M.D.*
200 Beacon Street
Boston, Massachusetts

David Wechsler, Ph.D.
Bellevue Hospital
New York, New York

Livingston Welch, Ph.D.
Hunter College
Park Avenue & 68th Street
New York, New York

Frederic Lyman Wells, Ph.D.†
19 Bowdoin Street
Newton Highlands 61, Massachusetts

Louis Wender, M.D.
59 East 79th Street
New York, New York

Frederick L. Weniger, M.D.
3811 O'Hara Street
Pittsburgh 13, Pennsylvania

Mary Alice White, Ph.D.
121 Westchester Avenue
White Plains, New York

Robert W. White, Ph.D.
Department of Social Relations
Harvard University
Cambridge, Massachusetts

John C. Whitehorn, M.D.
Johns Hopkins Hospital
Baltimore 5, Maryland

Cornelius C. Wholey, M.D.*
121 University Place
Pittsburgh, Pennsylvania

Robert S. Wigton, M.D.*
105 S. 49th Street
Omaha 3, Nebraska

George B. Wilbur, M.D.*
South Dennis, Massachusetts

Emanuel Windholz, M.D.
2235 Post Street
San Francisco 15, California

Lightner Witmer, Ph.D.
P.O. Box A
Devon, Pennsylvania

Cecil L. Wittson, M.D.
415 North 61st Street
Omaha 5, Nebraska

Lewis R. Wolberg, M.D.
55 East 86th Street
New York, New York

Lawrence Woolley, M.D.
490 Peachtree Street
Atlanta, Georgia

S. Bernard Wortis, M.D.
410 East 57th Street
New York, New York

Joseph Zubin, Ph.D.
722 West 168th Street
New York 32, New York

Past and Present Officers of the American Psychopathological Association

Presidents

1912	Adolf Meyer	1936	Nolan D. C. Lewis
1913	James T. Putnam	1937	Nolan D. C. Lewis
1914	Alfred R. Allen	1938	Samuel W. Hamilton
1915	Alfred R. Allen	1939	Abraham Myerson
1916	Adolf Meyer	1940	Douglas A. Thom
1917	Adolf Meyer	1941	Roscoe W. Hall
1918	Smith Ely Jelliffe	1942	Roscoe W. Hall
1921	William A. White	1943	Frederick L. Wells
1922	John T. MacCurdy	1944	Frederick L. Wells
1923	L. Pierce Clark	1945	Bernard Glueck
1924	L. Pierce Clark	1946	Robert P. Knight
1925	Albert M. Barrett	1947	Frederick L. Wells
1927	Sanger Brown, II	1948	Donald J. MacPherson
1928	Ross McC. Chapman	1949	Paul Hoch
1929	Ross McC. Chapman	1950	William B. Terhune
1930	William Healy	1951	Lauren H. Smith
1931	William Healy	1952	Joseph Zubin
1932	J. Ramsay Hunt	1953	Clarence P. Oberndorf
1933	Edward J. Kempf	1954	David McK. Rioch
1934	Edward J. Kempf	1955	Merrill Moore
1935	Nolan D. C. Lewis		

Vice Presidents

1924	William Healy	1941	Frederick L. Wells
	George H. Kirby		Lowell S. Selling
1925	J. Ramsay Hunt	1942	Frederick L. Wells
	Sidney I. Schwab		Lowell S. Selling
1927	Ross McC. Chapman	1943	Lowell S. Selling
	Edward J. Kempf		Flanders Dunbar
1928	Edward J. Kempf	1944	Lowell S. Selling
	E. Stanley Abbot		Flanders Dunbar
1929	Edward J. Kempf	1945	Thomas V. Moore
	E. Stanley Abbot		Robert P. Knight
1930	J. Ramsay Hunt	1946	Paul H. Hoch
	Herman N. Adler		Thos. A. C. Rennie
1931	J. Ramsay Hunt	1947	William C. Menninger
	Herman N. Adler		Ruth Benedict
1933	Albert M. Barrett	1948	Ruth Benedict
	Trigant Burrow		Lauren H. Smith
1934	Albert M. Barrett	1949	Arthur N. Foxe
	Trigant Burrow		Norman Cameron
1935	J. Ramsay Hunt	1950	Harry M. Murdock
	Smith Ely Jelliffe		William S. Taylor
1936	J. Ramsay Hunt	1951	Harry M. Murdock
	Smith Ely Jelliffe		Lauretta Bender
1937	Samuel W. Hamilton	1952	William Horwitz
	Ray G. Hoskins		S. Bernard Wortis
1938	Lydiard H. Horton	1953	David McK. Rioch
	Hans Syz		Merrill Moore
1939	Roscoe W. Hall	1954	Merrill Moore
	Douglas A. Thom		Howard S. Liddell
1940	George S. Sprague	1955	Oskar Diethelm
	Bernard Glueck		Howard S. Liddell

Secretaries

1921	H. W. Frink	1932	L. Eugene Emerson
1922	Sanger Brown, II	1933	L. Eugene Emerson
1923	Sanger Brown, II	1934	L. Eugene Emerson
1924	Sanger Brown, II	1935	L. Eugene Emerson
1925	Sanger Brown, II	1936	L. Eugene Emerson
1926	Sanger Brown, II	1937	L. Eugene Emerson
1927	Martin W. Peck	1938	L. Eugene Emerson
1928	Martin W. Peck	1939	L. Eugene Emerson
1929	Martin W. Peck	1940	Merrill Moore
1930	L. Eugene Emerson	1941	Merrill Moore
1931	L. Eugene Emerson	1942	Merrill Moore

1943	Merrill Moore	1950	Samuel W. Hamilton
1944	Samuel W. Hamilton	1951	Samuel W. Hamilton
1945	Samuel W. Hamilton	1952	Donald M. Hamilton
1946	Samuel W. Hamilton	1953	Donald M. Hamilton
1947	Samuel W. Hamilton	1954	Donald M. Hamilton
1948	Samuel W. Hamilton	1955	Donald M. Hamilton
1949	Samuel W. Hamilton		

Treasurers

1924	William C. Garvin	1940	William C. Garvin
1925	William C. Garvin	1941	William C. Garvin
1926	William C. Garvin	1942	William C. Garvin
1927	William C. Garvin	1943	Joseph Zubin
1928	William C. Garvin	1944	Joseph Zubin
1929	William C. Garvin	1945	Joseph Zubin
1930	William C. Garvin	1946	Joseph Zubin
1931	William C. Garvin	1947	Joseph Zubin
1932	William C. Garvin	1948	Joseph Zubin
1933	William C. Garvin	1949	Joseph Zubin
1934	William C. Garvin	1950	Joseph Zubin
1935	William C. Garvin	1951	Joseph Zubin
1936	William C. Garvin	1952	Bernard Glueck, Jr.
1937	William C. Garvin	1953	Bernard Glueck, Jr.
1938	William C. Garvin	1954	Bernard Glueck, Jr.
1939	William C. Garvin	1955	Bernard Glueck, Jr.

INDEX